David Profumo was born in London in 1955 and educated at the universities of Oxford and London. A former teacher and Deputy Editor of the *Fiction Magazine*, he is now a freelance writer and a columnist with the *Daily Telegraph*. His first novel, *Sea Music*, was awarded the Geoffrey Faber Memorial Prize in 1989, and he co-edited (with Graham Swift) *The Magic Wheel*, an anthology of fishing in literature, published by Picador in 1985.

DAVID PROFUMO

THE WEATHER IN ICELAND

PICADOR

First published 1993 in Picador by Pan Books Limited

This edition published 1994 by Picador
a division of Pan Macmillan Publishers Limited
Cavaye Place London SW10 9PG
and Basingstoke

Associated companies throughout the world

ISBN 0 330 32681 3

1 3 5 7 9 8 6 4 2

A CIP catalogue record for this book is available from
the British Library

Phototypeset by Intype, London
Printed and bound in Great Britain by
Cox & Wyman Ltd, Reading, Berkshire

For Helen, and our happy family, with love

AUTHOR'S NOTE

Some of the names and factual details included in the section entitled 'A Short History of Barbed Wire' are drawn from *The Wire That Fenced The West* by Henry D. and Frances T. McCallum (University of Oklahoma Press, 1965), and *Barbs, Prongs, Points, Prickers & Stickers* by Robert T. Clifton (University of Oklahoma Press, 1970).

I also gratefully acknowledge a Fellowship from the International Retreat for Writers at Hawthornden Castle, without the assistance of which this book would have taken even longer to complete.

The extract from *Salka Valka* by Halldor Laxness (translated by F. H. Lyon) is reprinted by permission of Harper Collins, and the extract from 'The Witnesses' from the *Collected Poems* by W. H. Auden (edited by Edward Mendelson) appears by permission of Faber & Faber Ltd.

And life in the place was like a kind of accompaniment to this absurd weather: its inhabitants went round in circles, toiling and moiling through one cycle of bad weather after another, without its leading to anything at all.

Halldor Laxness, *Salka Valka*

The author travelled with two pocket aneroids, a larger one left behind for comparison; three B.P. thermometers; Saussure's hygrometer; a portable clinometer; an *aréometre selon Cartier*; three thermometers (max. and min.); two hygrometers, the usual wet and dry bulbs; a prismatic compass; and Captain George's double pocket–sextant . . .

R.F. Burton, *Ultima Thule; Or, A Summer in Iceland*

The bolt is sliding in its groove;
Outside the window is the black remover's van:
And now with sudden swift emergence
Come the hooded women, the hump-backed surgeons,
And the Scissor Man.

W.H. AUDEN, *The Witnesses*

The colour of a Spider is somewhat pale, such as Ovid ascribeth to Lovers, and when she hangeth aloft in her web, with her legs wide and spread abroad, she perfectly and lively expresseth the shape and proportion of a painted Starre . . .

EDWARD TOPSELL, *The History of the Four-Footed Beasts*

I went into another room, where the walls and ceiling were all hung round with cobwebs, except a narrow passage for the artist to go in and out.

JONATHAN SWIFT, *Gulliver's Travels*

ONE

It was Christmas Day, and the last thing anyone was expecting was an Act of God.

My father was in the conservatory, treating the staff to his seasonal tradition of sherry before luncheon, when a section of metal guttering, loosened by snow thawing off the roof, tore away and fell sixty feet through the campanulate glass dome and impaled him fatally through the back of his skull.

The doctor was summoned while Flynn, our butler, cradled my father's wounded head. He must have been aware of me staring at him in silence, before lifting a tartan rug from the back of the wicker armchair and draping it up the body, but stopping short of the face and folding it tidily under the chin, as if to avert any final gesture.

'It is very bad, Mr Richard,' said Flynn, 'very bad.'

And then: 'I think you should follow me, Your Grace.'

And so it was that at the age of thirteen I ceased to be the Marquess of Waterstock and became instead the Eighth Duke of London. It is over thirty years since my father was murdered by the weather, and of course I don't use that name any more. Here in Switzerland my colleagues merely know me as Dr Slide – dukes, like the late United Kingdom of Great Britain, are a thing of the past.

I do not know you, and can never see you. Perhaps you may not even exist. Maybe as the world goes now there is no reader left for such a story, for the life and times of a defunct dynasty. Certainly Magda, who is combing her hair in the next room, singing away to herself, has no interest in my phantom limb syndrome. She knows me as a teacher at the Institute, not as an awkward, historical amputee.

Perhaps, even as I write, I become an irrelevance. The

3

humidor on this table beside my desk bears our family arms: a fructed apple tree, argent with peeping gules, and the sun, crescent, in its glory. And the motto beneath runs 'Fortissima stat arbor sola'. The lone tree stands strongest, that's it. But what if the tree falls, and no one hears it – does it make a sound? What is the half-life of a secret that is confided in no one else?

I rather think that some things have to be told as stories before they can really be said to have happened: but even then you can't be sure. In these maculate times, if I were you, I would be wary of trim resolutions – but perhaps it's not for me to say. Recent confusions in my personal life, combined with two decades of twin-fisted Scotch-drinking, make it difficult for me nowadays to address events strictly *seriatim*, so I shall begin with the day of my birth, and we will arrive at the rest in a roundabout fashion.

Besides – how long *is* an event? You can't tell until you unpack them, spread the assembly instructions out on the work-shop table ('Contains small parts: not suitable for a child of less than three years': I should say not). Events are retrospective, adult constructs. They involve time and labour. Children have nothing to do with them if possible: *they* proceed by a system of accidents and surprises, framed by sunsets and sleep. And I am inclined to believe that this is the only perspective on history which makes you want to wake up in the morning with a clear head, like a child.

I was born on 1 September (St Fiacre's day), 1956 – that makes me forty-two, to save you the trouble of counting. My father was not present at the event, because it was not in those days considered traditional – nor did people indulge in after-birth-omelette parties with their friends, or encourage women to go into labour in lead-lined capsules, or any of the other modern fashions.

Anyway, it was the opening day of the partridge season, and he had other demands on his time.

The obstetrician was similarly absent (en route to his golf links), because I presumed to arrive some twelve hours earlier than predicted. My mother, who had no choice but to be there in person, managed admirably with the assistance of a sturdy Irish midwife, and plenty of gas and air.

It is disappointing, since I am as arrogant as the next man (assuming there is one) that no exotic portents attended my introduction to what has now become Planet Earth plc. There were no sheets of flame in the firmament over Shrewsbury, nor reports of rainforest mammals seen bounding through the market square in King's Lynn. Had some agricultural labourer in Surrey chanced to look up from his machinery and espied a celestial host marching in celebration, with spearlight and pennons, I feel sure his vision would have found its way into the newspapers; as it was, the *Daily Telegraph* merely recorded a moderate heatwave in the Dorking area. Ideal partridge weather, as it happened.

When my father did come to inspect me, later that evening, he approached the wrong cradle in the nursery of the Welbeck Clinic, and began enthusing over a gently sleeping infant with sleek black hair: he was disconcerted to be advised by Sister that His Lordship was in fact the livid baby with glabrous pate and tomato visage whom he had instinctively avoided upon entry, due to the caterwauling, and that he had, in his paternal euphoria, mistaken the daughter of the Panamanian ambassador for his own son and heir, who was currently protesting at his first evening under the courtesy title of the Earl of Brompton.

According to the records of Buxton, the gardener, it was a gossamer day: the sure sign of a week's good weather. A tangle of silvery strands stretched across the acres of Spellbrook that were to become my inheritance. Lucky me: the air was full of money-spiders on the day I was born, a symptom of my good fortune. And I cannot pretend that I was not born with at least one platinum spoon in my mouth: it turned out that my family was, by any standards, exceedingly rich. This has had (I need hardly say it) a pronounced effect upon my subsequent life.

God's Summer, Gauze of Mary, Goose-Summer – even its origins are elusive, but linguistically strong. On gossamer days when they sense the winds can disperse them, they stand on tiptoes and release threads upwards into the air, by reversing their abdomens. Sinuous balloons of silk billow into the breeze until they conspire to lift the tiny aeronaut away from its place of birth, away from the heartlands of the meadows and into the virtual reality of the middle atmosphere, where the money-spinners offer grazing for birds on the wing, and they are at the mercy of cyclonic whims.

From dark cypress, bright gorse, the waxgleam of holly, they travel for miles and miles. You find these spiderlings on mountains above the snowline, in the rigging of ships in mid-ocean. But they survive. Their filaments of silk hang like arrested smoke, and then they are part of a diaspora, a net that catches the wind.

We have become blind to the glories of mass-migration. In days gone by (my text for this evening, as it happens) you could reckon the year by the seasonal movement of certain creatures. And I don't mean the cartoon lemming – but buffalo, salmon, passenger pigeon, mayfly, tuna. Migration now means humans so destitute that they are prepared to risk dying in transit, for lack of water. *Phylum Arthropoda* organized itself much more efficiently, thousands of years ago.

September is the sapphire month, and my father presented me with a pair of antique cufflinks featuring that stone for my christening. I am, in fact, wearing them right now. As I write. As I tell you about days gone by.

They are very elegant, and enhance my typing. They are links to a time when I was, virtually speaking, someone else.

Such objects have become important to me. Like talismans of my past – the sort of thing that we all harbour, in some shape or form.

Writing down anything on paper is an experiment; you get these strange, superstitious impulses – tugs at the sail, where there doesn't appear to be a discernible breeze – and a little anchor around the wrist, a bauble against drowning, is, however irrational, a source of comfort.

Before I take myself as a baby to ancestral Spellbrook, we need to have a word about St Fiacre.

After all, it was on his special day that I was born, and I believe in giving credit where it is due. Astrology tends to pass me by, but saints' days are generally there for a damn good reason. Torture, or a vicious extermination, in most cases; but history also embraces the obscure.

St Fiacre, of 1 September fame, was an Irish hermit who lived (or flourished, as the records would have it) in the seventh century. For which specific acts of saintliness he was eventually canonized, I do not know, but I do not like the sound of him very much. A misogynist, he set up shop near Meaux, in France, and devoted his life to the cultivation of vegetables, in the exclusive company of like-minded men. He has therefore become the patron saint of gardeners, and his official emblem is the spade.

But for physiological reasons, he is also the saint people invoke, worldwide, when they suffer from piles. St Fiacre is the one to dial if you are feeling anally challenged, or you have problems with your delving, or possibly both.

When I was five days old, Flynn brought the Daimler up to London and I was transported to Spellbrook, our family seat just south of Godalming, which was to be my home for the next thirty-seven years.

It was not a palatial residence, by any means, but there were ten principal bedrooms, and it certainly seemed vast to me as a child. Nor was it, strictly speaking, beautiful. I'm talking about it in the past tense, because the estate is not now what it was, but of course you can still go and see it for yourself, if you fancy a day out. I made the mistake of visiting it again earlier this year, and have no intention of returning.

The western façade, which you see as you approach down

the drive, is stuccoed and asymmetrical, giving it a Mediterranean aspect, with twin Italianate towers and elaborate balustrading which, for as long as I lived there, was entwined with arthritic wisteria. As the guidebook will inform you, the main body of the house was built between 1820 and 1826, designed by the architect Sir Philip Welby in the style that became known as 'classical picturesque'. The original owners were the Carr family, who had made a fortune in the West Indian sugar trade, and it was acquired by my ancestors in 1890, along with the estate itself, then comprising more than fifteen hundred acres.

If you stepped out through the french windows from the drawing room, and down on to the croquet lawn, you would have a view of the Great Park beyond the ha-ha, with its little serpentine lake of clear, applegreen water, the Chinese bridge at the narrows, and the artificial hill with its Victorian treehouse overlooking it. Beyond the woods lay Home Farm, to the east, and this is the prospect I enjoyed every morning, from my bedroom window, on the second floor.

Until my brother was born, my bedroom was referred to as 'the Night Nursery', to distinguish it from the Nursery proper, which was on the floor below. Like most people, I suppose, my earliest memories are of the place where I slept and awoke when very small. Above my cot there was a large print of Holman Hunt's *The Light of the World*, showing Jesus with his lantern, knocking on the door; above the fireplace hung a saccharine watercolour, under glass, of a ragged peasant boy, his cheeks flushed with piety, praying before his flock of sheep at sunset, with one of those impossible medieval villages on the hillside behind him, drenched in apricot light. To complete the theme, a sampler embroidered with the text of the Lord's Prayer was prominently displayed over the chest of drawers. I believe these items of decorative propaganda had hung in those very positions since before the Great War, and their images – along with the granary smell of the carpet – are the first associations I make with the experience of childhood.

I had a woolly dog called Ben with a zippered cavity in his

tummy, into which my pyjamas just fitted during the daytime. His coat had originally been creamy-white, but one night I was sick all over him and after Nanny had washed him he was popped into the oven for a little while, to dry out, and they overdid him, and he came out with a light tan. He was still quite warm from his ordeal when he was restored to my bed, and it was like cuddling a loaf of bread.

There was another thing about this Night Nursery where I slept until I was four: I used to experience occasional but recurring night terrors there, of a type I never encountered anywhere else. I don't know if it was something to do with the room itself, or merely a function of my age, but I can feel the fear of it in my throat even now. I am feverish and awake, and there is a kind of hissing noise in the air; the darkness of the room seems somehow to have expanded into the darkness of the sky, and the distances within my inflamed vision are gigantic. Great rhomboid shapes peel themselves away from the invisible walls and lumber around the airspace which is now like the arena of my skull, with little lights shivering in the distance, then looking suddenly close. They swish and buzz, like nocturnal insects. The cold gleam of the window's shape dances down, revolves, presses right up to my face, so that I feel I am falling upwards into a place without perspective, a chaos. My head is swollen and heavy, yet I am hurtling through an inflated zone full of inanimate energy, my face boiling and melting, my ears thick with those night whispers.

But when I cried out, Nanny would always come beetling in from her room across the corridor, carrying her torch, her hair in a net, a thick, blue woollen dressing-gown down to her slippers. 'There, pet. Did we have a bad dream? Well, it's over now, and dreams never come back,' would be her kindly lie, as she applied a cool flannel to my gasping face, 'Gone for ever, and good riddance – that's what we say, isn't it?' Yes, you could banish much with such verbal magic, in those days; in five minutes with a glass of barley-water, some rhythmic reassurances, and a little night-light floating its flame in a saucer, you could drive out demons. Provided you kept the faith; so long as you really believed.

Since my parents belonged to the final generation in a long line of the English tradition that held children to be an inconvenience until they could be treated as bonsai adults, I was effectively brought up by the staff at Spellbrook: and very happy I was, too. Here in the canton of Schwyz, where you cannot even engage the services of a daily cleaning-lady, those days seem more than a dream away. The resident indoor staff were Iris the cook, Mrs Pike the housekeeper, my Nanny Mottram, and Flynn. Mary, the wife of Begg, my father's groom, came in from the Stables Lodge each weekday as our maid. As well as being waited on hand and foot, I felt blissfully secure as the centre of attention of what I regarded as an extended family. In fact, I was lucky: these people were better than parents. Better than my actual parents, anyway.

In his wisdom, my father decreed that the servants should address me as 'Master Richard' (and later as 'Mister Richard') rather than as 'My Lord'. This was to prevent me getting ideas about my social station a little too early on in life, and was typically considerate of him. In fact, we were not a particularly formal household, but the business of nomenclature had to be resolved after a delicate fashion. My grandfather had been the first to break with tradition. When he inherited his title, male servants were addressed by their Christian names, and the female staff by their surnames, a Victorian habit that attached to the days where gentlemen called one another familiarly by their surnames, and their wives used the Christian names of their female friends.

So, when Flynn, who had been a batman in the Lifeguards during the war, became the butler at Spellbrook in 1946, nobody ever called him Michael. The exception to this rule was Mrs Pike, with her hairpinned bun, whom nobody – not even Flynn – had ever been heard to call Jennifer. She was of the old school, and actually preferred to be Mrs Pike to the rest of the staff, and male members of the family, but merely Pike to my mother, whom she regarded as her direct employer. And of course it was not desirable for me to call Flynn merely by his surname, like a grown man – right up until the moment I succeeded to the Dukedom, I knew him by my childhood nickname of Finny – the legacy of my toddler days when larval skills in pronunciation prevented me from managing the real thing.

Apart from the pleasing euphony it offered my youthful ear, this appellation was peculiarly inappropriate to Flynn, for his appearance had nothing in common with the aquadynamic contours of any fish (mind you, by that token Mrs Pike was in possession of a misnomer, too, being short and plump and generally benevolent). He could not be described as a compact man: stout would be the word, perhaps, with an impressive belly. In his striped trousers, black jacket, and powerfully restraining waistcoat (complete with golden watch-chain, though I never did see a watch at the other end) he was the most regular masculine presence in my early days.

He had immense hands – useful, no doubt, for carrying large loads around the officers' mess, but not the ideal prerequisite for a man who had to deploy crystal and bone china. His tread, though measured, was heavy. Finny proceeded slowly, but I rarely saw him flustered; he worked to his own rhythm, and the rest of the household had to pick up the beat.

Contrary to mythology surrounding such people, his girth was not the result of clandestine tippling, of finishing off the decanters after hours. He was, of course, custodian of the cellars, but for all the time I knew him he was a teetotaller. I am relatively certain that he had previously been a slave to the sauce, had peered over the brim of the pit, felt its flames, and seen the light; but I can't be sure.

Finny was a bachelor from Blackpool, and he had little time for the female members of staff. His attitude was one of studied intolerance whenever things were not running to his satisfaction, and he was fond of provoking Iris by rapping on her serving-hatch, and announcing, 'His Grace is still waiting, if you've got a moment.' He was not, shall we say, sympathetic to the idea of a soufflé, or the alchemy involved in an Omelette Arnold Bennett, and made Iris nervous whenever he considered her regime in need of improved efficiency.

His own favourite, which of course she had to dish up, was treacle tart and lashings of custard. On such occasions he was diplomatic enough to realize he should praise to the skies her epicurean handiwork, and Iris would tut, and jerk her head up in disdain, registering how far beneath her skills the preparation of such dishes lay, delighted with the approbation, perhaps even, just a little, hoping to find a way to his staunch heart through these regular offerings.

Since he had been engaged by my grandfather, Finny really answered to no one else when I was very small. By virtue of the fact that my grandfather was blind, he perhaps got away with rather more than he did when my own father began to pay his wages. This was one of the things that I found so attractive about him: beneath the patina of absolute propriety, discretion and attentiveness, Flynn was actually rather subversive.

I now think he deliberately left his hair and sideboards in need of a trim because his employer could not appraise the exact nature of his appearance. As the person responsible for guiding His Grace along the corridors to the wing where he had his apartment, Flynn virtually assumed *droit de seigneur* on behalf of his charge, and would actually push house-guests out of the path of their progress, if necessary. 'Excusing us, My Lady,' he might say, steering the old man between my mother and one of her friends, as they sipped a liqueur. Yes, he was a law unto himself, the central nervous system of the house, just impudent enough to be irreplaceable. He was a known quantity, which was important. In fact, that was the most important quality of all.

In the attic quarters of the south wing, Finny had a bedroom that housed a collection of wall-mounted daggers. It was an extensive black museum of weaponry that included a Mexican sacrificial blade, several flick-knives, a replica from Pompeii, a panga from Kenya, a device for opening oysters, a Maori spear, and a bleak-looking Commando knife with a black finish.

He claimed that this, and the submariner's compass pinned to the wall next to it, had been taken from a dead German during the war, but I'm not convinced he ever saw that sort of action (submariners would hardly have drifted across the horizon of his regiment on any kind of daily basis, so I suspect these trophies were the fruit of barter rather than ambush), but in any event, the soldier Flynn and the gentle Finny of my days at Spellbrook simply did not collide in the imagination.

I never saw him enraged, nor did I see him really unkind. As I said, with such people to love, it was better than having parents. In that respect, I really did enjoy a privileged upbringing.

Let me tell you now about Nanny Mottram. It was she who presided over my potty-training, chanted 'Jack and Jill', and taught me my alphabet. I had no idea how old she was, but to me she was like a grandmother, with the advantage of being always accessible. (I never knew either of my actual grandmothers, so this seemed important.)

She was in fact only about fifty-five. A neat-featured, bristly woman, with round shoulders, and a dry cough. For all outdoor occasions, quite irrespective of weather conditions, she would wear a soft helmet of grey felt. Unlike many similar nannies, she was not required to wear a uniform as such, but I can scarcely remember her not wearing a navy cardigan, and her shoes were always laced.

Partially hirsute, and entirely virginal, as I now conceive of her as having been, it is a smell that I remember most about her. The smell of something called Friar's Balsam, which was administered against the slightest symptom of catarrh, and involved a nasty ritual wherein you draped a towel over your head, and underneath this tent inhaled the fumes from a ceramic container full of hot, supposedly healing, liquid marketed under the above name. It was acrid, and stifling, and the stench combined tar with the worst notes of caramel. You were subjected to this for what seemed like an hour, but was probably half that time. Sucking and puffing, coughing and pleading, your face damp and in the dark, persevering in the ordeal only because you believed in Nanny Mottram. You had to keep the faith, even in that infernal tent.

But I loved her, believe me. As a sick person might cleave to a nurse, I realized that she was my lifeline.

'When I am older', I promised, 'I will climb into the sky, and dig out a star for you one night, and give it to you, and you can wear it on your day off.'

'That would be nice, pet,' she replied, never interrupting her knitting. 'A star. Now, that would really be something. They'll have to put a picture of us in the papers, when that happens.' And I wish I had managed it: Nanny Mottram was worth a constellation, at the very least.

It may look odd now, but the way my parents organized the household so that they were largely segregated from their children was considered absolutely normal among persons of their class; it was the culmination of an attitude that reached back at least as far as the Middle Ages, and is thought to have derived from the high levels of neonatal mortalities, which meant that parents protected themselves from inevitable anguish by not making manifest their attachment to any particular child until he or she was safely around the age of puberty.

Well, of course this is all rubbish. A typical stew of English neurosis and hypocrisy, cooked up by some vegetable-eating liberals researching the subject in one of those new universities during the Sixties. The real reason that parents of substance chose to marginalize their small offspring so systematically is that children were regarded as inconvenient and subversive and uninteresting, were no respecters of privacy, instinctively recognized your weaknesses, repeated things they had heard at embarrassing moments, disrupted mealtimes, made a great deal of noise, created constant mess, and woke at inconvenient hours of the day and night. It therefore made perfect sense that, if you could afford it, you hired sundry servants to deal with them, and relegated children from your sight for twenty-three hours of the day. This was, for centuries, the peculiarly English way, and its perpetuation down through the generations ensured that it was exceedingly difficult for you to get to know your parents – rather a strange start in life, had anyone bothered to think closely about it. But there you go.

Following their policy of divide and rule, my parents insisted on segregation at mealtimes: until I was seven, I only ever ate in their dining-room at Christmas or for my birthday tea-party. At all other times I was fed in the Nursery, off which Nanny had a little kitchen with a Baby Belling, a glass-fronted store cupboard full of tinned fruit, custard powder, tubs of Cerebos salt, and Quaker Oats, and a troglodyte fridge that gave off the sulphorous smell of hot pipes.

We said Grace both before and after each meal, for Nanny was firmly of the opinion that God was the provider, and she was also naturally an adherent of the Starving Millions school of philosophy. On one occasion she instructed me to go upstairs and pray for forgiveness from the Almighty because I had pretended a dislike of cornflakes. After twenty minutes she came and retrieved me, and watched while I finished my bowl.

She was at best a conservative cook, and had a number of dreadful specialities, generally involving hot milk. Nanny cooked with milk as others might use spices: she was much given to sago puddings, semolina, and other types of frogspawn, and her favourite Friday dish was something called Smelly William – a strip of fish (whiting or coley, I imagine) simmered in milk, the integument of blackish, scaly skin still adhering to one side, and all to be finished up, please, along with the boiled carrots for clear eyesight, and the twin bunkers of mashed potato.

Nanny Mottram only ever drank water. For lunch, she drew a jug of it straight from the tap, and to accompany breakfast she drank a pot of it boiled and plain, without even so much as a sliver of citrus added. She never took tea or coffee, and whether or not she regarded tannin and caffeine (of which she had perhaps never heard) as sinful addictions I do not know, but clearly they were unnecessary to her life, and she probably considered infusions to be unclean. What the inside of Nanny's stomach must have looked like, even then, I can hardly imagine. Perhaps it was already beginning to grow the thing it should not.

The law governing separate meals had one further ramification: Nanny would not eat in the Staff Sitting-room, so after I was safely in bed, the Cri-Call switched on, and the wireless adjusted to her satisfaction, Nanny had her evening meal brought up to the Nursery on a tray by the reluctant Flynn, and there, six nights a week for ten years, she consumed it in isolation. The strange thing is that I don't think she was ever lonely.

At certain specific times of the day, I was granted an audience with my parents, depending on their other commitments. If there were no house-guests staying (and most weekends there were) I was allowed to visit my father in the dining-room as he finished his breakfast, and this involved a rare excursion away from the nursery wing, and down the main staircase, with Nanny usually stopping to inspect my face before releasing me across the hall, tutting, licking the pad of her forefinger, and rubbing away at any breakfast-time tidemarks she imagined around my mouth.

'Walk, Master Richard, and don't run,' she would say – but if I appeared to be in a hurry, and in danger of shipwrecking myself on the marbled floor, it was not from any pressing desire to clap eyes upon my father. It was to get past the portraits along the panelled walls at the foot of the stairs.

I have never much liked painted portraits of anyone's family figures, whatever the artistic merits of their execution; they tend to be formal and pompous and large, and because of their shape they generally look down on you, unlike a photograph. Well, these were on the whole gloomier than most of the stuff you see in museums, and, since these (mostly male) personages were all my direct ancestors, it was hard not to take their forbidding stares personally. The only one of the ten who was smiling was Jane, the Sixth Duchess, who left my grandfather a widower in 1936, shortly after he succeeded to the title. Philip de László painted her sitting on the white bench in the Long Walk with a wide scoop-like flower-basket by her side containing peonies, and a pair of secateurs lightly held in her left hand. She is wearing a plain blouse, with Paisley shawl around the shoulders, and a pleated tweed skirt. She was certainly no great beauty – the nose is Roman and pronounced, the ankles thick as they disappear into her brown brogues – but the artist has imbued her small blue eyes with a brightness that was surely as accurate as her imperfections.

My least favourite was the full-length canvas of my namesake Richard, my grandfather's louche-looking elder brother, depicted in the khaki uniform of the Royal Flying Corps, a leather helmet on his head, goggles up, scarf folded around his throat. He is standing on the edge of an airstrip, with three biplanes parked in the background, and his thin, disdainful face exudes grim confidence. He is certainly not smiling. His hands hang very slightly away from his jodhpurs, like some cowboy anticipating a quick draw, and his stance (right foot turned out at an angle) suggests a man used to sauntering into whatever challenges life might concoct for him.

The picture was painted in 1916, the year of Richard Waterstock's death, by the youthful Colin Gill, himself on leave from the Front. I did not find it very edifying, on the way to the dining-room, to pass under the gaze of a great-uncle with the same name as me who had been blown to bits within living memory. It was like venturing down the tunnel of history, to emerge, just past the likeness of Samuel Slide, the First Duke, into the hall, and thence directly to the closed door behind which, on his own, sat the heir to the dukedom, my father, George.

I knock – the same, syncopated four beats every time. It could only be me at this hour: Flynn uses the door through to his pantry, and my mother takes her morning tea in bed.

Grandfather is unlikely to be roaming the house on his own and would certainly never knock – no, it has to be me, but my father always responds with a flat, uninviting, non-interrogative, routine, calm and slightly imperious 'Yes.'

I enter, and sit in the chair, two away from him. I say, 'Good morning, Father.' Depending on the contents of his newspapers (the *Daily Telegraph*, *The Times*, the *Financial Times*, in that order – he is a man of meticulous habits), or the contents of his letters (the precise movements of his paper-knife, the trim nails extricating the correspondence from the envelopes with chirurgeonly deftness) he may give me either the grey look (perplexed, and already running behind schedule: not an auspicious start) or else the blue (his eyes, unusual with such black hair, are this colour, and he opens them wide before commencing a conversation: the more promising response).

His hair is sleek, black, pomaded. My father toys with the little ceramic orange that holds his breakfast marmalade, decanted daily in dollops from the jar, by Flynn. 'Yes,' he says decisively. 'Good morning, Richard.'

A muscular man, broad shoulders, several inches shorter than the standard six feet most boys assume their fathers to stand; a grub-like cicatrice on the right side of his forehead, disappearing into the hairline ('Well, if you must know, it happened during the war'); the wire field of his eyebrows, the neatly clipped moustache ('Will I have one of those when I am a man?' 'Possibly. We will see.' Yes, that's it.)

'Is anything wrong?'

'No, Father. I was just looking. At your moustache.'

He raises a hand as if to touch it – as if it might have changed – realizes this is absurd, converts the movement into a gesture towards the rolls and toast-rack on the table.

'Have you had your breakfast?'

'Yes. With Nanny. I had it in the Nursery.'

'Well, then. See you after school.'

He had been thirty-seven – ten years older than her – when he married my mother. It was evidently a brief courtship, and though I never remember hearing them raise their voices against one another, they seemed to co-exist in a state of almost permanent disagreement. I wonder if they really knew each other very well before the wedding. When explaining anything to my mother, he would adopt a tone of patient exasperation, as if it were very probably beyond the bounds of possibility that she would comprehend any matter firmly based on practicalities. For her part, my mother gently goaded her passionately well-organized husband through the judicious tactic of creative mis-understanding – slightly reworking his arguments whenever it suited her, and throwing him off his stride with a fundamental question just as he thought the discussion had been resolved.

'But, darling – George – you surely can't mean we go there this summer?'

'I thought that was what we have been debating all this while, yes.'

'Well, I think there has been some mistake; I would not dream of visiting that part of France in August. It will be much too hot. It is simply out of the question.'

'Margaret – please. We are in danger of returning to square one. I am late enough, as it is. A decision has to be made.'

'Darling, I'm sorry. I have been wasting your precious time. I got it wrong, as usual. Do forgive me. Perhaps, if you are so very keen, you would prefer to go there on your own?'

'Honestly, Margaret, you've missed the point entirely. This really is most inconvenient. Why on earth can't you make up your mind?'

'But I have. We shall go to the Isle of Wight as usual.'

'I hate the Isle of Wight – you know that.'

'You'll enjoy it this year, I promise.'

Did my parents love one another? I find it hard to tell. There are so many shapes that love can take: there is duty, that is rewarded with a campaign medal; and crazed passion, that strikes like an attack from Special Forces in the night; and awe, which is the incomprehensible affection one supposedly feels towards a deity; and loyalty, which may occasionally be laziness. Whichever it may have been, I don't recall any signs of physical *tendresse* between my birthparents – none of that billing and cooing that initially embarrasses small boys, and later baffles them at the thought of frenzied couplings. No, I don't remember them so much as holding hands: which is strange, because my mother was beautiful, and surely desirable. Perhaps it was yet another of the nice proprieties observed by people of their social rank, their refusal to acknowledge the body of one's partner in life – but I now imagine the cause of it was something else. I do not think she ever really knew how unwell my father had been just before they first met, but my mother habitually had sole occupancy of her double bed (at least from the time my brother was born), and my father slept in his dressing room. If this was their love, it was of a remarkable kind, even for the English.

Up until the time of her marriage, my mother had been an actress – Margaret Whittaker, famed for her dramatic black hair (there was never any danger of me being a blonde), familiar as a model from the pages of *Vogue*, star of the recent West End thriller, *The Uninvited Guest*. Gave it all up to settle down with George Waterstock, SBS war hero, director of Hedges and Elliott, heir to the blind Duke of London.

Her beauty was avian: thin legs, perfect nails, two sweeping wings of dark hair. She had a trained and seductive voice, high cheek-bones, exquisite little teeth. Her skin was as pale and smooth as ice.

She would enter the Night Nursery when Nanny had made everything shipshape for the evening and, immaculately attired, a touch regal, emanating Patou's fragrance 'Joy', would compose herself in the little armchair by the window, run her hand through the back of her hair, and ask me (though she had usually decided on this beforehand) what story I would like her to read.

'What do you think, Rich? What shall it be, tonight? *The Selfish Giant*, perhaps?'

She loved Wilde, Kipling, the Norse Myths and Legends.

Time and again she performed them for me, and I have to say that when she was reading – when, in effect, she was pretending to be other people – my mother was quite enchanting. I fell under her glamour, as she spun me to sleep.

'It was a large lovely garden, with soft green grass. Here and there over the grass stood beautiful flowers like stars . . . '

I suppose it was because her low voice, with its practised modulations, was capable of accommodating anything in a story with absolute conviction, that these evening sessions made me feel so secure. I would settle further into the bedclothes with Ben, imagining I was suspended in a hammock somewhere in that orchard, the starlight of the petals glistening against the sky.

' "I cannot understand why the Spring is so late in coming," said the Selfish Giant, as he sat at the window and looked out at his cold, white garden' (and here she might hunch her shoulders, and narrow those eyes), '"I hope there will be a change in the weather." '

And then, as the Frost and the Snow danced about through the trees, pictures from her voice began to turn and twindle and dance before my flickering eyelids – the children running scared, the sudden birdsong one morning, the Giant's bearded ferocity melting at the sight of the boy reaching up for the tree. So far as I was concerned, it was a true story. I would discuss details of this, and other tales she rehearsed, as if they had been reported in a newspaper. Where *was* this Giant's castle, exactly, and how had he come by it? Did this happen a very long time ago? ('It must have, Rich, don't you think? Have you seen any giants recently?')

Was this Giant some kind of lord, like Grandpa? We had what seemed like a huge wall around one of our own gardens – was this wrong, and should we knock it down with an axe?

And why did he use an axe, which is meant for chopping trees, not bricks? ('It was the most powerful weapon he possessed, that's why.')

Each time these stories came around, in a delicious cycle

down the months, they hardened into my sense of what was real. I was both the Giant protecting his property, for instance, and the child conjuring colour and noise.

' "Nay," answered the child, "but these are the wounds of Love." '

At moments like these – great, sentimental, baroque moments when the full force of her passions and talent were weaving and whirling sounds to engulf a captive, and willing, audience – I was closest to the heart of my mother. It may have remained the voice of a stranger, a command performance, but these were the only sounds she could make, from her hinterland, that remotely corresponded to the language of love.

'And when the children ran in that afternoon, they found the Giant lying dead under the tree, all covered with white blossoms.' I can't be sure that I ever consciously heard her deliver the closing phrases to any story. Her carefully calculated cadences were designed to be soporific, after all, and if I missed the finale it was perhaps compensation for her that, in place of juvenile applause, she was rewarded with the spectacle – maybe the paradigm of human happiness – of her child contentedly asleep.

My mother is still alive and she looks remarkably spry on the phone, whenever she condescends to permit me a glimpse of her. Naturally I tried my best to persuade her to come out here and live with – or rather, near – me, but she was simply not having any of it. I worry about her living on at Durham Walk, in a city where civic amenities have still not been properly restored, but she has insisted on staying put. The rationing does not seem to bother her, and she is unfazed by the imploded sewers, the rats spreading Weil's disease, the rabies epidemic from the Tunnel. When I saw her earlier this year she had shuttered up the windows of the house against the Japanese mitten-crabs that have colonized the Embankment and crawl up the masonry, and she had not been outside for several weeks. But she was adamant about her decision: 'Things are definitely improving,' she said. And, in a way, she is right.

Now, though geographically apart, my mother and I have reached a better understanding (to get to know your parents it takes time, that precious commodity); besides, I hardly think she would enjoy this little country, which is famed for the freshness of its air. She is effectively a claustrophile, and in all my childhood memories of her she is firmly operating *indoors* – usually from her own little morning-room, where she had the company of the telephone, and Gilbey. She was never really a country person, and though she did her best to support my father during his relatively brief time as the actual lord and master of Spellbrook, I think she took very little pleasure in being the *châtelaine*. She preferred our town house in Durham Walk, her charity committees, the occasional company of those in her erstwhile profession, who were not really to my father's ascetic taste.

Where my father had chosen hopsack for his library, and claret for his dressing-room, my mother had finished the walls of her morning-room in powder-blue – and where his pictures, files and photograph frames had been dragooned into position, her own possessions merely looked as if they were resting temporarily, before continuing to migrate around the room.

Along one wall ran a painted Florentine bookcase, surmounted with a large silver witch-ball wired to the pediment. The shelves were crammed and jumbled with objects as well as books roosting in disarray – my father's recessed presses were faced in with a network of metal grilles (and no doubt shelved alphabetically by author, with writers of opposing gender housed at different ends of the room, I don't know) – but here the plays of Coward squeezed in between a series of *Art at Auction*, a broken run of Scott's novels was interrupted by a pair of tortoiseshell glove-stretchers and a *Life of Garrick*, a dried orange stuck with cloves hung from a blue ribbon below *The*

Arabian Nights, there was a nacreous Roman tear-vial in a
wooden stand, a Lalique crystal quill, a blown ostrich-egg with
a butterfly painted on it, and a stuffed oriole in a case, as a
book-end.

In the window stood her escritoire, the surfaces of which
were so permanently cluttered that my mother had to deal with
her correspondence from the armchair near the fireplace, with
a tray on which to lean. Although she invariably used a Shaeffer
and plain blue Quink, the desk hosted several assorted bottles
of coloured drawing and calligraphy inks (J. Herbin, Paris).
There also resided a cowrie shell, a Viennese vase (filled with
peacock swords and ostrich herls) decorated with a scene of
Salome dancing with the astonished head of John the Baptist, a
heavy Burmese corkscrew, and a scattered collection of vesta-
cases, stamp-boxes and card-holders in gaudy tartanware.

The whole place was volcanic with fine ash. Addicted as
she was to the smoking of Dunhill International, my mother
generally tried to appease the atmosphere by burning essential
oils, dripped carefully from a pipette on to an absorbent ring
resting on the crest of a warm light-bulb – but the result was
that her morning-room smelt of both tobacco and gardenias.
Planted strategically around the furniture was a virtual
anthology of flowered porcelain ashtrays, each with a metal
butt-snuffer in the centre, generally sprouting a filtertip like
some foul stamen.

When it came to real flowers, my mother was quite content
to snip, clip, trim, strip and primp them, once delivered to her
flower-room, but in the maintenance of the gardens themselves
she had no apparent interest. Besides, there were three gardeners
constantly at work, who had no need of her advice or assistance.

Peter Buxton was the presiding genius of the land immediately surrounding Spellbrook – a lean bearded man with a russet
tweed jacket and a pork-pie hat, the tops of his gumboots turned
down. Like Flynn, he had been in my grandfather's employ
since being demobbed, but he was a taciturn, more elusive
presence for me as a child.

Small children are seldom viewed with favour by those to whom the care of formal gardens has been entrusted: herbaceous borders are rarely improved by being beaten through during the search for a stray rubber ball, and the conversion of a stand of precious hydrangeas into an Arthurian fastness by surrounding it with a mass of pilfered bamboo sticks never meets with much approval. Buxton and I therefore hardly sought out one another's company. And this was also in line with Nanny's attitude, that 'outdoors' was nearly as suspect as 'abroad'.

Beyond knowing about the usual proximity of nettle and dock, Nanny Mottram was scarcely in the hedge-tutor class. She preferred to treat a walk outside as if we were safely perambulating some Royal Park in the capital, where you could look, but never touch. 'Don't do that, pet,' she would say, if I were to pick a stalk of grass, and poke one end into my mouth, 'or you will choke, and die.' Another taboo concerned the dandelion – 'If you pick *that*, Master Richard, you'll up and wet your bed, so you will.'

To Buxton himself she nurtured a complex antipathy. Should we chance to encounter him somewhere, stumping around in his corduroys, she would dismiss him with a nod; and on the odd occasions when he offered to approach and swap pleasantries, she would stiffen as if he were some avatar of Pan.

'That filthy man. Did you remark the state of his hands?'

But in reality this had little to do with hygiene and germs, and was just another scene in the enduring pantomime of superiority which such nannies liked to enact in order to stress their generic differences from the self-evidently unwashed underclass of all 'outdoor staff'. (When she eventually retired, Peter Buxton presented her with a magnificent potted orchid, and showed up his hands, back and front, for her inspection. They passed muster, and Nanny managed to laugh.)

When Buxton eventually retired, several months before my father's death, he was presented with a gold fobwatch. It was clear that he was so amazed he hardly knew what to say. I believe he may have considered it an insult, because he had always lived by the daily cycle of the sun, and told the important dates of the year, not by any paper calendar, but by the heraldry of his plants and shrubs – the Blenheim Orange would blossom on 5 May, the tea-roses on 12 July, and so forth, into winter.

It was quite possible, of course, when still there were well-defined seasons. Before time began its meltdown, making these strange arcs.

The guidebook you purchase at the Spellbrook kiosk today will be of little help in trying to imagine the gardens as they were when my eyes saw them from the vantage-point of only a yard or so above grass level, a boy running from place to place. North of the house was the walled garden, now designated the 'set-down point for groups, by prior arrangement', but then an area of two protected acres, safe from the depredations of rabbits, out of bounds to scumbering dogs, and dedicated to flowerbeds surrounding a central, oblong lawn.

Here grew the celebrated roses of Spellbrook, trained up and out from their fiercely antique trunks and along thick naval ropes slung between wooden posts, producing, every June, fountains and horizontally extended cascades of bunched, languet petals like something from an Elizabethan masque. Along the walls were trees pleached and in espaliers – pear, apricot and fig – and in September the wasps would get drunk on juice, and swivel angrily on their backs along the path, and I would take my revenge on them.

In the beds, huge Oriental poppies flamed in season, with hollyhocks and lupins, golden-rod and expensive-looking peonies – just reciting their names make me slightly heady, if not wasp-drunk. There were red-hot pokers, explosions of lavender, and slim forests of bamboo. When the crimson phlox was in flower, I would hunt Peacocks and Tortoiseshells with my net, and confine them until sundown in a balsa-wood cage, with a polythene viewing-panel against which they occasionally bounced and fluttered, before shutting up their wings, and making themselves thin, vertical and dark.

There were two gates to the walled garden. One led north

into the Long Walk, an avenue of cherry trees with some of the cutting borders for the house on either side. In late spring one year, when I was about five, I remember working my way methodically along this track and collecting the fallen blossom; I was carrying Ben, and stuffed my manna into his soft cave. That evening, when the flowers had bruised and fermented in the heat, I unzipped his tum and released an unfamiliar, brown scent, sour (as I now recognize) like ale.

If you took the western exit through the wall, however, you would in those days have discovered the glass metropolis where Buxton had his nursery and his forcing-houses. As you loll in the Sensureteria that has replaced it, and the kids vault happily among the hydrofoam castles and explore, under super-vision, the Virtual Corridors, Splatter-Zone, and Interfood Pro-gramme, it is now almost impossible to remember a time when the word 'greenhouse' referred to something with connotations of husbandry and skill, rather than a decade of 'Will it? Won't it?', successive international conventions, bickerings over stat-istics, computer projections, and data massaged until the point of implausibility by the industrial conglomerates, before admit-ting that, No, It won't, It has.

Like most citizens, I am fed up with all of this. It makes me sick, and I have no stomach for the ludicrous mismanagement of the immediate past. I don Skyblok and make jokes about it, even here, in this humourless neck of the woods, where scarcely anyone else quaffs whisky even when there has been a death in the family, and you have to motor for miles to buy a packet of lung-fucking cigarettes and shopkeepers (who stock the stuff, for heaven's sake) preen an eyebrow when asked for a carton of honest Gitanes, and sell it to you as if it were little better than a consignment of antique Spanish fly. It makes my blood boil, this notion that All Will Be Well. My synapses jolt, the ganglia crackle and make strange arcs, not entirely good for my metabolism, when I come across these double standards. You really should look after your own body; the Planet Earth will correct its imbalances. These things take time. We are finally working together. There are recovery mechanisms, scientific programmes, millions of committed individuals, several decades more than the alarmists would have you believe, we all need to ensure we are exercising our political rights, and, yes, thank you very much, that will be twenty-four ecks for the smoking materials, Doctor Slide, if you please.

Sod these new schizophrenics, the shopkeepers who are kinetically agitated by the Millennium. If there was a greenhouse-effect in the era when Peter Buxton held sway over Spellbrook, it was entirely different, and he rolled his own cigarettes, to boot. In the cast-off tins, from which his Old Holborn had been exhausted, I used to try the hatching from pupa to imago of various grubs I kidnapped around our garden. You'd have to search long and hard, high and low, to discover any such trophies on the chemically controlled surfaces of the gardens today – nothing to compare with that hirsute caterpillar, the colour of a Murraymint, I hoarded in a punctured tin convinced a Red Admiral would emerge, alarmed when what flopped out one morning when I opened the lid for inspection was a groggy brown moth, with a head like a bear.

But, *retournons à nos moutons* – Buxton raised a variety of fruits in his glasshouses: grapes, pineapples, the odd crop of greenish bananas, exquisite melons, and great, cetacean cucumbers. In times of plenty, vast numbers of the latter would become over-ripe before they were required by Iris, and Buxton would have one of his subordinates dump the excess on the midden, which I would then storm with my pen-knife, slashing and hacking at the flesh until I was king of the mulch-heaps. And in August, in the beds beyond, we would pick that archetypal children's fruit, the English strawberry, one gritty fruit in the mouth for each that got dropped into the trug, a dream of rubies.

Part of the sweetness of all this plenty was the knowledge that time was short. It was a natural harvest, anticipated throughout the summer, feeding only temporarily a taste stored in the memory. Now you can buy a macroponic version so big you have to carve it, on any day of the year, but it will never compare to those small, bloody, bristly fruit that just fitted into a child's cheek: another badge of progress, another strand of the seasons snapped away in the interests of efficiency.

I was four and a half years old, the perfect age for jealousy and an excruciating display of textbook regression, when my brother Cosmo was born.

For several months after her confinement, my mother was ill, and took to her bed, and I saw even less of her than usual. I was moved from the Night Nursery along to a proper bedroom of my own at the end of the corridor, away from those pictures and into a place where I was repeatedly assured, 'Of course, you are a big boy now.'

I didn't like this new state of affairs one bit ('Ah, he's just like his father'; 'Did you see him *smile*?'; 'Aren't you lucky to have a sweet little baby brother?'). So I tried a little lulu that proved remarkably effective. I suddenly could not swallow any food that had to be chewed.

It caused considerable trouble for Nanny, who grew alarmed at my refusal to ingest anything other than laboriously prepared purées, and before too long I was taken up to Harley Street, to the consulting-rooms of Sir Michael Stafford, the royal paediatrician, who depressed my tongue with his wooden spatula (first dipping it into a glass of milky antiseptic) and pronounced me anaemic, in need of supplementary iron, a special diet of beef extract, mashed spinach (they still hadn't discovered that the man who did the research on this obnoxious vegetable's supposedly fortifying properties had, quite literally, put a decimal point in the wrong position), and lots more milk.

This last ingredient naturally fired the imagination of Nanny Mottram, and before long I was staging a remarkable recovery. After a few weeks of her enthusiastic decoctions – ham bones boiled in milk, raw eggs whisked up in hot milk, milk and stewed spinach – I was prepared to ingest any amount of boiled ham with parsley sauce, beef crumble, or haddock pudding, in order to convince her I was cured.

Pleased as she was, she ascribed this reconstitution of the status quo less to dietary measures applied to the physical body, and more to the extra dollops of religious instruction that she took this opportunity of serving up to my fledgeling spirit.

Nanny was a Christian Scientist, and believed in the absolute curative powers of the Book. Medical nostrums were anathema to her, but a regular daily dose of a *text* was quite a different matter. So, when I moved to my new room and began my ploy to divert attention from the squalling infant Cosmo, I had not banked on my *Peter Rabbit*, *Little Grey Rabbit*, *Noddy*, *Flower-Fairy Poems*, *Struwwelpeter*, *Sooty Has His Birthday*, *Kings and Queens of England*, *Heidi*, *Rumpelstiltskin* and *The Enormous Turnip* suddenly being augmented – one hour after every breakfast, since it was the holidays, and one hour after bath-time, every evening for nearly four weeks, by which time, even by her lights, it was plain that I was once again whole in body and in tiny spirit – with the Text to which she was voluntarily submitting herself, and which, with no concessions to an audience aged less than five, involved such spectacular biblical topics as the numerous foreskins of the slain Philistines (it was more a question of, 'What is a Philistine?' than 'What is a foreskin?', since I imagined the latter were the skins that you sported on the four fingers of each hand), and the intricacies of that poor old magic realist, and author of the Book of Revelation, St John the Divine.

Again, I can't be precisely sure when my mother began to vary her own diet by augmenting her consumption of liquids, but it was certainly while Cosmo was still quite small. I imagine it was boredom that prompted her new habit, rather than the discovery of anything about the man with whom she was living – indeed, it might have been the very realization that their future together now held little promise of any new developments. The generation of their children successfully completed, and all the domestic machinery in motion, she must have felt as if she and my father were already perilously near the closing lines of their own personal drama, although she was still only a young woman. Perhaps that accounts for the distant look she often wore, like the dissolved gaze one might direct towards an invisible audience during the final tableau on stage (the querulous, faraway aspect gradually disappeared after his death: that I do remember).

She developed a penchant for gin, and took to spending many hours in her morning-room, perched in her armchair, fiddling with the contents of her scrapbooks and photograph albums, executing gros-point embroidery, or attempting to impose some order upon the zigzag pile of magazines, receipts and theatrical programmes that accumulated beside her chair – a heap of confusion from which sections periodically collapsed, like a caving iceberg.

My father referred disapprovingly to her bottle as 'your friend, Gilbey', and I used to think she really was closeted away with a person of this name. Sometimes I would creep up and press one ear to the panel of her door, to eavesdrop on their secret conversations. I could hear my mother's voice distinctly through the wood, but never that of any man. I asked her once whom she had been talking to, and she retorted that it was rude to listen in, and none of my business when she was speaking on the telephone. It never occurred to me that she had started talking to herself.

Her moods became more unpredictable. Sometimes, if I went to see her after school, she would peer at me and frown, as if at an improbable reading on some thermometer, making me feel awkward and unclean. But after she had enjoyed a particularly successful session with her liquid paramour there were also times when her face would take on a fetching little flush, an alcoholic alpenglow; and it was at such moments, when the chemicals had drawn the colour into her cheeks, that she looked most fresh and youthful, like a girl who has just caught her first sight of something thrilling. Her eyes did not assume the hooded aspect of the claret-drinker, but were wide, as if with wonder or belladonna, and bright with a light I now understand was lost for years in the labyrinth of matrimony.

I don't think she really liked children; but if only someone had handed me the right script – earlier, when there was still time – I would willingly have learned my way towards loving her.

It was one of the great pleasures of my childhood that my grandfather lived in the same house, and I now realize it was something of a rare privilege, because the British are notoriously bad at accommodating the idea of old people within their daily lives. In fact, our manifest distaste for the inconvenience of looking after the old is virtually a badge of our national incivility. Compared to other European countries, we have no recent tradition of providing for old people by setting them at ease in a position of high regard and seniority within the family home. As a result, most of us as children only come to know members of the family of the grandparental generation as remote figures, to be tolerated and endured during visiting hours (whether or not they are actually in a geriatric ghetto), and we are not discouraged from the notion that they live in the past, and that their opinions are of antiquarian relevance, at best.

In wiser societies, the views of the elderly (and sometimes even of the senile) are accorded a little more respect.

My grandfather was the head of our family when I was a child, and in retrospect I suppose my father deferred to him despite the fact that the estate had been made over to his stewardship during the war. Since I was myself somewhat awed by my father's impassive demeanour, it was probably this youthful and unformulated sense that he in his turn was answerable to some higher authority that invested the ageing Duke with some of his splendour and mystique.

Although he had the vatic mien of some Old Testament sage, with a fullish head of white hair (worn, I now realize, so unfashionably long that it would then have been considered a

mark of eccentricity), Arthur, Sixth Duke of London, aspired
to little in the way of *gravitas*. He was a modest soft-spoken
man, with a slight other-worldly quality – both childlike and
remarkably independent – that was immediately attractive to
me as a little boy. I used to identify him with that old actor
who played the original Dr Who, a series I was then enjoying.
Compared to the bustle elsewhere in the house, his apartment
on the ground floor of Spellbrook was serene, unchanging, and
he liked to refer to our family life as if it was enacted on some
battlefield, an on-going military saga like the Hundred Years
War, from which I would bring him daily dispatches. He was
a very patient listener, his manner was gentle, and he had the
most delicate hands with proud, greenish veins that fascinated
me: he might not have possessed the wisdom of a biblical
prophet, but he was in many ways the paradigm of an ancestral
presence. His visits to Trumper's, the Jermyn Street barbers,
might have been infrequent for tonsurial purposes, but he held
in fierce affection their eau de toilette that went by the name of
Eucris. The aroma faintly accompanied him everywhere, and
still I associate his presence with those citrus notes, and the
pervasive redolence of sandalwood. 'Brompton,' he would say,
'Brompton, is that you?' as I entered the conservatory where
he liked to sit (the excessive cost of heating his favourite area
was a frequent bone of contention between Arthur and his
waxen-faced son), but of course he knew it was his grandson
approaching, long before he beckoned me to his knee, because
Blanco would have heralded my approach as I emerged from
the corridor into the east wing.

Blanco was his parrot, a rather petulant African Grey whom
Arthur had taught to announce by name every member of our
household, and most of the regular visitors. Grandfather would
feed this beast a dried apricot each time he correctly identified
one of us seeking an audience, and family legend had it that he
had only, on one disastrous occasion, made a mistake: during
the war, the Bishop of London – who signs himself Londinium,
as opposed to London, a less neat but enviably venerable auto-

graph – had been invited down to Spellbrook for his annual luncheon, and Blanco, the holy fool and jester by appointment to the court of King Arthur, had ushered him into the ducal presence with a squawk of, 'Bloody Hell, Bloody Hell.' Dixit, quod Parrot. It is said the ecclesiastical luminary accepted his glass of sherry with a solemn face, and remarked, 'Silly bugger.'

I would clamber on to my grandfather's lap, and he would assume a most grave expression, putting the back of his hand against my cheek, and saying, 'So, little soldier – what news from the Front?' And seldom did he seem less than intrigued by the trivial reports I would bring him about my life in the nursery wing – how Nanny Mottram was cross with the hot weather, and all the flies in her kitchen; what was happening to Digby and Dan Dare in the latest *Eagle*; that Cosmo was now able to sit up, and was trying to crawl.

'Ah, Brompton,' he would say, with a pat, '*that* is something I would like to see.'

He had been blind since birth, and it was only by another accident that he ever became a duke in the first place. The youngest of three children born to Harry (the Fifth Duke, and an officer in the Grenadiers) and Anna (daughter of a Philadelphian tycoon) he was never encouraged when young to have high expectations of his life. His mother had contracted rubella during the second month of her pregnancy, and the blind baby Arthur was subsequently regarded as something of a family misfortune. His brother Richard, five years his senior, was the all-important son and heir, and his older sister, Martha, was destined to be beautiful. Arthur they regarded as slightly simple, a boy in need of protection and virtual confinement at Spellbrook, the purchase of which had been made possible by his mother's dowry just four years before his birth, but where he was to outlive them all.

For three years over the turn of the century, Duke Harry served in the war against the Boers, and then, at the start of the Great War, as a senior Staff Officer with Strategic Command. Richard Waterstock (as his portrait records) joined the Royal

Flying Corps as soon as he was qualified, in 1915. Along with many sons of the aristocracy, he was an especially useful recruit, since he was already an excellent shot. Amidst such martial activity, Arthur remained at home, saved by his disability. His mother never really forgave him for it.

With the heavy shells flowering in the mud beneath him, my namesake Richard was artillery-spotting above the lines at Verdun, on 9 April 1916, when his Moraine Bullet was shot down by an enemy Albatross. Fortunately, his machine did not catch fire, but he crash-landed in No Man's Land where a wire-field entangled the wings, and prevented him skidding into the trenches of the Hun.

He was rescued, unconscious, by a raiding-party of Canadians, and sent back to London for convalescence at Lady Ridley's hospital, in Belgravia. On the night of 2 September, just before he was due to return to his section, there were fourteen Zeppelin raids on the capital, and he was killed in a direct hit on the Grosvenor nightclub.

His mother was in mourning for the rest of her life; after the War, his father became reclusive, and hardly ever left the estate; Martha disappeared to Buenos Aires with somebody else's husband; and Arthur, the runt and now the heir, surprised everyone by marrying his childhood friend, Jane Watkins, the daughter of the local parson. A woman who seemed genuinely to adore this cloistered man of twenty-five, with his curious milky eyes, and even presented him with a son, to the equal delight of her in-laws, the very next year – a woman who would actually smile at the painter, when sitting for a portrait commissioned by a man who had never seen her in his life.

Jane was killed by pneumonia some twenty years before my own birth, but Arthur spoke of her quite often. 'She was an extraordinary woman, you know; you would have adored her, Brompton. Nothing was too much trouble for her. She had me to look after, as well as your father. Loved by everyone. She had been a friend of mine since I was a lad like yourself – would read to me, even then, and take me for walks. We sang in the choir together. They say she had a glory of a smile, and I can well believe it. You have seen her portrait, surely – is that not right?'

I suppose I loved my grandfather because, despite having led a rarified existence, he was not afraid to be passionate. In this respect he, too, was rather extraordinary. 'You will find that we are not very practised in the business of expressing our feelings, and I consider this a national failing. I hope you may be listening to what I say, though it is difficult for a boy to understand. A girl would follow it, however.'

'I understand, I understand.'

'Well, then. You must do great things with your life, but you should never ignore the noises that come from the workings of your heart. It is from these sounds that the complicated music of all human history is composed. In the end, this is what matters.'

'Yes, grandpa.'

'Yes, Brompton. Remember this.' (Old men, old men: they are fond of such pronouncements. And of course I was not listening properly, even then.)

But he was rarely quite so solemn. He understood the need that most children have – to be silly on occasions, and to have an adult share in the exuberance and anarchy of their laughter. For the first seven years of my life I could count on this whenever I was with him, whereas with my own parents my behaviour was almost perpetually irrigated by a slow fear of appearing childish (I have made up for it since, but it's not the same).

Despite the fact that he had never been able to see so much as a buttercup, my grandfather had a remarkable affinity with flora; and his particular delight was the orchard he created through the medium of Peter Buxton. He was the amanuensis with whom Arthur London collaborated in his mind's eye, and between them they achieved a kind of immortality by devising the pomological specimen known as the Spellbrook Seedling – an apple now cultivated from Australia to Canada, and a triumph of cross-pollination.

They were seldom happier than during those meetings when, Buxton having read out the relevant entries in Robert Hogg's *Fruit Manual*, or E. A. Bunyard's *Handbook of Hardy Fruits, Apples and Pears*, they lit upon glamorous variations with which to experiment the following spring. But he certainly maintained an ironic perspective on his hobby, saying that it had nothing to do with the Garden of Eden, which had been an orchard full of potential that suffered badly from a lack of general foresight.

For a man who had made the daughter of the local vicar his Duchess, and who was so familiar with the Bible (read daily to him by her, and latterly by Flynn) that he could *recite* the lesson in church once a month, hoary-headed Arthur could be pleasingly irreverent. He had a reedy, rather melodious voice; I remember it less from his religious recitations than from the several occasions when he regaled me (on my own) with a fluent litany concerning the evolution of the English apple. I suppose it was the first real obsession to which I was ever exposed. On an autumn promenade through his orchard, he would jab his stick in the direction of the various trees that represented significant stages in the gradually complicating pedigree of the Pomona – beginning, just to the left of the gate, with the ancient Permain and Costard, through the French Pippins, the Sussex Goldens, the Elizabethan Queenings and the russet Leathercoat until the story broadened out with Codlin cookers from Kent, the wilding Redstrake and such Victorian beauties as Beauty of Bath, the Houblons and the Paroquets.

These names were my childhood spells, rendered more potent by his insistence that 'The apple is our family tree', as indeed, heraldically, it is. Emneth Early, Cutler Grieve, Gloria Mundi, Mr Prothero – they sounded like a leash of exotic racehorses. 'Never forget, little soldier, the fruit that can be gathered from what is rooted deep in the past.' I wondered, even as a child, how he could adore what he could not see; but he was adamant that their form and colour were tangible to him, and that the best attributes of such a fruit were its texture and smell. 'You need ears to appreciate an apple,' he would say, feeling along the underside of a branch, and gently twirling one into the cup of his other palm. 'Here, bite into this, and listen for the sound. You must learn to trust all your senses. Do you hear that, through the sizzle of the juice? That noise is the reason this tree has been growing here for so long. It is like the applause at the end of a first night in some theatre. They tell me your eyes work well, so what do you see as you look up above us? It must be a splendid prospect, surely? It is a box-office success, it will run and run.'

Sack and Sugar, Braddick's Nonpareil, Striped Beefing, Sunset. The five packed acres of history where he used to fret about the perils of scab and mildew, hatch plots for the eradication of the Capsid Bug, and discuss with Buxton the intricacies of grafting have now been torn open and made over to a Visitors Reception Centre, with a sterile metallic signpost by the gate, which points to the Historium, the Heritage Walk, and the Gift Shop.

At least they have not yet ploughed up the graveyard. He was buried there in 1963, and I'm glad to say that the sapling planted by my father later in that year continues to flourish: the Spellbrook Seedling sent down its young roots into the particular soil beneath, and each May continues to put forth pointed green sepals enclosing trusses of pink and white blossom, an olive stem, and below the flowers that slightest of swellings which suggested, with careful husbandry, where one might have expected fruit.

I may be quite wrong, but I do not think another small boy will ever experience that crack and spurt of off-white ripened apple flesh as I did in the company of my grandfather, Arthur London, when the garden of my world seemed so young.

TWO

We were not always a family of Dukes, obviously.

In my recent years of voluntary exile, I have been trying to understand something of what has happened to the various members of my family down the generations, the swirls and currents that have conspired to fetch me up on this particular stormshore. But it is not easy, this process of detection: it is an inexact science. You hear so many people say, 'We just want to know The Truth.' But, what is that? It's a picture as complex and amorphous as the shapes on a weather map, derived from some satellite screen. It depends what you're looking for, it depends what you are equipped to recognize. And it is a moving target.

The truth is polyfaceted, compounded of shifting multiples: it is as plural as the sky at night.

What light we see comes into our eyes from a great web of starfields, supposedly infinite in extent. But the accumulation of all their luminary emissions amounts to no more than a general glow, the achievement of a mere series of glimmers. If the universe is actually boundless, then why is there so much darkness in the night sky? Touchstone, in *As You Like It*, explains, 'A great cause of the night is lack of the Sun'; but if there really are uncountable other suns, each a million miles in diameter, burning away across the heavens, why does our sky not positively blaze at night, or at the very least resemble a poorly tuned television monitor? Why these isolated little pin-pricks, instead of soft, but ubiquitous incandescence?

One answer seems to be that those stars that would be supplying light in the dark places lie so far from our view that even their first pulses have not yet had the time to reach us. Because the perception of starlight is an ocular aberration: what we are

recording is a picture of these bodies as they once were, sometimes long ago. We see what is no longer there, and some of
what is there we cannot yet see (and if we are not very lucky, we
may never perceive the light from some stars, crossing the voids
to us even now, because we may not be here, or anywhere,
ourselves).

So, when a person attempts to peer into certain sectors of his
past, with the equivalent determination of one of those boffins
staring into the tunnels of space for evidence of light emanating
from fresh sidereal configurations, by which he may plot the
architecture and genealogy of the cosmos, he must accept that
what seems clear may no longer be so; that what appears obscure,
or optically thick, could yield a clue, given patience. Given time.

In theory, if we could delve deeply enough with our instruments into space, we could see far enough back in time to glimpse
the spark at the Moment of Creation. In effect, we would be
gazing directly into the face of God.

When this happens, it will no doubt make a great story in
the Astronomers' Club Saloon Bar and Late Nite Allstar Eaterie,
where photographs will be handed round, and the good old boys
who always knew they could do it if only they hung in there,
(and siphoned off the research funds that could have made water
fresh, and children keep their sight, and basic pulses arrive each
day for consumption at migrant camps not five miles outside the
major cities of three continents), and so long as they kept their
vigils, stuck to their theories, restricted themselves to furious
auto-erotic sessions of manufriction and nocturnal emissions,
came on all strong with their esoteric papers, and the occasional,
worldwide blockbuster of popularizing flim-flam and carpcrap
to keep us laymen on tenterhooks, make us suck our teeth in
admiration and anticipation about the glories, the wonders, the
sheer, life-enhancing developments that would become our collective, global dues as a result of the result of their results (when
they come) – well, I meet some of these people from time to
time, here, in the staff common room of the Institute, and I can
tell, as they activate their sachets of water (Did you never learn

about the lunchtime beer?), that they would not spot Sir God's physiognomy, not if it popped up in some press release after the sensible Prokrisp lunchbox, and nine minutes of humming and nodding over the subsequent herbal tea.

Forgive me; this is self-indulgent. My feelings about the expensive star-peerers are not strictly relevant at this stage. I just don't see why they should be funded, when we're so manifestly heading up several other perilous creeks without any paddles, in a procession of barbed-wire canoes. A snapshot of God's face would no doubt be very interesting, but at this stage of our World Family history, I can't help but think it a bit of an indulgence.

After all, there's a sporting chance there won't be too many folk here to leaf through the album, anyway. I know He has become a celebrity again, but I think we should get all this speculation about Sir God into a proper perspective. Quite honestly (and here I am proffering you My Truth), I don't think we should continue to give Him the benefit of the doubt. I am firmly of the opinion that He would care, if he existed, and would intervene. The Acts of God of which I, personally, have any knowledge, suggest otherwise.

So I will presume some other force has been at work in the fortunes of my family, until I am confronted with something that suggests the contrary. I will think of us as having been subject to the strange weather of what goes down in the record-book as History.

Samuel Slide was born in the year the South Sea Bubble burst, in the village of Brompton, then just outside Westminster. His father was a shipping clerk from a family of Huguenot refugees called de Slyde who had left La Rochelle in 1684. Samuel followed his father into the book-keeping profession and began to work in the accounts office of the East India Company until, at the age of twenty-five, he boarded a tea clipper and set sail for India itself, as one of the Company's factors.

Within ten years he had made his first fortune, from 'shaking the pagoda tree'. Although his salary was modest, there was money to be made by the adventurers from private internal trade, exempt of taxes, through the *dastak*, or free pass system – cottons from Madras, Gujurati indigo, Bengalese saltpetre, traded and bartered while travelling across the sub-Continent on Company business.

According to Robert Hodgson's excellent biography, *The Nabob of London*, there were two reasons for Sam's extraordinary success, and they were both a combination of luck and skill. In the early part of 1747, while en route to a silks merchant in Jaipur, his entourage was set upon by a gang of dacoits whom they surprised ambushing – literally red-handed – a beleaguered party of Banyans. The bandits were driven off by Sam's men, who then discovered that the man whose retinue they had saved was the son of one of Rajasthan's wealthiest sarafs – the caste of money-changers and brokers on whom all Europeans depended as intermediaries for business transactions throughout the Mughal economy.

The grateful father gave Sam access to this powerful network on extremely advantageous terms, and it meant that, unlike his fellow speculators, he could easily transfer debts and credits across India without having to tie up much of his actual capital. He concealed this singular advantage from the Company's other operatives, and converted his profits at irregular intervals into gemstones that could be conveyed back to London as unobtrusively as possible. In this way, throughout the period of Clive's ascendancy in India, Slide managed to repatriate a considerable sum of money, which was invested according to his instructions by Alexander Hunter, his lawyer in the City of London.

Having exploited his privileged connection with the web of the sarafs, Sam had another stroke of luck that brought him very rapid profits. He had established a quasi-monopoly on saltpetre, and had taken the risk of financing out of his own reserves three factories devoted to the manufacture of gunpowder. Towards the end of his spell in the East, he could practically name his own price to keep the Company's rifles primed during the struggles against the French that culminated in the defeat of General Lally at Wandiwash, and his eventual surrender (after a siege of eight months, and highly lucrative to my ancestor) at Pondicherry.

Samuel Slide returned to London in 1766, during Clive's first term of governorship. In his absence, Hunter had put the profits to good use: they had established a thriving chandlers and munitions company, completed the construction of Slide Wharf (just up from the East India Docks), and built up a broadly based body of stocks as a reward for his enterprise. He left India just as the heyday for personal profiteering was about to enjoy a drastic decline.

At the age of forty-six, he entered a new phase of his life; he acquired Waterstock Park, a Palladian mansion set in 3000 acres of Northamptonshire farmland. He raised sheep, and began to supply his own woollen mills in the Midlands; so that while the ships plied his wharf in London with Asian textiles (at a 10 per cent surcharge) for re-export to the Continent, he was simultaneously developing an interest in the production of domestic cloth – an industry in the process of mechanical revolution.

By all accounts his life at Waterstock was on the grand scale befitting a nabob. With its dramatically landscaped gardens, fashionable folly, and serpentine lake, it was a minor palace. The house was filled with the appurtenances of an exotic adventurer – great rugs of woven silk, dark hardwood furniture from the Northern Territories, and animal skins on the walls. He surrounded himself with a retinue of forty servants, many of whom were brought back from the East. These included a number of Anglo-Indians, rumoured to be his illegitimate offspring.

He had a reputation for lavish hospitality (there was a little playhouse for weekend theatricals) but seems to have been quite austere in his own habits. Although he maintained a splendid cellar of wines, he never drank alcohol himself – a fact that was considered highly eccentric in those days, especially since water was so dangerous – and had an aversion to tobacco, forbidding its consumption in his presence. There was some talk of an addiction to opium in his years in the East.

When in the capital, Slide's economic influence naturally drew him into powerful political circles, and he became a devotee of the Tory party. As a businessman and entrepreneur he did not align himself with the Whig grandees, who considered themselves a race apart, preserving their landed interests for future generations. His docklands interests attracted the admiration of the Earl of Sandwich, who was created Admiral of England in 1771, and through him Slide was introduced to the circle of Lord North, who became Prime Minister the same year. He created my ancestor the Earl of Brompton, Baron Slide, and the new peer cemented his alliance with the Tory ministry by marrying North's youngest daughter, Caroline, in 1773.

His star firmly in the ascendant, he was well received at Court, in particular by the hapless Queen Charlotte, whose husband was stricken with insanity, brought on by porphyria and enfeebled genes. At one time, George III was determined to conclude every sentence he uttered with the word 'peacock', and it was Brompton who persuaded him that this pavonine noun was so majestic a word that it should only ever be whispered sotto voce, for fear it should fall upon vulgar ears.

When the monarch finally recovered his senses in 1789, a great alfresco feast was held at Waterstock in celebration, with three hundred estate workers and their families dining off spit-roasted deer – an event commemorated inbils by George Morland. The following year, on the occasion of his seventieth birthday, my illustrious ancestor was granted by the monarch, at the request of the Younger Pitt, the Duchy of London, and in recognition of the great sway of trade he had attracted to the city, the courtesy title of Marquess of Waterstock, for his son, and all future heirs.

Managing to acquire a Dukedom was fortunate enough in itself, but bagging the title of the capital – with its archetypal connotations as the epicentre of an emergent empire – well, that was an extraordinary bonus. I can't help thinking the monarch might still have been a few annas short of the full rupee when he acquiesced to Pitt's suggestion, but there you go. Our family has certainly never had any complaint about his magnanimity, and the name has always looked rather impressive on our subsequent documents and letterheads.

It was surely a fine example of the ancient honours system sometimes getting things right. Sam had both riches and land to support such a title and hundreds of tenants over whom he held political control. He was elderly, he was incontrovertibly distinguished (unlike some of those who subsequently bore his title, I grant you) and he had proved himself a natural leader of other men. This was the original requirement of the highest rank of the peerage – Duke derives from *dux*, a leader. On the Continent, the equivalent would have been a Prince (though I doubt even that would cut much ice here in Switzerland, where a doctorate seems to be the only title that creates much of an impression). I remember my grandfather – who was not exactly a stickler for such matters – explaining to me that, in strict protocol, an English Duke (those Irish ones are a different genus, on the whole) takes precedence over the Dalai Lama, who, with his millions of devoted followers, is presumed to be a leader of lesser import than the owner of a clutch of farms in the Home Counties, or a man who spends most of his year in tweed plus-twos trying to kill birds, the rest of his calendar taken up with watching his highly trained animals running and jumping, as he sits on a bench with his binoculars.

But then my grandfather Arthur was very confused towards the end of his life. I'm sure that fundamentally he appreciated the essential vertebration that such aristocracy afforded the rest of society. I feel certain he could not have been blind to these self-evident, historic and often self-sacrificing benefits. I mean, the facts speak for themselves.

Samuel and his much younger wife Caroline had three children, of whom the eldest, Rupert, briefly succeeded to the Dukedom on his father's death in 1796, but died, without issue, himself five years later, when he was asphixiated by a piece of fish.

Although I like to think we have never been a family of exquisites or eccentrics, like the Marchmains, or, indeed, the Tantamounts, those fictional daguerrotypes that have caused so many to mistake the shadow for the substance, I have to admit we have produced some black sheep. And when, in 1801, a morsel of cod throttled the great Sam's heir, it was perhaps unfortunate that the estate and titles passed to his younger son, a wastrel named after the Indian maverick, Clive.

The Third Duke squandered what was in those days an almost unimaginable fortune. He speculated disastrously in mineral rights, indulged his penchant for heavy gambling in the company of the Prince Regent, and took to brandy. He had a daughter and a son (Hugh) by his first wife, Alice, and then lived alone at Waterstock for several years. There were rumours of a scandalous nature surrounding the death of a serving-girl who was, according to some sources, discovered mutilated in the meadows, and then he made a most unsatisfactory match with Constance, Lady Askwith, by whom he had two further daughters. By this time, he was heavily in debt, and in 1828 the estates at Waterstock had to be sold. Seven years later, estranged from Constance, and leaving behind him his son and three importunate daughters – Charlotte, Victoria and Dorothy – he hanged himself in the Green Man tavern, off the Strand.

Waterstock passed into the hands of the Shadwell family, industrial plutocrats from Pontefract, and ultimately to a reclusive Canadian who had made huge amounts of money in the pulp-mill industry, and used to visit England every summer. He abandoned the house when it was requisitioned as a training-camp during the Great War, and returned to find it in a state of ruin. It was riddled with rot, the roof-leads had been torn off, and the neoclassical bath-house had been used for target-practice.

The house was demolished in 1921, so neither I, nor my father, nor (of course) my grandfather, ever got to see it.

Hugh was only fifteen when he inherited the title: the estate and the fortune were gone, though there was a town house in Durham Walk which his stepmother had bought with her own money some years before, and which has remained in the family ever since (my own mother still lives there, today). In contrast to his father, Hugh was a studious and sober young man, and he was advised that the best prospects for a virtually penniless peer lay in the Imperial patronage system. He obtained a position in the Household of the youthful Victoria as an equerry, and eventually rose to become Deputy Chamberlain at Windsor, with special responsibility for the Queen's Collection, and the Royal Archives. A discreet and retiring courtier, he married relatively late in life the Hon. Gwendolyn Carey, a Mistress of the Bedchamber, and the youngest daughter of Lord Launceston, a West Country squire. They had one child – a son, Henry, who was born in 1860.

Harry Waterstock was educated at Harrow, where a godfather paid the fees, and he was groomed for a military career. Due to the great expense involved in maintaining horses in the more fashionable cavalry, he opted for an infantry regiment instead, and bought a commission in the Grenadiers. He thus became the only member of our family to serve in the Thin Red Line, but this was hardly going to restore the family fortunes; when he succeeded to the Dukedom (in 1882) he was an impoverished lieutenant who owed money to his uniform-maker. But he had been born lucky.

It may seem absurd to us now – although there is little to be learned from history if you impose your own perspective on past behaviour, and judge people's reactions by modern standards – but there was a certain *fin de siècle* panic amongst those families (of which the Londons were not one) who did still possess stately houses and extensive holdings of land. There was a new political climate creeping in over the heartland of the Empire that boasted it never suffered from sunsets, and the aristocracy, feeling the pressure, feared a watershed. The Reform Acts had transformed the electorate, the traditional systems of rent had been challenged and modified, the feudal ground-base was being demolished by the Land Leagues, the radicals, and dangerous progressives. The old Whigs even thought they could smell revolution in the chill new air, but they were just over a century out in their predictions. They looked at Europe, with its numerous *déclassé* nobles, and shivered; there was a libertarian Ice Age coming, and they were to become an endangered species. Fortunately for many of them, there was a society dedicated to their preservation.

Some grandees who were feeling the cold went in for a bit of notorious hunter–gatherer activity: they conducted heiress safaris in North America. Marlborough and Curzon were notably successful, but Manchester was perhaps the most blatant and desperate of them all. He conspicuously scoured the United States for a rich trophy, and eventually settled for the wretched Helena Zimmerman, with her plump portfolio of mining stocks from Cincinnati. Such New World transfusions were the cause of much unhappiness, but the truth about other peoples' marriages is perhaps the most impenetrable subject of them all. (For several million quid, I reckon I could just about live with anybody: I mean, look at our old Royal Family.)

Harry London attended a ball at Londonderry House in 1887, to celebrate the Golden Jubilee. He was attired as a sultan. There he was introduced to Anna Clay, eldest daughter of one of America's 'golden élite', Michael T. Clay, who had spun a fortune for himself during the barbed–wire boom, and had diverse interests in the steel and cannery industries. Anna was dressed as Cleopatra. The first thing she said to Harry was, 'Tell me, Duke – are those jewels real?' He apologized that they were not. 'Well,' replied Anna, extending her hand, 'Mine are.'

They were married the following year.

And so, just as the rest of his peers were fretting over their futures and deploring the inroads made on their ancestral properties, Harry London literally waltzed his way into a financially secure future for at least a century's worth of his descendants to follow – his surviving son, Arthur, my father George, and me. Enjoying the fruits of a chance meeting that brought us Spellbrook, and grafted on our millions. Our unfair advantages. The whole shooting match.

His friends dubbed Harry 'the Canny Duke', because he had seen his chance and made a smart move, and because his new money derived from the Chicago canneries. But the truth seems to be that he married for love as well as money, and it was all due to the invention of an artificial thorn-bush.

I've still got a photograph of myself, taken in the year my grandfather died. There is nothing especially remarkable about its
composition, but here in the mountains it happens to be one of
the very few visual records I retain of the early, distant phase of
my life.

I must have been seven, and I am looking very serious for
the camera – languorously leaning against one of the stone gry-
phons that flanked the parterre outside the north wing. I am
dressed like some naval cadet – white shirt and trousers, blue
shoes, and a blue-peaked cap, with a golden anchor on a badge,
and some grandiose piping. Behind me, the door to the flower
room is open; it casts a shadow against the interior of the house.
As I look at this picture, I cannot help fancying that someone
was about to emerge from the gloom – no, that is too portentous
a word, a word thrown up merely in hindsight – that some
person was about to walk out from the obscure area behind me,
and stand in the spring sunlight.

Why should I imagine this? It would have been Flynn with a
tray, perhaps, or a folded message to deliver, when convenient,
to whoever was behind the lens; it might have been my mother,
fresh from some business with her vases. Whether or not anyone
actually did step out of that doorway behind me, I cannot, of
course, remember; but I am now convinced there was someone
lurking beyond the flap of the door, and it has become one of
those strange certainties that so often associate themselves with
otherwise random items of memorabilia. All I really know is that
once I looked like that, and now I look like someone else. What
has happened to all those smaller people I used to be? How did I
ever get here, from there?

It is now almost two in the morning. I am sitting in my
study, with the remnants of a quart of bourbon on my desk. It
seems to me I have precious little in common with that boy in
his nautical cap – yet, if he is a stranger, what hope have I of
coming to know anyone else? I may have inherited his memories,

but as a person I am a completely different shape and size, and I have forgotten things like his wonder and sense of trust. If we were to meet, I think I would merely frighten him. He would be polite, then avoid me. Some haggard friend of his parents, he might think, yet another inexplicable alien from the planet where adults are produced: a stranger, a grown-up, an irrelevance.

I have always been vain, so let me describe myself: my eyes – my best feature, I feel – are dark grey, and my hair is full and black, with a little weave of silver. Magda accuses me of looking saturnine, which probably alludes to my aquiline nose, and the fact that I frown suspiciously at most people. I do so because no other attitude makes any sense at all. It is also partly a legacy from the time when I rather liked to affect *superbia* and the disdain that I imagined attached to my social rank. Looking at newcomers and letting them know you are unimpressed is a very simple skill to acquire, if you have the requisite arrogance, and perhaps the unfair advantages on your side, to start with. Here in Schwyz I may be plain Dr Slide, but I would not want you to think I had lost all previous behavioural quirks and quiddities. When undesirable callers present themselves at our door, or the Common Room bore suggests a motion that runs contrary to all the currents of common sense, I can assure you I am still capable of the genetically transmitted patrician hauteur: *l'hauteur de l'auteur*, as it were.

But I do have to admit that I am a little bit out of condition these days. I don't take all that exercise they recommend around these parts, sensible though the whole thing may be. Quite frankly, I have always regarded the aerobic and callisthenic classes as a bunch of pathetic primates attempting to achieve things for which their given bodies were probably never really designed. Personally, I would prefer to predecease these fanatics by ten years, and in the interim continue to inhale my lungfuckers, drive everywhere rather than walk, and stick to my drink. It is a way of life that makes me less unhappy. But I don't look great in the morning. I can't disguise this, so I don't attempt to, any more. I am not what I was. I am what you might call a whisky duke.

So I am, and am not, the same person as that boy in the picture. I no longer think like him, and could not be held responsible for his actions. Or could I? During the Eighties, a defence was offered up on several occasions for those suspected of war crimes during the Nazi Empire: they were no longer the people who had perpetrated these acts, it was a long time in the past, it was history. The defendants were innocent, because they were not the persons they had been. They now had children of their own, they did not subscribe to the overall programme to which they unwittingly contributed: it was, in effect, a quite different person of the same name, a previous incarnation.

That didn't wash, and you can't play games with the past, anyway. But consider this: if you bought a house some thirty-five years ago (on the date when that snapshot was taken of me, then Richard Brompton, but a few months later to be called Richard Waterstock) and you redesigned its façade, gutted and transformed its interior, built extensions, made conversions, stuck on battlements, a conservatory and a couple of garages, you might arguably still be staying at the same address, but are you really inhabiting the same house?

A guide was once conducting a party of tourists around a castle in County Wicklow; on the wall in the gun-room were nailed several pike skulls, ancient trophies from the nearby lough. Pointing to the largest, he proudly proclaimed that the fish, when caught, had weighed all of sixty pounds. One of the visitors enquired about the tiny skull next to it. 'Sure,' came the reply, 'and that was the same pike, when it was younger.'

I do not have much time for the historically mendacious sport of angling, but the idea of separate and distinct stages of physical incarnation offers more than a little comfort. If I could only reach out into the chemical perspective of that picture, and touch his shoulder and say, 'Listen. This is what you must do. I know, now. I would listen to this advice, if I were you.'

If I were you. No phrase so encapsulates the lonely essence of each human being's isolation. We cannot know what it is like to be another, and we do not even know how we are perceived.

Then, I was a boy who had a family, a home, a homeland; I had not even grown old enough to have real ambitions. It was a time of plenty, comfort, spring sunlight. I was surrounded by advantage and buoyed up with privilege. This was my larval form, before the moth struggled out, with his sore bear's head. Tomorrow I will be someone slightly different, too. We just go round and round.

So, here we are on the cusp of the millennium, with the noughts soon coming up on the mileometer. I moved here in '94, the year before the Push that turned the United Kingdom into the British Republic. There is a small community of ex-pats here, mostly in Zurich and Geneva; but many more (like the Yorks) opted for America. At the time, I could see little point in swapping the stockaded Spellbrook for some hilltop bunker in Vermont, where security would be even more of a problem. Switzerland was the obvious choice for me: I already had funds here, and my father had taken precautions of setting up his own financial fire-door against any possible monetary collapse as long ago as the Sixties. You can't move funds out of Britain now, of course.

Like practically all revolutions, it took place during the summer – but, being a peculiarly British affair, it was attended by very little violence. There was an uprising by predominantly Conservative males against a Queen who had allowed the younger, female members of her family to disrupt beyond endurance the image of monarchy, and large numbers of people considered this was responsible for the social entropy afflicting the nation. The armed forces were already doing much of the work necessary to keep the country running, and ridding the place of the Windsors seemed a cathartic act: I don't think many of them had the first idea of what was to come.

The various Royals exiled to Canada and California landed rather comfortably on their portfolios (£223 million in old money was the gross figure generally quoted), and I think they should jolly well be grateful to General Fenwick for letting them off so lightly. There wasn't a single throat slit, nor a cobblestone thrown. Instead, they got one of the great golden handshakes of history.

When I came here, I did not think of it as an irreversible measure; but since revisiting Britain this year, I realize my exile must be permanent.

The lifestyle of the Swiss has had a bad press: it is known for honesty and cleanliness, the parsimony of its inhabitants, the attention to detail. In an increasingly tabloid Europe, this is hardly the sort of stuff to get a country into the gossip-columns, but I like it here. Foreigners say it is dull; but dull is safe. Elsewhere, neurosis offers its own colour-wheels, for those who prefer it. Here, differences of opinion are legally sanctioned and minorities officially tolerated. Belonging (as I suppose I always have done) to a very small minority, this feels good. It has proved the best possible antidote to what I was leaving behind, and so I have shaken the British dust off my suede Gucci loafers for the last time. Go back to a military republic crammed with submissive, indolent people, where the State controls the liquor stores, and the trains run on time, but you are not always free to use them? Where the jails now hold the highest number of citizens *per capita* of the population anywhere in Europe, and you have to obtain a special licence to drive into the centre of any city? Return to a State that forcibly relocates individual members of families around the country, according to the demands of regional workforces, and where all the Church property has been annexed for 'economic rationalization'? No. I mean: No, thanks. Pass the cuspidor, there's a good citizen.

I now live in a farm-house just outside the town of Schwyz, the capital of the oldest, and most conservative, canton of the Confederation and the place from which this origami country took its name. It's a tiny state, and the capital is more of a *dorf* than a *stadt*, but it is far from sleepy: *Homo Helveticus* is a notoriously quarrelsome species, which offers much in the way of entertainment. You wouldn't come here for the cooking or the architecture, but there are some fine old patrician houses, and some good examples of bourgeois baroque, and civic squares with plane trees and geraniums. Even the air feels clean-shaven and cologned, as if the national propensity for hygiene and orderliness had sublimated to affect the climate itself.

Behind the town tower the two peaks of the Mythen, the mountainous Mitre, where if there is any snow in winter the ludicrous skiers ply the slopes in their fluorescent uniforms, faces camouflaged in coloured Skyblok, like computer-generated images of urban guerrilla fighters. But down here it is pastoral, quilted, agricultural land, which I can admire without the responsibility of husbandry. There are acres of cherry orchards, though I no longer have Ben for company as I wander through the blossom. Even these days we get a fair amount of rain coming down like buckshot on my sloping roof, and the place whispers prosperously with water. There is a weekly market, when farmers still bring pigs and goats and cheese to sell, before retiring to drink and bicker in the shade – a touch of Ruritania, in fact, except when the *föhn* comes down and gives us all headaches.

And, no, I do not possess any cuckoo-clocks (a German invention, as it so happens).

Our neighbour, Herr Sitt, is a successful printer, whose hobby is brass-rubbing but whose passion is democracy. His attitudes are virtually typical of the place. We engage in disputes about my occasional barbecue parties for the students, and from time to time I threaten his cat with a stick; but when it comes to discussing the agenda for the local council, or co-ordinating civic plans for Swiss National Day, we shelve our differences, and deliberate on equal terms the budget for fireworks and *pâtisseries*. Nothing could be more different to my life at Spellbrook, and it is a relief to live somewhere regulated entirely by committees.

This remains a self-centred country, one that has always taken itself seriously. It preserves its identity because it is regulated through a system of indirect democracy by its inhabitants. Its constituency is a known quantity. The Swiss have traded certain rights to privacy (remember them, all you New Britons?) in return for collective control. We may have to carry 'smart' ID cards that can offer the authorities a considerable amount of personal information (a policeman who stopped me for speeding logged out details of my Genevan Reserve account 'by mistake', and I almost laughed at his expression when he saw the size of it, though it doesn't do to laugh at the policemen here, either) but it helps if everyone is equally accountable.

We legislate partly by referendum, which is a far cry from the House of Lords – another system which was theoretically unsound, but worked in practice (though I wouldn't venture such an opinion in front of your new President and his Army Council, if I were you). Only last month, in Bern, our own President (Willy Steiger) had a Government motion on paper-rationing overturned by a popular referendum independently organized by Herr Sitt himself. I don't suppose we will hear the last word about that particular triumph for many months to come.

There was a time when the cantons were scoffed at for their neutrality, their hermetically sealed caution, their conservatism. Over the past three decades they have been voluntarily innoculating themselves against the enormities of modern European developments, and this resolute immunity has paid off. By refusing to adapt to the accelerating pace of change that has characterized the other, supposedly progressive, nations, the Swiss have largely escaped the information sickness that afflicts what used to pass for the civilized world, the plague caused by the ether being infected with too many electronic impulses, spreading panic and deception. Obeying its own Coriolis force, it circulates eastwards from the American valleys, leaving zombie survivalists and HIV ghettos in its wake as it crosses Europe and on towards the Steppes. In the southern hemisphere it sweeps from the African nuclear dictatorships across to the new badlands of South America, where the World Co-operative has written off the collective debts of the Fourth World countries, so they can concentrate their resources on the manufacture of narcotics like Ultramarine, Hero and Johnny-K.

These days there is a delusory network wrapped around reality like a membrane produced by the interdependence of all the media: there's so much information in the air that nobody knows what to think any more, and it's hard to make any decision – hard even to remember whether or not it is still necessary. But the Swiss are immune to most of this: they have never taken advice from others, and they have no intention of their system breaking down.

Decisions, decisions: they wear you down, weigh so heavily that the ice starts to crack beneath your runners. There was a time when we only had to concentrate on making choices about our immediate lives – one lump, or two? Shall I turn back for the umbrella, or catch the train? Should I speak my mind, or hold my tongue?

But now every trivial dilemma comes surrounded by a corona of global fact, opinion, gloss, interpretation, graphs, warnings and projective packaging. You can't see the orchard for the apple trees. People are terminally confused, and outlandish cults and fetishes proliferate; anything seems worth a try – psychotropic therapy, biobionomy, Breath for Love, magneto-colonic tuning, polar photometrics, molecular irridology – even Calvinism is proving popular (a Swiss joke, obviously).

A decade ago, popular science books liked to impress the lay reader with all that stuff about quantum mechanics, and Heisenburg's Uncertainty Principle (the odd fashionable novelist got hold of it, too); but you can forget Planck's constant, and all that wave-particle duality these days, because we've got our very own, bran-fresh Uncertainty. We've worried ourselves sick, and we can't make our minds up at all. It was precisely this type of congenital dithering that lead Britain into the web of totalitarian government, but at least the citizens of the republic are spared some of the more demanding aspects of the daily indecision that exhausts most other anxious Europeans: their uncertainty has been removed, along with their freedom of choice. They can continue to think what they like, so long as they do what they are told; for many of them, this is actually something of a relief.

As well as this change in the political climate, you might say there's been a revolution in the weather. For centuries, it's been obediently going round on its planetary carousel, and now it appears to have had enough: the floods of Sri Lanka, the creeping dustbowl of the Great Plains, the rising oceans. People are building arks in their allotments. We are beyond speculation now: we have engineered an ecodystopia.

The weather, the weather: that favourite topic of conversation, especially among the English. It shaped our national character, all that weather coming off our island coasts, holding us in thrall: we saw it only in soft focus, though, with a kind of dissolved anxiety that suggested that it was symptomatic of other, equally intangible and unassailable aspects of old England. It accounts for our countrymen's phlegmatic shrug – well, you can't do anything about it, can you? (Yes, yes, you can.) Hang up a length of old seaweed, lick your finger and set it to the wind, then carry on regardless (those blokes on the telly never get it right, anyway). If anyone had bothered to point out that our history depends on climate, the English would have thought a great deal of fuss was being made about nothing.

Those days have now gone, and jolly boating weather is unfortunately all too common. The climate is taking its revenge. 'Mad February drags his father into the sunshine and beats him', runs a Spanish proverb – well, who drove him to distraction? Who systematically infected him with rashes and boils, lit fires under him in the forests, piped carbon into his bedroom all night, blistered him with gas, strangled his oxygen supply, and shot a couple of holes in his roof, nineteen miles high? The atmosphere turns around, and spits in our face, with black snow, red rain, earthquakes and summer storms that drive blades of grass through sheet metal. The air is so laced with smoke and suspended chemicals that even in the neon streets of our cities we witness huge, industrial sunsets. We have spent centuries grumbling about the weather; perhaps the time has come for us to ask, 'What does the weather think about us?'

And of course the media respond to this new anxiety, feeding our new sources of uncertainty. Satellite channels are dedicated around the clock to telling us the latest stories of the planet's moods and metabolism. With gaudy kinetic flow-maps, we are informed how the weather is going to affect the history of our own little day – our locomotive methods, our choice of clothing, our health, our eating habits, our recreational prospects. These programmes are the predictive summaries of each person's dangers and delights. The weather is no longer vaguely trailing the news, it is dictating it. We tune in to frequent bulletins, as if monitoring the hourly health of some hospitalized monarch. In the new Britain, the weather forecast has become an integral part of patriotic propaganda; gone is the pantomime cosiness of the BBC (the standing in-joke at the Met Office used to be: 'There's a deep depression over Iceland'). It is now a civic duty to be appraised of the forecast, to take precautions, to be prepared. It is illegal to ignore these warnings. It is compulsory to participate in the National Weatherwatch Scheme, if your name is 'selected'. There are severe penalties if the rescue services are summoned to help you during economically unnecessary travel. The military are using the weather as a curfew.

So, if you're searching for a *zeitgeist* for the end of this particular millennium, there he is, in his lightweight Spyrex suiting, sweating under the studio lights – the weatherman, telling you the stories of tomorrow.

THREE

Although his other commitments did not leave him enough time ever to act as Master of the local fox hounds, my father was none the less keen on hunting. In the courtyard behind the house, next to the wood-store, the game-larder and the converted brew-house, was a stable-block where lurked Begg, the melancholy groom. He was a young, sandy-haired man, as I first remember him, with mutton-chop sidewhiskers that gave him an owlish look, and he bobbed his head around slightly as he spoke, like some superannuated prizefighter from a fairground. He was a slow, diffident man, of uncertain opinions when it came to anything other than equestrian matters, and this caution was manifested in his idiolect, for, whenever possible, he would end his sentences with the word 'like' – 'It's hanging up on the back of the tack-room door, like', – as if any information he might impart could only be presumed to have provisional qualities of reliability.

There was never any question of me not learning to ride, and it was my father's clear intention that once I was proficient I should accompany him cubbing, and thus learn the etiquette of the field. Now, I have no particular objection to this pastime on ethical grounds – nor, of course, did most of those protestors and saboteurs who achieved so much publicity earlier in the decade; what they were reacting against was the feared image of the mounted man in uniform, the Imperialist echo of another Thin Red Line. It is ironic, though, that this sport should have been rescued from the statute books by the Channel Tunnel. Rabies is a perfect focus for English xenophobia, and the cavalry regiments (once an endangered species themselves) didn't have to work too hard at persuading the authorities of the newly practical value of maintaining their precious horses.

No, it was the horses, not the riders, I disliked. Apart from their peculiarly comforting smell, horses of all sizes intimidate me; I lived in constant fear of being kicked as I edged around the loose-boxes, and derived none of the delight that children are supposed, always, to do from the simple act of offering up sugar-cubes on the palm. This was unfortunate, because riding lessons were compulsory, and I even had my own pony, Flea, a skittish little grey from whose back I frequently slid in the paddock, to the consternation of Begg. 'Knees tight, Master Richard,' he would shout, 'Like there was a fiver between them and the saddle, like.' But it was hopeless. Quite how anyone managed to live with these brutes and depend on them during all those centuries for rapid transport, I cannot imagine. And all the maintenance and gear! The buckets of feed, the tedious saddle-soap, the curry-combing and inspection of pasterns (or were they fetlocks? I'm as ignorant here as Dr Johnson), the anxious wrestling with the bit (Flea, as good as his name, was a nipper) and, worst aspect of all, the creeping, hemlock feeling of defeat, ignominy.

I made the mistake, at the age of eight, of attempting to explain something of all this to my father. 'If I were you,' he replied, 'I would spend rather more time concentrating on posture, and less spent in general complaint.' And so it had to continue. But I never got up on a horse's back after that Christmas when he was killed.

When it came to the shoot, however, I was a little less of a disappointment; and here I must make mention of another man who really did seem to loom larger than life during my childhood years. Because, in Charlie Sanga, we had the only black gamekeeper in the whole of Britain. But to arrive at the clue to his story, we must again go back down the family tunnel: for I now realize that Charlie would never have worn a pair of tweed breeches in his life, if it had not been for something that happened to my father before I was even born.

George Waterstock was a sixteen-year-old schoolboy at Eton, when his mother died. He managed one year reading history at Cambridge, before joining the Royal Navy in 1940. He spent the best part of the next two years on a training programme working with miniature submarines in the waters off the north coast of Iceland – work to which I imagine he was especially well-suited, given his wiry, almost jockey-like physique. He was then seconded to the Special Boat Service which, in 1943, was based at Athlit, in Palestine, under the command of Major the Earl Jellicoe. Secrecy was such that those at home imagined this motley group of marauders was engaged in something cushy, like guarding a fuel depot, but it seems their chief task at that time was to prevent the Germans taking control of the Aegean.

After the fall of Leros, the SBS managed to persuade Turkey – though officially neutral – to allow them to launch some of their 'engagements' from inside their territorial waters; and it was from there that my father and a party of four launched their caïques in the dark, on the evening of 12 March 1944, their target being the island of Calchi.

I have never been absolutely clear as to what happened next. One source has suggested that my father was working for military Intelligence, but, like many of his generation, he hardly ever spoke of his wartime experiences. I remember asking him – as a boy, naturally interested in theoretical bloodshed – if he had ever actually killed anyone. He frowned, and looked irritated, and said he supposed he must have, but one did not discuss such things. I might have been enquiring whether he had ever suffered from dandruff: he clearly regarded my question as vulgar.

Maybe he would have spoken to me about this – and another matter, now too late to explain – had he survived until he considered me mature enough to comprehend (and how old would I have had to be, I wonder, before he thought me sufficiently grown-up – twenty-one? thirty? Would I still be waiting now, hoping for that summons to his library, the spreading out of journals and papers, the offer of whisky before a peremptory cough, and then, 'Look, Richard, this is going to be difficult. But there are one or two things it might be better for you to know . . . ')

But the winter carried him off, and he left that business unfinished. All I knew until recently was that my father was considered a war hero.

His group landed on Calchi and began their recce for concealed locations that could be used during a forthcoming raid on the radar installations at Scarpanto. But they were spotted by a German patrol, there was an exchange of fire, and Trooper Baring lost his life. My father and the three survivors took to the hills, and two nights later they stowed away on a fishing smack bound for Rhodes. It was intercepted almost immediately, and they were taken prisoner.

At my father's Memorial Service I met for the first time one of the men who had been in this party. He did not introduce himself by name, and, when I pressed him for it, he said it was not important, as it was all a thing of the past (well, that's precisely the point). 'You know, he was a very brave man,' this stranger said. 'He had already made it over the blind side of the boat, and we were still not far from shore. He could have saved himself. But he heard them say they were going to shoot us, right there on the deck, and he hauled himself back up the side, and identified himself. They knew who he was alright and they really wanted him alive. So they took us off. He saved my life. I just wanted you to know that.'

But I never did hear anything about this from his own mouth. What could have been going through his mind as he crawled, drenched and dazzled, around the wheelhouse and stood in the ferocious moon of the searchlight, one arm over his eyes? Was he grim, and resolute: did he give them his grey, challenging look, or did he think he was going to die? And in his later years, in retrospect, I wonder if he realized how important the implications of that moment of capture were going to prove for those of us waiting in the shadows of the future.

Of course not. There was a war, and these things – worse things – happened.

Their unit was already notorious for the destruction it had brought to several outposts and munitions centres in the area, and although my father was only a lieutenant, it was suspected from his title that he must be on close personal terms with Jellicoe (though in fact I doubt that he ever was).

He was severely interrogated concerning the Service's planned operations, and was dispatched to Austria, where he was interned in the infamous camp outside Innsbergen. I now know that he was subjected to torture. He was presumed dead by the Navy, and awarded a posthumous DSO, in recognition of his actions in the Aegean, and other, unspecified, operations while serving with the SBS. The Russians invaded Austria in April 1945, and the camp was liberated. George Waterstock eventually returned to Spellbrook, a quieter and more reserved man. He retreated to Cambridge, where he completed his degree, and then in 1947 he joined Hedges and Elliott, an insurance firm in the City, where he specialized in maritime liabilities.

In 1952 my father made a trip to Kenya, ostensibly on holiday. The Mau-Mau activities were escalating, with militant Kikuyu engaged in terrorist acts against both the white community and recalcitrant members of their own tribe. Hundreds of rebels were swearing the oath to Stanley Mathenga and Dedan Kimathi, hiding out in the forests of the Central province. Their atrocities were becoming newsworthy, generating their own, often ill-founded mythology. There were the spectral Ptemba brothers, who continued to disappear from police custody, the Scissor Man, who murdered and mutilated two white women in Nakuru, the caste of oath-takers who indulged in cannibalism. (This state of affairs could not be tolerated, of course, and before too long the Governor had declared a state of emergency, and troops were flown in. It was the same old story: 64,000 Mau-Mau supporters brought to trial over the next four years, 20,000 Kikuyu placed in 'detention camps', 11,000 rebels killed.)

It was perhaps no coincidence that the Princess Elizabeth was also visiting Kenya at this time, only to be summoned home with the news that her father had died. I do not think that my father had severed all his previous links with the Intelligence services, and the frequent travel that his business entailed at that period would certainly have made him a useful, if informal, set of extra, roving eyes.

The immediate legacy of this trip, however, was that he had assigned to him as a driver and guide a young member of the Yaaku tribe, whose qualities apparently so impressed him that he invited Charlie to begin a new life, back in England, where he became apprenticed to the Head Keeper, Owen.

I first recall Charlie when he was in his early twenties; an arrestingly handsome man who stood six foot three on his bare feet. He had close-cropped hair, and a head burnished like a horse-chestnut. He was physically one of the strongest men I ever knew, and was possessed of uncanny stamina. I remain convinced he was closer to what we might think of as a magician than an ordinary mortal, and I was not the only one in awe of him.

The Yaaku originated from the Mukogodo Forest, where they had been hunter–gatherers, but Charlie had spent most of his life around Doldol, just north of Mount Kenya, where the nomads had come to rest and herd cattle. His father Kitumu was the *jumbe*, or head man of the tribe, a position accorded to the man considered closest to the ancestral spirits of his people. His name meant 'spear', because he, too, was tall and slim – and potentially deadly: one of his roles as medicine-man-cum-high-priest was to be the tribe's official poisoner. He was also guardian of the ceremonial stones, ritual purifier, and the undisputed equivalent of our Lord Chief Justice. The way Charlie made it sound to me, as a child, his father was just about one of the most powerful men in the universe. And I have no real reason to suppose that he was not.

Certainly, his remarkable son had learned a lot from this man: the skills he brought to the Surrey countryside were not exactly familiar to many of its inhabitants – a fact that caused my own father a very real degree of satisfaction on numerous occasions. Even through the clouded atmosphere of southern England, Charlie could continue to count the moons of Jupiter – at least, he claimed he could, and there was no way of disproving his assertion, and I for one never thought of taking the part of the little boy who exposed the facts about the Emperor's New Clothes. Quite the contrary: if Charlie Sanga pointed out something in the skies, and I could not see it, then I was always prepared to accept that he had light coming in to his eyes that my own faculties were too deficient to detect, or decode. And I believe this was metamorphically true, as well; I think he managed a view of our family from the outside – often the best point of vantage – that was denied us. He was the best sort of stranger for a community such as Spellbrook then was: he had no interest in pronouncing his opinions, but preferred, when it was the time to make a contribution to some discussion, to tell stories.

There is a lot to be said for this communal tradition. But only as long as they are stories of the past, stories that have become myth. Projections of the future have relatively little value, though they may titillate and alarm. The whisper of myth is valuable, to some, because it refuses the aura of that now irrelevant question, 'Did this happen?', and replaces it with something more likely to cast light, in these obscure times, and that is the whole issue of '*Does* this happen?'

So that when Charlie told me he had lost the tip of his index finger on his left hand while finishing off a cheetah, on his twelfth birthday, as prescribed for all the pubescent males of the Yaaku – an encounter which also accounted for the deeply scored scar that ran down either cheek of his face – I imagined him wrestling bare-handed with such a beast, and begged him time and again to recount his exploits in the bush. It was not until I was much older, and myself approaching that period of puberty which was so curiously befuddled by the embarrassments of my own tribe, that Charlie admitted the facial scars were perfunctory, and universal amongst the Yaaku of his age, and that the fingertip had been amputated by his father after it was crushed in the door of a truck, and was in danger of turning septic.

All the same, he wore the severed bone around his neck, on a chain, having carved it into the rudimentary shape of a leaping cheetah. For Charlie, it was completing some sort of bodily cycle, and he claimed it gave him strength.

Owen had a little trouble with Charlie at first, because among the Yaaku it was customary to hunt animals and birds while clad in white, the colour of light and extinction. This did not sit well with the foliage and undergrowth of the Home Counties, where not since the time of the druids had anyone patrolled the copses attired as a ghost. When Owen presented Charlie with his tweed uniform, the Kenyan merely smiled; and though he subsequently wore it, this weak affectation of camouflage was not really necessary in his case, since, irrespective of garb, he seemed capable of disappearing into his surroundings at whim. Although he had to teach his apprentice, from scratch, everything about rearing-methods and predator control, Owen found him a ready pupil, and was impressed by his tracking skills. Charlie was able to scent many animals – not just dogs and foxes, but also certain birds, rodents and humans. Which was just as well, because once word got around that there was a 'coloured' working on the estate it attracted the unwelcome attention not just of the usual local poachers, but of the odd racist gang from London, who thought they knew a good target when they saw one. These incidents recurred sporadically throughout his years at Spellbrook, but no one ever got the better of the man known in the village as Charlie Sambo.

Although it happened before I was born, there was a curious incident concerning some poachers who thought Charlie fancied himself as a 'hard man', and decided to teach him a lesson; by the time Begg recounted it to me, as a child, it had already become enshrined as part of the local folklore and was proof, Begg assured me, that Charlie could make himself invisible – 'It's been seen, like.' Charlie was out on patrol one night when he heard a commotion from one of the pheasant pens. As he was crossing a paddock to investigate, he was suddenly caught in the headlights of three vehicles which had earlier converged into position, two across fields and one up the road. Four men entered the pool of light: one had a lurcher on a leash, two held clubs, and one was carrying a kitchen-knife (these were the days before every intruder on the estate carried some kind of gun). They had him pretty well surrounded, and the only weapon he appeared to have was his torch. He dropped this on to the grass, shrugged off his jacket, and began to run directly at one of the vehicles, shouting in his tribal tongue. Then, when he was no more than ten yards away from one of his assailants he made a great leap, and, in the words of the man's later statement to the police, 'just seemed to disappear into thin air'.

They were still searching for him, in some confusion, when two squad-cars arrived fifteen minutes later. How Charlie had made it back to his cottage, three miles away, and telephoned them within such a short time was never explained; he merely informed the sergeant that he was used to running very fast. The police said the gang had been drinking, and their accounts did not agree with each other (two of them, from opposite sides of the field, claimed he was running directly at them). Whenever I asked Charlie if it was true he had made himself disappear, he would answer, 'Well, some of them men thought so, and that's the important thing.' Personally, I believed every bit of it.

In the latter years of the United Kingdom there was a growing neurosis about the ownership of property, the ethics concerning its protection, and a dangerous notion that it was immoral for people to possess exclusive rights to land. But Charlie had never needed any persuasion about the role he had to perform at Spellbrook – not because he was servile, but because in his tribe the concept of property was fundamental, and the theft of animals was a very serious business. He told me a story about Yaaku justice that not only illustrated this, but also his principle that it was what people *thought* had happened was the most important thing.

Two men had cows that were due to give birth about the same time. One morning, a stillborn calf was discovered in one stockade, with a healthy calf in the next; but the man with the dead beast came to Kitumu and claimed that his neighbour must have switched them round in the night, and was trying to pass off the live one as his own. Kitumu assembled the council, and heated the blade of his short sword in the central fire. He told both men to stick out their tongue, and announced he was going to apply the blade to each one in turn – the liar would be burned, but the innocent man would feel nothing. And so it proved: the man making the accusation never flinched, and the other roared with pain, confessed, and 'He then gets fined three good goats, and people call him liar.' The reason this worked, said Charlie, was that everyone believed it would: the guilty man was frightened of his father's powers, and his mouth went dry – the other had confidence in this type of justice, and his tongue was protected by his usual saliva.

No, with a father like that for an example, Charlie Sanga never needed any guidance regarding the exercising of his duties at Spellbrook. When I was four, Owen retired and Charlie took his place as Head Keeper. It was not hard to tell who had been the sorcerer, and who was the apprentice.

Although my grandfather Arthur was still technically the owner, it was my father who ran the estate when I was little, and I will say that from the start he impressed upon me the need for its care and regulation. I do not think he ever actually gestured across the prospect of our acres, and said, 'One day, all this will be yours,' but he certainly made me realize that it should never be taken for granted, and had me accompany him occasionally to meetings with the farm manager or the forester, so that I would not grow up with the idea that Spellbrook ran itself, or that it existed purely for my childish enjoyment. It was typically considerate of him.

I now see that in fact his husbandry of the family fortunes was really outstanding, though I have never been much of a businessman myself. He was always adamant that the landed base of the estate should not shrink to below 2000 acres (it was still 2400 acres in extent when I sold it), and he resisted the temptation to sell off parcels of land to the local councils when planning permission was granted. 'This might make the land worth a great deal of money,' he would say, 'but its value to us is even greater so long as it remains under our control. You must remember this. Your outlying acres are the most important. The centre of the estate is more flexible. Do not shift your boundaries.'

I now find it hard to appraise him objectively, of course, but I think he did his best to be a responsible parent. (I must choose my words carefully, here, but sometimes I grow tired of struggling against my language.) His aloofness was often perplexing, and his business-like manner was seldom irradiated by any gleam of discernible humour, but then I'm sure he found me an irritating, trivial-minded fidget of a companion in those days, and I don't think Cosmo fared any better. It did not appear that my father was especially fond of children. Perhaps it would be fairer of me to say that he was impatient for us to grow up: that adult relationship would certainly have proved interesting.

The Great Park beyond our croquet lawn was plagued with stubborn thistleries, against which my father had conceived some kind of personal antipathy. He kept a special cutter in the umbrella-stand – a tubular grey metal shaft, with a semi-circular blade at the bottom – and when he had a spare moment he would march out into his field and attack the weeds. I accompanied him on one occasion (it was August, and very hot) and he became quite suddenly enraged; he began hacking at the bases of the juicy stalks with terrific, controlled sweeps of his forearm, grunting as each was sliced and felled, then a sharp hiss coming through his teeth, the sound of a gout of fat being dropped into a hot pan. 'They come back, again and again,' I could hear him say, 'they return, whatever you do. I must' – snick – '*must* get rid' – clack, scrunch – 'of these things. I will have them torn out by the roots.'

He was moving rapidly, cutting from side to side, now oblivious to my presence. I became nervous as his face grew an unfamiliar look of exertion and stress, his breathing chopped into pronounced panting, darkness crept across the damp back of his blue shirt. 'Get rid,' he was saying, 'get *rid*, and cut them *out*.' The grey blade flicking sap, the bristly clusters jerking, falling.

Suddenly, he stopped. My father leaned on his weapon, and closed his eyes. Whether from sweat or dust or flying spores, I could see that they were streaming. 'Enough,' he said, and we walked slowly back towards the house, in silence.

Despite the seriousness that he brought to bear on the care of Spellbrook, my own perception of the place was that it had been there as our family home for so long that it might have been for ever, and that it was unchanging in its character and routines. In a secure childhood, such delusions continue – along with a personal conviction that one is never going to die – up until about the age of seven. And to these same years we owe much of the visual dimension to our later memories, since they furnish the archetypes, the pictures, of many things to which we incessantly refer. The child's mind is so busy storing and sorting out these snapshots, this archive footage, that it does not harbour much in the way of emotional recollection – states of mind come later with the hormonal cyclones and the adolescent depressions, when time starts behaving irregularly, and missing some of its beats, and nobody will admit it, no one helps to understand it.

My first few years now seem to have occupied a long historical era, like the Plantagenets or the Stuarts; a shapely, sinuous period, where events arose and fell, as if to the beating of great wings. I was part of a large, almost unchanging household; there was a hierarchy; I had to make very few decisions; my slow year was articulated by seasonal rituals around the estate. I have become nostalgic for them, of course, and the memories are selective, patched up, conflated, cosmeticized. The feeling is quickened by geographical distance, by the knowledge of failure, by the realization that I can never offer anything similar to a child of my own, by the maudlin legacy of alcohol. But I surely did not dream it, this vanished order of rural England, rinsed with birdsong and latticed with sunlight. I am no longer capable of such dreams. I have hardly even remembered a dream for years.

Until they sent me away to school, and my visual references were scrambled out of all previous proportion, I have a picture of something that seems to particularize each of those early seasons at Spellbrook – so that even now, when we cannot strictly speak of spring (the cherries of Schwyz blossomed in February, this year), the very vibration of the word brings a shimmer of a scene, and something of the sound as the wind sung across my line, and I am standing on the hill beside the lake, with Nanny sitting below the tree-house, conspicuously uncomfortable as the weather dishevels her appearance, one hand clamping her precious grey hat, the other grasping the throat of her cardigan, and she is not even troubling any more to follow the progress of the box-kite we have set aloft, the kite made for me and Cosmo by Charlie Sanga (my brother is only three, and has stayed indoors with my mother), and it is tugging away at the broiling skies, riding the bucks and the buffets, its star-shaped spider-face painted by Charlie peeping and twirling in and out of view – and, as I lengthen the leash still further, I drop the spindle, and it bounces and rolls down the path, with turn after turn unravelling in great jerks, beyond my grasp, as I scramble after it – and Nanny Mottram is now calling against all the wind, 'You just watch you don't fall, Master Richard, and ruin those trousers,' but it's beyond my control; the star-spider makes a couple of final faces, its black crêpe paper legs rustling and hissing, like fireworks tearing off; it inverts suddenly, and crash-dives into the lake. The kite begins, very slowly, to sink.

Charlie made me another one, because he said kites were

important, they pulled the skin of the sky the right way round after it had become wrinkled, sleeping through the night. I expect he had to fashion several more, down the various springs, to compensate for entanglements in poplars, frayed cords, and my insistence upon showing my brother how everything should be done, before I had the least mastery of it myself. But each time Charlie would paint the same markings and attach identical streamers because the whole point of flying these kites was to commemorate Sitobo, the spider-god.

'Here, Richard, is your new kite. The new can be better than the old, but take good care. Not like you were, flying all over water. This is Yaaku spider-kite, and now I tell you why.

'A woman, when she was just thirteen years old, before marriage, was out to wash the clothes early one morning, in the cool before the sun rising. And as she goes to the lake, a big noise behind her, a great noise – too early in that morning for it to be good. A figure stands there, dressed all in skins of bird, his mouth is made of gold. And the Yaaku girl cries out, for she sees this is the Morning Star. He has watched her, who knows how long, several months watching as she comes to this same place every day. The Morning Star has come for her, as his love.

'They went up into the sky, and she lived among his people – the place was all bright, and it dazzled, and she got sick for her home, like you would, and very sad. Then she died. The sun did not rise that morning, and the people of our village were in fear and sadness, and the sky was black with cloud, with the animals making a great noise. But there was a boy, about your age, I think, maybe, and he was sent to settle the cattle, and he makes a great shout that there is a hole up there in the dark, and the people run to look; and the story says that it seems the sky is weeping, and it makes tears of gold from its eye; and a thread comes down, with Sitobo at the end of it, and the dead wife of the Morning Star in his many arms. But as she touch the ground, the woman come alive again, and each day the sun rise if we are thankful, and no man harm the spider.

You send up his picture, and make him happy. But not over water, where he drown.'

When it comes to summer I hear the strum of insects against the pane, the pinking of finches around my mother's bird-table, the mutter and spit of Peter Buxton in the prelude to the eventual moan of his lawnmower. We have the thick, sour nidor of cut grass, common to the experience of almost every child, even in the cities, and – though this must be less familiar, a ritual that astounded even Charlie, with his wealth of legend – the annual visit of Carter, the mole-catcher.

Although Buxton struggled to combat them, moles were evidently beyond the expertise that he could bring to bear on the croquet lawn, and the grassed walks. Every year he tried traditional remedies, such as poking bits of holly or lengths of bramble down their runs. When this did not work he would pour in sump oil from the engines, or dose dead earthworms with strychnine (for which I'm sure he never had a permit) and dig them into the infested areas. But whatever triumphs he may have thought he achieved, the craters and earthworks proliferated, and his last resort, the final blow to his professional dignity, was to summon another specialist.

Carter walked with a limp and a broken-coated terrier. He would prowl the lawn, and the park where many among his quarry dwelled, scouting for fresh burrows, and shooting the moles across their snouts with his .410 as they surfaced. The corpse would be retrieved by his dog, and hung by its claws from the nearest stretch of barbed wire, along the lines of a gibbet. (The gibbet system was designed to terrify people – to dissuade potential copy-cats, or, as they had it with Admiral Byng, '*pour encourager les autres*' – but I fail to see how the suspended and putrefying bodies of these trophies could have communicated their warnings to the busy cousins way beneath the topsoil.) It was a way of proving his hit-rate, and Carter took a professional view of the challenge: it was, in fact, only his hobby, because in real life (ah, what a loose term!) he drove long-distance haulage lorries. I reckon he enjoyed his forays, but to me he had a forbidding aura, and I would watch his operations from the relative safety of the parterre, and never went along with him into the fields. I am only guessing, but I bet he had a son in the Forces during the Push. There were thousands and thousands of men like Carter in the United Kingdom: naturally, they weren't all trying to exterminate moles, but they were firmly ensconced on an interface between the urban and the rural – a position that had historical antecedance of which the inner-city 'Green', the civilian who kept a pet or two, disliked certain farming practices, and objected to so-called Blood Sports, was largely ignorant. It was not entirely fortuitous that the governance of Britain fell into the hands of the Forces, whose officer class had always maintained that the countryside was a *spielplatz* for their sporting activities, and the ancillary trades that always attended them.

Which may be all very well for those who have struck a satisfactory deal with the administration: it could only be at a certain cost, and I am glad I never had to be part of it. Whatever populist delights they now crank out of Spellbrook, I know, for a fact, they will not emulate the extraordinary fun we had with the shooting around the crops. I don't suppose they even have hares there now, but we did. And trying to shoot them was part of our seasonal harvest, my Indian summer image of the place. There were miles of hedgerows in those days and our arable fields were smaller than the great cereal expanses that were later deemed more efficient, and when the combine was applied to a field of wheat we would patrol the shaven margins, three abreast, and take potshots at the rabbits and hares as they bolted for cover across the stubble, in panic, to avoid the advancing machine. I shot my first rabbit in this way, at the age of eight, tumbling him head-over-heels in a flurry of fluff – a jack rabbit with an orangey neck, and a mouth still half full of corn. Iris made him into a little casserole for my supper, with only a mild grumble about the trouble in skinning and dressing him.

But perhaps it was in winter that Spellbrook looked its

most impressive, when the leaf was off the trees, and you could see how far it all extended, and the house looked robust with its towers set against an anthracite sky. Another trick of the light is that one seems to recall snow around Christmas, though it certainly happened once when I was quite little. The Great Park became a bloom of virtually unbroken white, like a freshly painted room, locked and left, and as I looked out of my bedroom window, the sky now hard with stars, I had a long vista of our own acres giving off a dull gleam, like submarine phosphor.

Even in later years when it became fashionable among the filofax classes (remember them?) to decry Christmas for having been hijacked by commercialism and for causing suicides and generally not coming up to scratch (it may not be a holy day any more, but we'll take the holiday all the same, thanks very much) we celebrated Christmas as a household with unanimous commitment, and unvarying rituals. It was not a time for improvisation. A week before, the forester would deliver our selected tree, and secure it in a tea-chest in the hall; my mother would cover the box with a swathe of her favourite tartan material, and then begin to unwrap the decorations from their tissue-paper. Some of these had been in our family since the beginning of the century – delicate globes of Venetian glass, painted tin birds with sprung perches that could be clipped to the boughs, hollow, gilded angels with satin wings – everyone had the chance to place one item, for luck, though it was Finny's precarious duty to mount the ladder and fix the star at the apex, a task he made appear as daunting as any challenge faced by a steeplejack.

On Christmas Eve there would be the ordeal of a visit by the rector and his team of hand-bell ringers, who would solemnly regale us with rather syncopated renderings of 'Silent Night' and 'Rudolph the Red-nosed Reindeer', grinning and shuffling and rearranging themselves in between numbers, while my mother exclaimed, 'Oh, yes: *that* is my favourite' about alternate tunes, and, 'Rector, I *do* congratulate you', when she felt we had all suffered enough. I think only Grandpa genuinely enjoyed it, and he would clap enthusiastically at the end, make a final request, and then invite everyone to dig into the refreshments – bottled beer, mulled wine, and cider-cup for the younger campanists, with the inevitable mince-pies, sausage-rolls, and cartons of dates.

'Truly splendid. They get better each year, I think,' my grandfather would say. 'Now, Flynn, if you would be so kind as to give me a hand . . . ' and he would begin to rise from his chair, at which juncture another ritual began, with Flynn folding his arms behind his back and issuing a formal invitation to the family to come to the Staff Sitting-room and 'take a seasonal drink with us, if you would give us the pleasure, Your Grace'. And Grandpa would raise his eyebrows with delight, and accept this annual surprise with great eagerness, and we would all troop in (Cosmo and I were included) and Finny would pass round his tray of minuscule sherry glasses (a trophy from a visit to Spain), carefully producing a tumbler of bitter lemon for himself, from the side-table, and then he would propose a toast to the family, while Cosmo and I smirked into our Ribena at the gravitas of these proceedings, and also in anticipation of the hanging up of stockings, the calling to Father Christmas up the drawing-room chimney, and the prospect of certain booty on the morrow.

And then on the day itself we would attend church *en famille*, and my grandfather would recite the lesson from the Nativity, and then the little reception in the conservatory for the inside and outdoor staff, followed by lunch for all (including Nanny) in the dining-room, the Queen's speech, and then the presents under the tree. One of the entertaining aspects of this was the moment when my father opened his present from my grandfather: for every year it contained an enormous wooden box of crystallized fruits, from Fortnum and Mason, a delicacy which I never observed my father to consume at any time, though he dutifully expressed thanks at what he must have realized was becoming a ceremony beyond eccentricity. 'Well,

Papa, Christmas would not be Christmas without Mr Fortnum and Mr Mason. How delicious!' Then he would place the embarrassing box below his chair, at which point his father would say, 'Aren't you going to offer them round? And you know, I do believe Blanco would like one, if there are any left.'

The final event for us children would occur at tea-time, when there would come a knock on the window, and my mother (enjoying her performance) would exclaim, 'Did you hear something, boys? I think . . . yes, there's someone at the window' – and, drawing back the curtains as if unveiling the plaque at the opening of some civic building, she would reveal, his cheeks rouged and face flocculent with white beard, Flynn disguised as Father Christmas. With a little difficulty he would squeeze through the casement, and go through a cheerful routine that culminated in everyone receiving their final present of the day, from the pillow-case he employed as a sack.

Finny's theatricals were not confined to Christmas. When either of us boys had a birthday party, he would bear the cake into the dining-room, each year dressed in some different disguise – a pirate, a policeman – with the full panoply of props and wigs appropriate to his role. For a man who was otherwise a paragon of propriety, these were the rare occasions when he had licence to appear as the Lord of Misrule – my mother encouraged it, I'm sure, but I can't think why my father toler-ated it. Possibly he just regarded it as childish and pointless.

In this respect, my brother Cosmo was his father's son. He rarely smiled at antics, and I think he regarded fun and games as a necessary evil; right from the start he had a tidy mind, and preferred to play by himself, and concentrate on a single toy, rather than scramble from one to another in a fever of industry. Nanny Mottram was delighted by this, and would hold his behaviour up to me as an example: 'Just *look* at how nicely your little brother is playing, with all his animals in straight lines, just as they should be. You should take a leaf out of his book, Master Richard, and learn to *organize* yourself better, so you should.' Perhaps she was right, but I never had much ambition to resemble Cosmo, then or later. There was something frail and distant about him, which was not conducive to fraternal connivings and mental fantasy games, so that we tended to go our separate ways. Where I scribbled and scrawled, Cosmos (though four years younger) was already interested in attempting careful shapes; he was reading at the age of three, and would quite often sit in the nursery with Nanny, listening to music from the big wireless. He was definitely my mother's favourite, since he preferred to stay indoors. This did not promote the kinship there was meant to be between us, either, and I'm afraid I used to tease him and disrupt his solitude and hide his crayons and tell lies about what he had said and done and, yes, I confess that I have never been very fond of him, though I cannot remember a single unkindness from him to me.

Perhaps it is true, what my mother said to me when Nanny reported I had deliberately knocked his water-pot over his painting: 'You know, Rich, I'm not sure you're going to grow up into a very nice person, after all.'

So Finny read the situation, and reserved the finest act in his dramatic repertoire for me alone. This was his impromptu Quasimodo, and I think, had my brother ever witnessed it, he might have fainted to the floor. (I'm being unfair now, even now, but who said anything about life being fair?) Without warning, he would emerge from his pantry with his oiled white hair wildly dishevelled, affecting a terrifying crouched and lurching gait, and clacking his false teeth (the legacy of many years of liquorice allsorts); and while I fled towards the hall in exquisite horror, he would quickly recompose himself and proceed past me as if it had all been some figment of my imagination, as if any variation in his steady progress would be unthinkable in one who was charged with embodying the orthodoxy of the entire household.

He was rather more of a major-domo than a *valet de chambre*, and as he grew older his habits increasingly hardened. Any tradesmen or artisans who arrived at the back-door were deemed to be entering his private fiefdom, and should there happen to be a new milkman, window-cleaner, postman, or reader of meters, he would be subjected to a probationary period of several months before any summons was forthcoming to tea and biscuits in the staff sitting-room. And as he slowed toward retirement, and dandruff weathered his collars, Finny built up a stubborn resistance to newcomers that must have seemed incomprehensible to anyone delivering a parcel, or a consignment of oil for the central-heating. But so far as he was concerned, when first he had been engaged by my grandfather such people were servicing a great house, and he would not accept that their successors saw it as a task no different from the other houses in the area, and that twenty minutes being detained by an elderly man in a dingy room was more a kindness in humouring him than a benison to which one might aspire, an honour of which one might care to boast over ale that night at the inn.

My father was not a gregarious man; he rarely visited his London clubs and, despite his interest in horses, kept well away from events like Royal Ascot. Conviviality did not come naturally to him, and even the pursuit of his personal pleasures seemed to be attended by a desire for efficiency, and the minimum of idling about. His driven temperament was not conducive to anecdotal conversations either, nor protracted periods spent sitting in the company of others. He was, though, a decent host, and through the three main winter months of the pheasant season there would be regular house-parties of guns staying at Spellbrook on weekends. These kept my mother very busy, and she was at her best when her personality was reflected off the company of others, although the sport itself I'm sure she found dull. This was true of my grandfather, too, but he enjoyed holding court at the dinner-parties, and was certainly an enthusiastic eater of all types of game.

'Ah, George: this is English partridge, surely? I much prefer the little native Englishman to that red-legged French intruder. Quite excellent. Tell me, did you shoot it yourself?'

'It is difficult to say, Papa. The birds are all bagged up collectively, as I believe you know.'

'So much for the hunter–gatherer, then. At least I know how my apples arrive on the plate.'

'It is necessarily a combined effort, such driven shooting. Several different skills are brought to bear on the operation, of which marksmanship is merely one.'

'The whole thing executed with, um, military precision?'

'Ideally speaking, yes.'

And my grandfather would nod, as if impressed, enjoying the exasperation caused by his pretended ignorance, leaving his son thin-lipped and perplexed, wondering if the old Duke ever really paid attention to anything he was told.

I was much too young to shoot in the line in those days, but I was encouraged to accompany my father, and stand quietly behind him at his numbered peg, carry his cartridge bag, or join the beaters for a drive or two. The latter was surprisingly hard work, especially if you had to wade through a field of wet kale, or negotiate the spiky lower limbs in a stand of evergreens, and all the time keeping an eye on the others, so the line was straight. But it was an instructive experience, not just because it gave me an early, interior knowledge of our coverts, but because it introduced me to the beaters' eye-view of a day's shooting, without a sense of which no estate owner can properly conduct the day's sport.

To be honest, I was rather in fear of them, at first, these weather-beaten men with their flags and leggings, their tele-graphic forms of conversation, their evident lack of excitement at whatever occurred. They made strange sounds as they trudged through the thickets, sounds I mimicked eagerly to win their acceptance, but my treble was no more than a parody of the gruff 'Aye-aye-aye-aye' they produced to startle a crouching bird into flight, or the shout of 'For-warrrrd!' as the pheasant cleared the trees and thrummed its path towards the waiting guns. Then a report, maybe several if there had been a 'flush' of birds, and Charlie might hold the line for a moment, during which his men would pass comments about how the various guns were performing: 'Missed 'un clean, that time' – 'Which

bugger's that, on three?' – 'That'd be Sir Robert, I reckon' –
'He want ter buy himself some decent ammunition, if his lordship's goin' ter invoite 'im back' – 'Ey, watch yerself, Will.
Boy's on yer left.' These were the first adults I ever heard talking
like this, and in my rarified world their weekly appearance in
the courtyard as they mounted the trailer and disposed themselves along the bales offered the thrill of a commando raid.

On the morning of the day he died, my father presented me
with a beautiful matched pair of Purdey twenty-bores with 24-
inch barrels. I was to be allowed out with his guests on the
Boxing Day shoot, a significant rite of passage. (Before I even
got to fire a pellet out of them, of course, the initials he had
had engraved on the silver butt-plate were no longer mine.) I
brought them out here to Schwyz, but it is years since I ever
shot at a bird. The natives do a bit of rifle-shooting among the
crags, but it doesn't interest me; I haven't glimpsed a chamois
since I moved here, and it's not much of a place for wildlife,
unless you're fascinated by marmots, or fond of rats.

Herr Sitt's cat might prove tempting, mind you, one of
these evenings, as he pads around my shrubbery, marking out
his territory with sprayed urine. Yes, perhaps as a treat to myself
on my next birthday I will pop his clogs for him as he arches
beside one of my fence-posts and lug his body, slain in the act
of micturition, sticking-plaster tongue lolling as I drag him by
the hindpaw, and slump him on my neighbour's doorstep. I
will activate the chime, and peer into the lens, saying, 'Listen,
buddy, watch my lips move: do the words "Private property"
mean anything to you?' The very prospect of it makes my
trigger-finger curl slowly, with delicious anticipation.

It may be some time since I saw a pheasant, but these days
the commando raids are for real. As a naturalized citizen (and,
boy, does it ever cost you to join this particular club) I am

automatically a member of the militia – I am, in fact, a lieutenant in an infantry brigade of the Landwehr, the National Defence Corps. In my bedroom there hangs a blue–green uniform, and in the security cupboard (with the Purdeys as strange bed-fellows) my flyweight R-42 Cloudburst stands to attention in its rack. Every other month there is regulation target practice at the local rifle club, to which every male between the ages of twenty-one and fifty must, by law, belong.

There are no conscientious objectors here, thank you very much indeed.

We go on training weekends occasionally, and I am rather taken by the idea that, in an age of belligerent devices of almost preposterous levels of sophistication, there should exist a band of men prepared to respond at once to a Vidcall emergency tone, and lug their equipment up to defend some mountain passes. But I can assure you they are deadly serious about the training: we may be neutral, but by Jesus there's a well-armed presence.

There was a sudden fall of dirty snow this July, and our brigade was called out to take advantage of these rare conditions. I got to wear my fur cap for the first time with my combat suit. The eager volunteers of the ski-corps slooped around their own specially contrived test-firing course, while we were sub-jected to a rather complicated lecture and demonstration about temperature-controlled explosives, and then invited to traverse a slope on our bellies, construct a small impasse of diversionary APW anti-personnel wire (a hogfucker of a material to fiddle with in sealed mittens, even before it is juiced up) and then bury a strip of necklace-mines at a uniform depth of sixteen centimetres. Well, it's the least you can do for your country; and there was some hot chocolate to be had later from the field canteen – with a drop of something wet from the little hipflask Finny gave me for my twenty-first, as a jumpstarter – and it was while we were stamping around for the Sno-Lynx to arrive that I saw them bringing up the pigs.

It was a medical unit, and they had three large pigs in

a cage on runners behind their vehicle. Major Moltke, our commanding officer, signalled this party to a halt, and warned them they were entering an official practice zone: it transpired that they had in fact come in search of our brigade, at short notice because of the weather conditions. They were a team of surgeons who needed to rehearse the treatment of wounds in an area above the snow-line, and requested the use of one of our marksmen. Fortunately, Moltke fancies his prowess with the rifle, and so he volunteered his own services for what followed.

They constructed a wooden frame, like a low set of goal-posts, and then dragged the first pig out of its prison. They pulled it over to the target area, and injected it with an anaesthetic, then hung it belly-up from the crossbar, in a sling. Moltke then withdrew fifty yards, and shot it twice in the haunch with his Cloudburst, and then ran forward and put a further, regular bullet into its stomach from just a few feet away. The medical orderlies then retrieved the animal on a covered stretcher, conveyed it to the tent, bandaged its wounds, administered transfusions, and prepared the stricken pig for emergency surgery. This took around half an hour, and was filmed to a running commentary from one of the surgeons. We could see a little of what was happening, through the flap in the side of the tent, and with only the animal's abdomen exposed between the surgical drapes it was not hard to imagine these identical procedures being performed on one of our own number. The only difference (one hopes) was that when the operation had been completed, the pig was killed with a pneumatic bolt through its skull. Our transport arrived just as the medical experts were arranging the second animal in its cradle, and the Major had agreed to stay on beyond the call of duty and continue to assist in this essential research. We went back down to the base camp with hardly a brave militiaman uttering a word.

I don't believe the pig we saw was anaesthetized at all. I can't be sure, because we don't get issued with scanners for snow-ops, but I reckon its eyelids were not hanging open because it was upside down: they were wide open because it was paralysed, but fully sensate. That would make for better results, scientifically. Data gathered from an assessment of the recovery prospects of a pig that has felt no pain can hardly be compared to what might be the case when a man is wounded, fully conscious, in action. That animal was shot, its system registered the exquisite muscle-shock of three missiles, the first of which caused the body to arc into the air under the impact, and swing silently with such momentum that Moltke had to wait for more than two minutes before he could be sure of his second target-point. Then they repaired it to their satisfaction, and they disposed of it. The very process of disposing of corpses, under such conditions, was presumably all part of the experiment.

If the day ever comes, and something crazy happens, like the Italians deciding to annexe the valleys, I will turn out for my spell of duty like the rest of these men, but I hope we won't be fighting in the snow. The picture of that trussed pig, with the thin spray of blood behind him in three long projections across the snow, is not any kind of mock-up for the way I intend to go. But I have to say I am hatching plans for the cat. I definitely have some fresh ideas in mind for Herr Sitt's increasingly expendable-looking pet.

Well, that's just about seen off the Highland Park (seventy centilitres of it in one, fell evening, but it's been a bad day: with good malt here costing 52 ecks a bottle, it's just as well I'm still pretty rich). I'm loaded for bear, and firing at shadows. A maze of smoke and mirrors. If that cat should chance to mince across our yard, right now, as I prepare for bed, I could catch it in my Starpoint scanner; I could make Ribena of it. We will see. But it is late, and although tomorrow is Saturday and I do not have to teach, I have Magda to think of. She will turn, wearily, in our bed, and ask me where all this is leading (she is only twenty years old, for Sir God's sake), but she knows I shall disturb her no further. The drink has replaced any sex. She knows how I slouch each night to an alimentary orgasm. Magda is a lovely girl, but I don't suppose I will be able to hold on to her for ever. Not even if I donned my fur cap, and crawled across a snowfield, in the uniform she says looks cute.

My mother used to drink, and I believe she still does; perhaps I inherited this passion from her, along with my dark hair. That's it, blame the folks; turn it all around, and say it must have been the parenting. I don't care. Quite honestly, I'm not interested in the blame industry. If my insidious, masculine lovers are called Johnnie Walker and Jim Beam, so be it. They have the colours of sunlight. My mother drinks gin, which is subtle, and retains the colours of air.

And what, exactly, did I inherit from my father? Several titles, an embarrassment of riches, a level of intolerance? But not his phobia, I hope, not the legacy of any family strangeness, something which goes with the title.

I have just time to drag in the blue smoke from one final, *papier maïs* lungfucker, apply a last belt of squirrel-oil, before retiring (and I could now retire, having a job) and turning everything out, and going as quietly as possible into the dark.

FOUR

My grandfather was only in his seventieth year when he died in February 1963. It would be nice to record that he was found stretched out in his orchard, killed instantly by a heart attack, or discovered quietly dead in his sleep, sitting in the conservatory with his faithful parrot, but this is not what happened. He suffered a stroke that rendered him bedridden and incontinent and, I think, frightened for four months, before another finally ended his life. I was just six at the time, but I could understand that he was dangerously ill from the way everyone else in the house lowered their voices when discussing his condition. I asked Nanny Mottram, 'Is he going to die?' and she was the right person to field this inevitable enquiry, because she was strong in faith: 'Each and every one of us has got to die, pet, you know that. But His Grace has lived as good a life as he was able, so there will be nothing for him to fear in the hereafter.'

But when I went to visit him (I had never until then even entered his bedroom) he was not always composed, and once or twice scared me by not seeming to realize who I was, or calling me 'George'; at other times he seemed a little more resigned, and would make me laugh by asking questions about his Irish nurse Pauline, when she was out of the room. 'Quick, Brompton, before that woman is back here again, what does she really look like? They keep telling me she is small, and dark, and young, but that's not what her voice sounds like. Tell me – is she old and fat? Is she? I want the truth, now.'

I said, 'She's not *too* young, but she's not fat, not like Iris, and her hair is black, like they say.'

'You wouldn't lie to me, would you, little soldier? Well then, come and give me a kiss, and be off and find your tea.'

I kissed him on his forehead, and said, 'I love you, Grandpa'.

No, I never lied to Arthur London.

If I think of his death as the end of an era in my life, it is not just because I missed his presence in the house: shortly after the event I was informed by my father that the following spring I was to begin attending a boarding-school. I did not like the sound of this, since I was quite happy at my little day-school just outside Guildford, but I was not offered any choice in the matter. There was still a theory, dished up largely for parental convenience, of course, that sending a boy away for a decade, to spend most of every year with no access to his home, was the only way to promote 'independence', get him used to living with other boys (why this wholly artificial *ménage* should be thought desirable, I cannot imagine), be instilled with discipline and enlightenment by 'experts, who really *know* about children', and introduced to the inestimable benefits of compulsory, competitive team-games. Well, however thin you slice that, it's still baloney.

I never even went to view the school prior to that January day when my mother cheerfully steered the green Daimler up the drive between the rhododendrons (all right so far, quite like home) and scrunched to a halt outside the front door of what was known as the 'private side' of Stockhill House, a Jekyll and Hyde edifice if ever there was one, a purpose-built Janus of an institution dating from the noonday of the Empire, surrounded by sentinel pines, and hidden away in so-called Royal Berkshire, a county through which I subsequently could never drive with sufficient rapidity. The trick to the survival of this red-brick abortion was that the fee-paying parents saw one of its faces, while the inmates, patients, pupils, squaddies, call them what you will (my new appellation was 'squit') saw quite another. But since nothing in my experience could possibly have prepared me for this, I did not see through this disguise as my mother pulled the door-bell of what, so far as I was concerned, appeared to be an ordinary house, rather uglier and slightly smaller than our own. But as I crossed the threshold, I was becoming someone new and unfamiliar. The phase of my child-hood proper was falling away behind me, like the jettisoned first stage of a rocket after escaping the Earth's gravitational field.

On this winter's day, some hours before the rest of the school was due to return for what was pompously known as the Hilary Term (what was this, some kind of university?) six little boys and an assortment of parents (my father had an unavoidable meeting in the City) were entertained to a stand-up tea in the Headmaster's dining-room. There were sandwiches with chocolate spread or Marmite, a walnut cake, a banana cake, some glasses of rather bitter squash, and two plates of Kit-Kat biscuits. It was a fiendishly staged pantomime of wel-come and hospitality, presided over by Mr Vaughan and his nice wife; already I was deep into enemy territory.

'Oh, Rich, the food looks scrumptious,' said my mother with a reassuring smile. Did she know – were all those parents all part of it? – that this was but a sham, a publicity stunt being pulled by the authorities to tart up reality, like the twists of seasonal tinsel the police put round the aerials of their patrol-cars, come Christmas, to seem festive? Or had she sold herself the idea that it was all going to be for the best, and that 'Love is shown in the letting go', and that it would be all right for *me* because I was quite clever, or a marquess, or some such other will-o'-the-wisp nonsense? We six stood around, uncomfortable in our short new haircuts, and felt we were being fattened for some sacrifice.

'You're sure to settle in splendidly,' my mother informed me, kissing the top of my hair, 'and of course I'll write and tell you all our news from home.' She cupped my chin, but I resisted looking her in the eyes, as usual. 'Don't forget to eat *lots* of fruit and vegetables,' she said, 'to keep up your energy for all the games. You'll be a star, Rich, I just know you will.' (Oh, yes, darling, you were *marvellous*.) And then she left.

It was the last time for ages we were to see the inside of

the Vaughans' domestic quarters: there might be visits to Mr Vaughan's study, but that was strictly speaking more of a transit area between someone's home (where there was real furniture and recognizable food) and the hinterlands we inhabited, supervised by people we never saw in the real world, a place decked out with bare parodies of beds and chairs and clothes and cutlery, a cartoon interior that was less like any prison I have ever seen and more of an alien dimension in which everything familiar from one's domestic past (and here I admit I was probably not typical) had been slightly distorted and demeaned.

The feeling of abandonment was novel, and at first it simply did not sink in. When Mr Smedley, the deputy head, approached us, the parents now safely on their way, the six of us instinctively gravitated together like trout in a restaurant tank as the waiter closes in, grasping his dip-net. Smedley advanced, rubbing his hands together energetically like some dreadful party-entertainer, and announced, 'That's it, then, boys. Time we were setting sail. Welcome aboard. Let's go and find your berths, shall we?' He was a plump man with grey hair and a pink face, and I doubt for one second he had any connections whatsoever with the Senior Service (except, just possibly, in an off-duty capacity), but he was fond of jargon, and liked to think it lent even more dignity to his already lofty position of command. We followed him into the hull of the school, in silence.

Of course it was no grimmer than dozens of similar establishments trading, in those days, on a shoestring budget and an ancient reputation for supposed excellence, and the hardships were merely relative. (They seemed real enough to a pampered child at the time, however, and we would never have sent Peter to such a place, had . . . No: not now.) As I say, lack of even a modicum of creature comforts came as a rude surprise, but the most odious aspect of my years at the Hill was the relentless dragooning that attended every conceivable portion of one's wakeful hours. I came to hate the place for its pettiness, its clockwork efficiency, its fake *esprit de corps*. But mostly I resented the power that the school exerted, the inexorable pull it seemed to exercise over my life, the way in which it dragged me out of the soft meadows of my childhood proper and into the coarser thicket of communal existence. I will never forget that: it was quite unforgivable.

There were about ninety boys at the Hill in my time, arranged into eight dormitories, each of which was named after some important battle in British history. You began in Hastings (not, on the face of it, a very promising start) and graduated through Bannockburn, Bosworth, Flodden, Naseby, Malplaquet, Trafalgar and Waterloo – at which juncture perhaps military history was exhausted, or becoming too threateningly modern to be worth commemorating. There was a single poster on the back of the door to each dorm, depicting the eponymous battle or, in the case of Malplaquet, which was too obscure for any company to have manufactured an illustrative poster, and which had presumably been designated by some history master from long ago wishing to immortalize his erudition, a rather dull water-colour of a soldier in a shako, done by Mrs Pugh, the visiting art-teacher. It would never have done to invoke commandoes or fighter-pilots, the only historical images that we found fascinating from the pages of banned 'trash' comics, and other misleading examples of modern literature.

Each dorm was under the charge of a monitor, a senior boy invested with such heady privileges as having a slice of toast each morning at breakfast, sporting a starred tie with his maroon and grey uniform, and being allowed to read after we were consigned to darkness, with a little light clamped to the top bar of his iron bedhead. It wasn't such a bad system: the monitors changed dorms every fortnight, and it gave you a chance to have some contact with the swells at the top of the school, some of whom were inclined to organize fun (elsewhere a commodity conspicuous by its absence), like a dormitory play, or after-lights quizzes and competitions. But any form of 'ragging' – getting out of bed for fights, or games – was out of the question, and any boy sanctioning that would be summarily 'de-monitor-ized', and ignominiously reduced to the ranks. Short of expulsion, which was very rare, this was the worst humiliation the hierarchy of the Hill could threaten. This was as stunning a ritual as anything meted out to Chuck Connors in the title-sequence of *Branded*, and involved the disgraced pupil coming to stand on the dais by the Headmaster's table after lunchtime Grace, facing the rest of the school, and hearing Mr Vaughan outline his misdemeanours in public, following which he had to remove the special tie from around his neck, and walk out of the dining room alone, ahead of all the rest of us.

This happened only twice during my five years in residence – once to a charming boy called Paisley, who had a gold tooth, and once to me. But we'll come to that, in a roundabout fashion.

The master in charge of dormitories resided in a little suite of rooms on the second floor, and he was the nocturnal deity of Stockhill House. His name was Mr Gardner, but we knew him as 'Swish', because he was empowered to beat boys with his cane, if he so decided, without reference to the headmaster. Swish was an Old Boy who had returned to teach at the Hill in 1913, and had only ever left to fight in the Great War, when he had been slightly wounded in his left (non-swishing) elbow. You could see him in those very early, sepia-toned staff photographs that lugubriously adorned the main stairwell. Then fresh out of Cambridge (a classics graduate, naturally, though he taught everything from maths to French), the moustache dark and impressive, standing proudly at the rear of the group behind the senior masters enthroned before him in their wickerwork chairs with their striped blazers and dundrearies, their watch-chains and Imperial stares, confidently waiting his turn, having settled on his destiny.

For three years his face is absent, but he crops up once more in 1917, back on sick leave, his arm in a sling, but by now so many of the other faces are absent that he has made it to the row of chairs, never to have to stand for the school photograph again, in forty-eight years. We believed, but wondered, that this could really be the same man who padded along our very corridors in his crêpe-soled brogues (to render more silent his approach) – could this have been his entire life? If so, then perhaps there was more to the place than met our eyes. This was not convincing, but it was a haunting possibility: that the Hill might, for some adults, actually *be* a version of real life.

It was chiefly the appalling aspect of his age that made us more respectful of Swish than we were of the rest of the staff – the papery, almost mummified skin that stretched across his cheek-bones, his inefficient deaf-aid, his nearly perpetual truculence. He was no mere mascot, either, but the living embodiment of school tradition, the resident historian, the peripatetic *lar* of the entire building. He had slept in these beds (they weren't quite that old, but so we believed it), thundered down the same turf with a rugby-ball tucked under his arm, won a scholarship to Radley (you could see his name in gold on the board in the Library, every day), but he was never any kind of hero or role-model, being much too old and cantankerous and scary. He may have enjoyed a venerable status, but as an example to us all he was frankly terrifying. I never heard any boy express a wish to follow in a single footstep of Mr Gardner's.

Rumours about him abounded. He had suffered shell-shock, and been in a mental hospital; he married his nurse, who became an assistant matron at the Hill and later killed herself (there is no photographic record of this sad person anywhere up the stairs, but the fact that there is no staff picture for 1918 is thought to furnish positive proof – it was later removed at his request); he had actually been responsible for the death of a pupil, a long time ago (again, nothing so specific as names or details, but a good legend all the same for scaring the new squits in Hastings). The real mystery, which never occurred to us in our relative innocence about systems of preferment, was why he had never been made Headmaster, and why, that being so (he must have realized he was passed over in this respect well before the Second War) he had chosen to stay on, a stalagmite in the school's seldom less than gloomy history.

He was not exactly disliked, but nor was he renowned for his kindliness. After half a century of confronting the attempts of little boys to negotiate themselves out of trouble, he had become, quite understandably, entrenched in his attitudes. His favourite comment was, 'remarkable' – a word which signalled the impending dismissal of lame excuses, bald lies, wrong mathematical solutions, hopeless requests and other such occupational irritations with which, for fifty-one years, he had been dealing on a daily basis, for thirty-six weeks of every year, man and boy, father and son, with little in the way of discernible variations. 'Ha, quite remarkable,' he would bark, before proceeding to remedy the imbalance caused in Nature by the incessant and unsatisfactory mental performance of children.

There was one treat associated with him, however, and that was the nightly business of fetching his ice up from the kitchen. It looked as if this was a random process of selection, because he chose boys from all over the range of dorms, but there was never a sign of favouritism, and I suspect he worked to a careful rota. We all got our chance, even the known villains. Swish would enter a dormitory at seven o'clock, clutching his blue Thermos. He then requested the monitor to allow a particular boy to run an errand for him, namely to ask Lizzie the cook for some ice-cubes to go with his whisky. When you returned in your dressing-gown to deliver what he needed, he would nod, and say, 'Ha. There you are. Thank you. Put it there, on the table.' And the etiquette was to bid him good-night, and turn for the doorway, at which point (and I never heard of an instance when it did not happen) Swish said, 'Do you like grub?'

Even now, I find this the perfect example of a rhetorical question. 'Grub' was our code-name for sweets, tuck, sock, call it what you will, and it was the staple of all the barter and bribery systems in operation at the Hill. Grub was the powerful equivalent of narcotics in some prisons. We were denied tuck-boxes, and the only source of confectionery was the grub-trolley, wheeled into the Library with great ceremony after lunch on Tuesday, Thursday and Sunday. There might be tins of White Heather assortment (six bits each, the hands to be shown to the master in charge, after selection, in order of seniority), or a glass jar of barley sugar, a carton of Milky Way, a box of toffees. There was no other legitimate way to obtain this prep-school snout, this youthful version of *soma* – except by Fetching The Ice. Because at that moment when Swish asked you if you liked grub, the received choreography had it that you turned, and said, 'Yes, sir', and he hoiked two butterscotch balls out of a tin as a reward for your services, and you would thank him, and scuttle back to your bed, and crunch them noisily, at once, to maximize the envy of your compeers, and then sink to sleep with the delicious feel of granulated sugar ground into the topography of your teeth, making you unique beneath the roof, the evening's chosen votary, having redis-covered the sacrament of the world beyond the dark shrubs.

What I found most bewildering was the lack of privacy, and the inescapable presence of other boys, whatever it was you wanted to do: the prep school was overtly dedicated to prepar-ing you for a life of self-sufficiency and independence, yet the only time you were really able to go it alone was when you were sitting at your desk. Like most similar schools, the Hill offered a lifestyle that was one long round of rosters and rou-tines, roll-calls and rituals, so that after five years you just felt you had been plodding round in circles like a blinkered horse in an old brick-mill.

Everything was rendered down into lists and timetables, pecking-orders and classifications – the team-lists, the form-orders, Mr Smedley's 'Order of the Bath', the school chart in the Library. The latter established the names of all pupils in a hierarchy according to age, along with dates of birth and a weekly record of conduct marks, published for all to see. The punishment system involved masters awarding marks for bad behaviour, and the scale ran from two for being late, right up to twenty for crimes of unusual enormity such as gross insolence, aggravated assault, and, perhaps piracy on the High Seas. Each afternoon during tea the Master on Duty would call 'Silence', and then read out the name of every boy, in reply to which he had to report any marks clocked up on the day. Usually, you said, 'None, sir', but there were always some miscreants, and the *Schadenfreude* as we listened raptly to the record of the day's scandals could be very considerable. If a boy said 'Ten, sir' there would be a slight sussurus in the dining-room, as he had to explain the reason for this penalty, but if the reply was a mumbled, 'Twenty, sir', the anticipation amongst his so-called peer group would be so pronounced that it took a moment for order to be restored. The record tally that I ever heard was when Fulton replied, in a strangulated voice, 'Forty-five, sir': that just about brought the house down, followed as it was by an arithmetical breakdown of his day's infringements that comprised more crime than most of us were capable of in a school year. It is strange the way these lists seem to enter the long-term memory of children at that age – I can still remember the particular sequence of the mark-book where I had to be alert (you attracted marks for not replying at once, naturally): Dennison, Benchley, Borthwick, Parker (later, Parker Ma.), Montague, Waterstock, Prideaux, Addams mi. (later ennobled to plain Addams), Henniker, Turnbull. It is an information-strip that time has reduced to no value, a synthesis that once regulated years of my life, a little run of words that has become burred on to the sleeve of my memory.

It is a miracle that I don't still dream of The Acrosses.

Let me explain: the main lavatory block at the Hill was located across the yard from the changing-rooms, and as a result it was called 'going across', when you needed to answer Nature's call. This was the official euphemism, not for the journey but for the act of urination itself, irrespective of the location where it was performed – along the lines of the American use of 'go to the bathroom'. There were several urinals and water-closets in the regions of the dorms as well, and it was still 'going across' when you utilized these ancient examples of the plumber's art, and it was still 'going across' when you did it in your bed at night, by mistake. There was a bizarre extension of this code whereby defecation was called 'going across properly', the adverb presumably functioning as an intensifier analogous to the scale of Number Ones and Number Twos. None of this would really be worth setting out in detail if it were merely a question of the quite prevalent social phenomenon of lexical deodorization, but it was only a prelude to a system of excrementitious policing that somehow typifies the literal basis upon which such education rested, a kind of *mens sana in corpore sano* that would not have disgraced a physician at the Court of the Sun King.

After breakfast there was another rota that came into play, the Across Sheet. When you had done your stint you reported to the master with his clipboard 'Properly' or 'Non', and your square was accordingly filled in with a tick or cross, before you went to fetch the next boy in your particular chain of hygiene. I did not find that regularity of bowel-movement was encouraged by the need to go to stool under starter's orders, nor by the concomitant business of reporting on your success (or lack of it) to some unqualified Australian athlete masquerading temporarily as a maths teacher. But it was even worse for your first few terms, because you had to report to one of the matrons, who then came to inspect your consequences of eating, to prove that you were telling the truth, thus investing with further embarrassment a subject about which certain sectors of English society have traditionally been repressed enough as it is. However, like most of the systems at the Hill, the Across Sheet enjoyed its own peculiar logic, though what its side-effects might have been for those boys who later in life became tycoons, poodlefakers, Members of Parliament, polo-players, estate agents, or took up any of the other admirable vocations for which such an unimaginative education is traditionally necessary, I cannot guess, and am perhaps in no position to debate.

We've probably all turned out to be a clutch of psychosexual infantilist anal-retentives of the breed that was originally desired, for the preservation of Empire.

You might say that very little was left to chance in this community – no doubt safer that way, from the point of view of the authorities, but 'better safe than sorry' may not be the ideal way to learn. When it wasn't the teaching staff to whom you were answerable, then one of the three matrons would be requiring you to show proof that you weren't biting your nails (in the surgery, every Friday), that you were carrying a pocket handkerchief (to be brandished each morning as you descended to breakfast), that you were not infested with nits (once a year, just before the end of summer term, by which time it was conveniently too late for the matrons to do anything about it, and the problem was exported beyond the school gates), or that you had made your bed, tidied the contents of the basket beneath it, or put your dirty underwear in the correct dumpbin every Tuesday evening. You can see, perhaps, why I do not much object to being a Swiss citizen who has to carry an ID card.

The Head Matron throughout my time there was a gruff, plump little spinster named Miss Hooper, a turkey-person who fretted around in a brownish uniform, a slight hobble from her bad hip making her gait identifiable to our ears before she ever penetrated our dormitories. (Just settle down, now.) The extent of her medical knowledge was probably not great, but she remained a curiously reassuring presence, without by any stretch of the imagination becoming a surrogate figure for our nannies or mothers. I say this despite the fact that she once diagnosed my first verruca as a corn, and accordingly sliced away at it with an excruciating razor-blade every Sunday evening for a whole month before Dr Bevan gently corrected her during his next visit, and proceeded to freeze out the excrescence with something from his smoking vacuum flask.

Stockhill House was one of the few places I have ever lived where it was thought to be a stroke of good luck if you were taken ill. Next door to Bosworth were the two Sick-rooms, twin havens of quiet and relative comfort for those running respectable temperatures, or suffering from some infection that might result in a pandemic. There were jolly posters framed upon the walls – photographs of kittens with balls of wool, wheeling sea-birds, horses at full tilt across a hillside – and you had your own bedside table, with your travelling-clock, plastic jug of squash, hairbrush and a loaned radio. You could sleep during the day and ignore the bells, savour the exquisite, exclusive pleasure of hearing the rest of the troops thunder downstairs at the appointed hour to begin their daily programme, and, if you were very lucky, or suspiciously contagious, you might have one of those rooms to yourself. There were boxes of jumbled soldiers, jigsaws and games of L'Attaque to play as you convalesced, great bound volumes of *Punch* and the *Illustrated London News* to leaf through for the cartoons and pictures, and – best of all – your food.

The first morning I awoke in one of these idyllic rooms (I was going down with mumps, and shortly after had to be sent home) the breakfast tray that was brought to me seemed as though it must have been some mirage. A bowl of Ricicles, an egg poached softly and uniformly in a metal cup, toast with real butter – I wondered if, in my fever, I was dreaming. I feared I might have died and been reunited with my loved ones on Planet Earth. Because this was not Stockhill fare, this was human food, food you did not fear: this was a meal. It was not hard to see why boys resorted to deception in order to have their recovery periods prolonged – holding the thermometer over the radiator, pretending to rush off and vomit in the Acrosses, press hairbrush bristles into their flesh to approximate rashes. But Miss Hooper had seen it all before, and malingerers were soon banished to their dorms, with the taste of toast and honey just a happy memory.

As adults, we eat, in part, with our memories. The fictions of Proust have set this fact beyond contention, but I need no delicate *madeleine* to unlock the flavours of my schooldays. The food at the Hill was so uniformly an adulterated, degraded and unappetizing version of what one might have been lucky enough to have been served at home that I even came to think wistfully of the Escoffier-like skills Nanny Mottram brought to bear in her Nursery kitchen. The cook at the Hill was Lizzie, a large, hot woman with facial sideboards, a woman who toiled against the odds and with no prospect of gratitude, but a devastatingly bad cook, for all that. She could boil mutton, weave a fish pudding, reconstitute potato-powder into a semblance of mash, heat cauldrons of industrial beans, and sear any number of carmine-coloured beef sausages – all, apparently, to the satisfaction of the school authorities – but the rudimentary physics of boiling an egg were evidently beyond her. Either the yolk would be cemented to the rigid albumen structure surrounding it, to the extent that both were resistant to the fierce probe of your alloy spoon (the introduction of a blob of margarine, as general lubricant, notwithstanding), or else your egg would be so underdone as to release a chlorinous spurt of gas, its decapitation revealing glutinous liquids that brought the exhalations of a swimming-pool to the already questionable delights of such a communal breakfast table.

With the several, cumulative, and unforgettable discoveries that one made in the quaint contents of what were dubbed her Shepherd's Pies (Mondays, without fail), I can only say that I would not order a dish with this name even from the chefs of the Connaught or Simpson's in the Strand, both of which establishments continue to flourish and serve glorified school food to the uniformed heirs of the new Republic. One can have too much of a bad thing, after all.

The only legitimate way of supplementing this diet was with cakes. Each boy was allowed two of these per term (plus one extra on his birthday), and if it was of sufficient size, and divided up into more than the twelve slices needed to go round your immediate table, you were permitted to distribute the surplus to chosen friends at other, very possibly cakeless, tables. This afforded you a little moment of power as you criss-crossed the room with your plate of offerings – here was the chance for a public display of friendship to a boy outside your form, the bestowal of personal honours that also included a complex system of barter, bribery and reciprocation that was positively Masonic in its intricacies, with those hoping to be numbered among the elect putting on a dumb-show of imploration if they caught your eye, the favoured clapping you on the shoulder as you bent forward to invest their platters with a fragment from the distant world more precious than any moonrock, more welcome than a long drink in summer.

Some boys were almost celebrities by virtue of their cakes: Hamilton's mother cooked (or had her cook do so, I'm not sure) a biscuit-cake that was a nonpareil – of peaty complexion and heavy with crushed digestives and dark chocolate, deliciously moist; the Addams brothers used periodically to come up with an iced orange sponge; after a day out, I would sometimes return equipped with one of Iris's ginger cakes, which were excellent even when the slices had to be spread with margarine. But the mother and father of all school cakes was produced by Chandupura, a boy who later drew me into some trouble, and who became quite effortlessly one of my schoolboy idols.

He did not arrive at the Hill until he was ten, so it must have been for his eleventh birthday that the great confection was produced: it was so large that it fed the entire school, including the staff, and was a facsimile of his Maharajal palace in Madhya Pradesh. At the end of that meal he sat behind a separate table that was heaped with wrapped gifts, and as we filed out he presented each boy with a parcel containing a toy. I think my ancestor, Sam, would have been amused at the spectacle of one of his linear descendants receiving gifts *from* an Indian, rather than the other way around, but the spirit in which these were handed over was so casual that they could hardly be accepted as if they were anything more than natural largesse. To Chandy, this was merely an amusing little apology for what was really a state occasion, and he remained as languid as ever, looking remote and sleek, refusing to be impressed by his own extravagance.

Last chance for food came after prep, when there was a table spread with certain of Lizzie's *mauvaises bouches* that were dignified with the term 'supper'. Great metal jugs held hot Bovril, weak and sour, or thin cocoa made with water and powdered milk, or packet soup (tomato or leek seemed to be the only flavours), with hot lemon squash in winter (not a good thing with which to scour your stomach just before bed). To complement this liquid feast you had the choice between two baskets, each containing half-slices of plain white bread. Depending on the weather, and on which member of staff was on duty that evening, you might be lucky enough to transform your bread into toast, by impaling it on the blade of your penknife and dangling it down in front of the single electric fire in the Victorian fireplace. There was inevitably fierce competition to achieve pole position as toaster, and it was considered a triumph if you completed your cuisine before the order came to ascend to the dorms. As usual, it was a case of the survival of the fittest, and I can't claim that in that respect I was ever very fit. After a while you simply gave up trying to jockey for position, and accepted that you were to sup on dry bread while those who got to scrunch toast were boys like Chandy (who tended to saunter up and wave aside the opposition) or berserkers with a bone missing somewhere in their heads, like the notorious Fulton.

Perhaps it was not Fulton's fault that his knuckles grazed the lino as he trundled about his business, but he was almost pathologically irascible, and taunting him was a regular bloodsport at the Hill. He was three years older than me, and was pointed out by another boy on my first day: 'That's Fulton, and you want to watch it if he gets into a bate. He's the school zombie.' Our delight was compounded by the fact that he was a godson of Mrs Vaughan, a person who did not figure centrally in our lives but whom we glimpsed from time to time during the more clement months wandering a little erratically around her cutting-borders, as if to langorous music. She was not in much of a position to discharge her godmotherly duties, and so it fell embarrassingly upon her husband to deal with the boy's sometimes life-threatening volatility.

The first time I witnessed one of Fulton's fights I could scarcely believe the degree of noise and physical violence towards which he had been goaded: one minute he was walking away from his picadors, and the next he whipped round and charged, bellowing, his cheeks lit with rage, and dragged one of his verbal assailants to the floorboards. They were quickly surrounded by a circle of hecklers, several boys deep, all ululating like an emergency siren, waving their hands rhythmically up and down in the air, as if literally fanning the flames of his temper. The skirmish was just getting nicely under way when Mr Vaughan appeared in the doorway of the Library with two prospective parents on a familiarization tour around his educational establishment. Somebody would have spotted them straight away – there was nearly always a boy posted to 'keep *cave*', but it took some minutes for a warning to percolate through to the centre, when the circle instantly dissolved to disclose Fulton steaming like the Minotaur, with his tormentor's head (still, fortunately, attached by the neck) locked under his right arm. Mr Vaughan turned to his astonished guests and merely said, 'This, as you can see, is the Library, where at present they are rehearsing the school play.'

The emphasis on playing games at the Hill was the feature which really left me most bewildered and estranged, because I excelled at none, and was scarcely competent at any. I detest soccer to this day, but to have admitted that at school would have amounted to sacrilege and would have been the foolish type of honesty that might rebound on you in other, insidious ways, off the pitch. Playing with a football was taken very seriously by most of the younger staff, and team spirit (that most useless of peace-time attributes) was regarded as a religious tenet, a credo on a par with the need for regular excretion.

Listen, if I'd been any good at games I have not the slightest doubt that I would have enjoyed my time there most thoroughly. As it was, I realized quite early on that it was going to be tough for me to succeed, and I did not want to give my more athletic contemporaries (Browne, Hamilton, Palmer) the satisfaction of seeing my aspirations thwarted. So I made it look as if I didn't care – although this wasn't such a smart solution, since there was no enlightened programme of alternative ways to spend those grey afternoons, and sooner or later during your career at the Hill you were bound to be co-opted into playing for some team or other, however humble. The prospect of this made me exceedingly nervous, since I have never relished being the weakest link in a chain – as well as being called 'yellow' and 'spastic' by the other boys, and being accused of 'letting the side down' by Mr Lawson, the First Eleven coach.

The only advantage of playing in a match was that Mr Lawson issued all players with a single orange-flavoured Dextrosol before the game – this was partly an inducement, but also I think originated from a fear that our putrid diet might otherwise be exposed to the enemy if one of our number collapsed on the field of battle through malnutrition. If it was an Away match, one was subjected to the hostility of the Home supporters, which I tended to take personally (a stupid mistake) and not as a tribal thing, largely because I didn't feel I belonged to any tribe myself. In retrospect, I don't think any of these neighbouring schools appeared preferable to the Hill, and it was actually something of a relief to clamber back into the minibus and return to the devil I was beginning to know, even if I had scored an own-goal or failed to execute a wall-pass, or some other manoeuvre that was entirely beyond me, and was therefore 'sent to Coventry' by the captain for the rest of the day. What I remember most keenly about these rival establishments is their distinctive corporate smells – I expect we had one too, but, as with accents, you only notice deviations from what you regard as the norm. At Benniston Hall, for instance, both boys and buildings reeked faintly of boiled meat; Slatebrook was redolent of polish, Wentworth unmistakably carbolic, and the aroma at Ashleigh Court I have only ever detected elsewhere in the Big Top of Bertram Mills' Circus.

You were allowed out three Sundays a term with your parents, and that was it. You left after morning chapel, and had to be back by evening chapel, and if you were staying in school you wrote a nice letter home instead. These were little more than official bulletins that followed the helpful guidelines chalked up on the board by your form master: the week's permissible topics were prescribed (Saturday film, *The Ladies Who Do*; result against Slatebrook; weather) and anything smacking of creative variation, or words that masked homesickness – any cry for help, in fact – was subject to benign censorship, because the contents of every letter were read before you, prior to being sealed, and would be re-presented for a 'fair copy' on the grounds of poor calligraphy or defective spelling, until you came up with a properly turned and sanitized version of what had transpired since your last communication.

I can see the logic – diaphonous as it was – wrapped round this pretence. Small boys often perceive the world from a misleading viewpoint, being only a few feet above the ground, unlike their masters, who enjoy a lofty over-view. To report back home any private interpretations, such as 'Mr Lawson was very cross with me for missing a header, and told me I was chicken,' or, 'Our form was all given ten marks because no one would own up to scribbling on the blackboard, which is unfair, because Montague did it' (useful, and duly noted, but hardly of parental interest), or, 'The team was beaten at judo yesterday, for the thid time', might impart a false impression of the progressive life of the Hill or fail to cast light on its really important aspects, I can see that. But the result was that it was virtually impossible for parents to keep tabs on what was going on, always assuming that they had a desire to, and they often regarded neat letters and end-of-term Reports as propaganda, and cosy chats during most infrequent visits as suspicious until proven otherwise. Which, I'm afraid, mine did not.

And so the world of the school became such an alien dimension from the arena of one's home that it was hardly worth trying to explain it, and you learned another lesson, inadvertently – that people are quite happy for facts to be hidden, and there exists a series of tenuous compacts, on which adult life depends, that makes a virtue of silence, and gives its blessing to discretion. This was an integral part of the 'preparatory' process of the Hill, I must assume, although it was only years later that I was able to diagnose it in such terms. At the time, it seemed an absolute betrayal of everything I had ever been brought to believe at home. But I succumbed to this new code, and kept the confusing faith. I might have been no good at games, but the Hill possessed me for most of the year, and no amount of homesickness, apathy or resentment could prevent the place from claiming me for its tribe.

Sundays out with your parents were curious, limbo hours that were both longed-for and dreadful, brief, tantalizing exeats into the exterior, insufficient and tense, precious but embroidered with anxiety, the lingering awareness of imminent separation. In the early days, we went back to Spellbrook on a couple of trips, but they made me badly homesick, and I could only spend a few hours at home before we had to consider the traffic, and 'head back, for now'. Such a day would involve my mother in several hours' driving to and fro, and was not in the end considered to make the best *use* of our time together, so such plans were dropped in favour of a quiet visit to the Haywain Hotel, where we could take things easy, and not have to bother with all that travel.

I came to hate the very sound of the word Berkshire – the matrix of place-names, Bracknell, Staines, Binfield, Egham, that combined into a grid-reference for much of my fear and loathing. The Haywain at Bullbrook was an unlovely Twenties' building, with a self-important plaque by the front door announcing that the local Rotary Club dined there on the second Monday of each month. Bustling as it may have been during weekdays, playing host to heaven knows what heady combinations of Masons, British Legionaries, Women's Institutarians and members of the Grand Order of St Willibald of Eichstätt, mid-afternoon on a March Sunday it was as thrilling and hospitable to a listless child as a provincial dentist's waiting-room. It did not sell confectionery, there was no television in the lounge, its dull lawns were unredeemed by clock-golf or even croquet. My mother would produce comics for me to read in the interval between the clearing away of our set lunch (usually roast mutton followed by trifle) and the arrival of the tea-trolley at 3.45p.m.

Once a term my father came too, and he liked to attend morning chapel beforehand, sitting in the parents' row at the back and chinking the change in his pocket during the intervals between Mr Vaughan's often improvisatory performances on the new electric organ. Then, if the weather was good (and sometimes it was on the side of the angels) he would drive us to an antiques emporium nearby, the Owl Tower, where the proprietor discussed vesta-cases and porcelain figurines with my mother, and I prodded the weeds in the fountain in an effort to flush out any goldfish – and thence to a huge horticultural nursery run by Commander Amery, a former naval acquaintance of my father's, where we would have a picnic, a real treat. Flynn would have packed the racing-hamper with pasties and cheese puffs, crustless sandwiches containing cucumber and Patum Peperium, containers of Coronation Chicken, a Thermos of hot sausages, bottles of apple-juice and Chablis. After our meal my father would ignite a powerful cigar, and while my mother had one of her little naps, he and I would join the Commander for an inspection of shrubs and bushes.

Parents did not, by tradition, come to evening chapel, which was really no more than a glorified roll-call to ensure that all boys were back. There was much snivelling from the boys who had been out, as Mr Smedley in his lay-reader's surplice intoned the doleful crepuscular prayers, and we took to heart the sentiments concerning the terrors of the night, before filing out between the two boards listing the Old Boys fallen in the wars ('But Their Name Liveth For Evermore'), including R. P. Slide, Marquess of Waterstock 1897–1902, the

dates of his residence at the school. For those who had just
kissed goodbye to their parents for the next several weeks there
was sorrow and regret and tears to negotiate after lights-out, as
one stared up through the dormitory curtains at the impossible
stars.

'The sun and the moon were married,' Charlie told me,
'and for their children they have the stars. But they never can
decide whether to live in her darkness or his light, and the sun
get angry that his wife not doing like he wants, and she takes
children and hides them away. Then he chases after her with
spear and big shield all day, but when he asleep they come out
into the dark fields of the sky, very quiet so they not wake him.

'But some time the sun catch up with her, and they struggle
during day, and we take our drums, and hammer – hammer
and shout at the eclipse, to drive them two apart. And so it
remains.'

The chief interface between the Hill and the outside world,
and the main social event in its calendar, was Sports Day, at
the end of June, when the school polished up its Janus features
to their brightest and paraded itself as One Big Happy Family.
The teachers sported their best club ties, Mr Smedley donned
his panama, Miss Hooper was in full medical uniform with a
watch pinned above her left breast, and the Vaughans strolled
around like some Presidential candidate and his wife, all smiles
and handshakes, sometimes putting a hand on the shoulder of
some startled boy, while hymning his achievements before his
beaming family, nodding and waving their way through the
throng. A marquee would have been erected on the First Eleven
pitch, for refreshments that included delicious (and surely
imported) food – cardboard dishes of strawberries and whipped
cream, salmon and cress sandwiches, scones and jam, mering-
ues, bottles of Coca-Cola, pear flans. There was not a single
cauldron of powdered leek soup to be seen.

The parents probably had no reason to be suspicious of this
party atmosphere, the culmination of weeks of dragooning boys
into heats and eliminators, the strict instructions to return to

one's family after the race (so the teachers could identify who they were), the penalties for any misbehaviour. Quite a few of the fathers – my own included – were Old Boys for whom such occasions offered fellowship and the pleasing sense of continuity, a spectacle of colour and permanence that drew out many an anecdote about athletic prowess and careless high jinks. They must have realized that this event was all a sham, the impression of effortless efficiency in no way a paradigm of the everyday life of the school, the whole thing staged for their benefit, but it suited them to succumb to the delusion and collude in the notion that this was the quintessence of Stockhill House, with their sons literally putting their best feet forward.

It was carefully arranged that we should all be involved in some race or other, but I need hardly say that I never won any prizes on the track, although I did come second in the annual exhibition at the Carpentry Shop for my hardwood table-lamp in 1967, an achievement that was unfortunately eclipsed by the Duke winning the Fathers' Race that same day, and my overhearing him respond to the congratulations from Hamilton's father – one of his erstwhile contemporaries at the Hill – that it was just as well someone in the family could run in a straight line.

FIVE

When I was nine, I asked my father why so many people seemed worried about the meaning of life.

He gave me his grey look, and felt his moustache. 'Are you worried about it yourself?' he enquired. I said I just didn't understand what the question meant (I still don't, as it happens), and he narrowed his eyes, as if taking aim, as if drawing a bead on my latest manifestation of insolence and chicanery. 'Very well, then,' he said, the tips of his index fingers tapping together beneath his chin, 'I will tell you. If it will help to set your anxious young mind to rest, then I will explain. These people of whom you speak are worried about the meaning of life, because they assume it must have some essential shape – but it doesn't. It just goes round and round. Like the weather in Iceland.'

Actually, the coldest thing about Iceland is its very name; it has suffered from this, as people sometimes do. Now, of course, since the events of February it is too late to do anything about it.

Geologically speaking, Iceland was a late European baby, an afterthought of the clapped-out old continent, not much more than twenty million years old. Like so many offspring of ageing mothers, it was never quite right in the head. This scabby, leaking, incongruous landmass was discovered by the Vikings in 870, when the only mammals living there were arctic foxes: there was no aboriginal population, and so the human history of this island is unique in that it has been recorded in its entirety, from start to finish, and in a single language virtually unchanged in over a thousand years.

The slaves and prisoners originally settled there by the Norsemen called it Snaeland, but after the disastrous effects of floating pack-ice upon his crops one spring, Floki Vilgerdarson dubbed it Ísland in a fit of pique. In 982 the explorer Erik did come to land on a country composed of ice, but he chose to call it Greenland. Later they gave him the sobriquet Erik 'The Red'. In the year of the first millennium, his son, Leif Eriksson, landed in North America and christened it Wineland.

So much for the reliability of names and titles.

Iceland is a country of such anomalies that if it had not existed you would have been hard pressed to have invented it. Lying on a great submarine ridge, it is in effect the tips of the mountain-tops of a drowned continent, a desert in the middle of an ocean. No more than 300 miles across, it is host to two hundred volcanoes; it has rivers of stone, rivers of fire, and rivers that run blue with phosphates. The air reeks of sulphur and dead fish. It boasts no iron, timber, oil or coal. Throughout its history its exports, apart from the flesh of fish and whales, have only included swan quills for the use of librarians at New College, Oxford, volcanic pebbles to stonewash denim clothing, a curious literature, and limited amounts of quarried feldspar used in the manufacture of optical equipment. Snow-melt causes tufa and dirty cinders to cascade down its hills, and where there is grass the action of the snow has reduced it to tussocks and knolls. Littered with volcanic scoria and dinosaur outcrops, the place looks like a mineral battlefield.

One cannot help wondering who chose the godparents when this *lusus naturae* converted to Christianity in the numerologically pregnant year of AD 999, but there must have been a wicked fairy at the feast. Perhaps it was worse than that. Danish legend held that Iceland was Satan's only successful attempt at emulating the Divine Creation, and that the volcano Hekla was one of the mouths to Hell. Certainly the demons would have found it handy for the relentless burning and freezing of the damned (whose cries were heard by more than one traveller, emanating from this crater), for flame and ice were the twin devices in the infernal heraldry of this physically inhospitable island.

Great contradictory rivers of air circulate above it, bearing dust, spores, chemicals, water, spiderlings, birds and relentless, ever-changing weather. My father was quite right: the weather in Iceland goes round and round, its clouds dashing past the sugarloaves, the tabletops and the lateral moraines as the climate chases itself by the tail. It is a microcosm of the unpredictable New Weather we now enjoy across the planet. 'If you don't like the weather,' they would say, 'then just wait a minute.' You'd get all four seasons in one day, but after centuries of this you just accepted that it did not make much sense – the ocean currents from the Atlantic Drift pushed up from the south, the Arctic sweep washed conversely down from the east of Greenland, they collided and cavorted around the coastline, and there was little point in complaining about it.

This cracked, dribbling, debauched landscape may look as if it is suffering chronically from some unmentionable disease, but no one has ever been able properly to take its temperature. In the north (where my father was based at the start of the War) it will snow in June, but even in winter the air seldom sinks below zero in Reykjavik. So where would you introduce your thermometer into this schizoid little foundling? How do you gauge the fever associated with some alchemist's wet dream?

There is a central glacier, three thousand feet thick, which is fossilized weather; it contains the impacted snowflakes belonging to winters now a thousand years in the past. By drilling down into this ice, glaciologists can retrieve a frozen archive of the acid, dust and pollen levels in atmospheres long gone. These things leave their signatures, but if you want such truths you have to dig for them while you still have time. You have to bring them to light before they disappear.

The weather in Iceland seldom delivers its promises. They say the inhabitants are always anticipating a summer that never quite arrives, and dreading a winter that doesn't really materialize. Meanwhile, they live exhausted by hope and fear, as the elements run rings around them in an eternal, mesmerizing circus.

Jack and Jill went up the hill, and were transmogrified into Scandinavian constellations. The Younger Edda tells how Hjúki and Bil walked off to a well named Byrgir, and were drawn up into the heavens to follow the movements of Mani the moon, where now they presage his wax and wane. Their bucket Soegr, and their yoke Simul, have become the moonspots that symbolize the changes in weather and rainfall affected by the lunar cycles.

God's laboratory it may have been, but Iceland was never a place to visit for the cooking. After the British occupation in 1940, when the island was regarded by the forces of the Axis as a gigantic, unsinkable enemy aircraft-carrier (like the 'stone frigate' of Ascension Island, during the Falklands War) my father spent enough time there to have an idea of the national diet, and he once said to me that, even in the face of wartime rationing back home, this was the most unpalatable food he had encountered anywhere in the world, outside captivity.

Ingenious though the farmers' wives and daughters were in their recipes, there was no getting round the paucity of tasteful ingredients, even in a good year. There might be occasional luxuries such as fulmar eggs for omelettes, or crowberries to go with clotted *skyr*, but the problem once again was the weather. The ground around the coast kept freezing and thawing throughout winter, splitting the soil into frost-heaves, and confusing the crops and the vegetables. An ear of corn in Iceland encounters obstacles as formidable as those facing a thistle forcing its way up through the tarmac of an international airport. A sunflower would suffer a nervous breakdown just trying to keep track of developments. In 1884, a Danish merchant planted an apple tree in his garden in the capital, and it didn't even blossom until 1909, in which year it produced a total of five fruits. Small wonder, then, that the islanders never expected to live off their land – it would have exhausted the optimism of even a Peter Buxton.

Water was the staple source of their subsistence, and the three main resources that Iceland possessed were demersal, pelagic, and geothermal. The first two fed them, and the latter kept them easily at room temperature, though it was to prove the death of them after centuries of being a blessing.

The Icelandic herring was a world-class prize, and the islanders used up every last aspect of it but the smell. For cod they were prepared to go to war, and they used to make shoe-soles out of its skin, and measure distances over the lava-fields of the interior (where later the NASA astronauts were trained) in terms of how many pairs of such shoes you could expect to wear out during a journey. Cod were caught on longlines, then split and spread to dry on wooden racks, and the nutritious stockfish consumed as a delicacy, spread with a little butter. Fresh fish depended on the weather conditions for putting to sea, and fresh meat was even more seasonal; after the annual slaughter in the autumn you might have been lucky enough to get some boiled-down knuckle of mutton, or a pudding composed of sheep's-head stuffed with blood, but thereafter all flesh would be smoked or salted. By some quirk of tradition, the islanders refrained from harvesting the prolific avifauna which, during the migratory season, might have afforded considerable variations on their diet, but an infusion was sometimes concocted from the half-digested bog-whortle flowers taken from the crop of a native ptarmigan, or *rhyper*, though few visitors ever recorded it as having been a drink of much worth. But then alcoholic beverages were very restricted in their availability because the authorities quite wisely predicted that the climate had such a debilitating effect on the temperament of the islanders that unrestricted access to real drink might before too long spell oblivion to this long-suffering tribe.

For sheer repellence, however, nothing could rival the effect upon the tastebuds of a foreigner when it came to the national dish known as *Hakarl* – it would unseat the gastric juices even of those who had survived a decade in British boarding-schools. To achieve this gastronomic abortion you first had to bury a dead shark in the sand. Its putrefaction would be accelerated by synchronized urination upon the carcass at regular intervals by members of your household, their friends, visitors, and pet dogs. After a couple of months it would be triumphantly exhumed, and little flakes chipped off its brittle vestiges, just as one might have reluctantly tackled ship's biscuit in the days when my ancestor, Sam, took to the seas in his clippers. With the assistance of a little illicit corn-brandy, the ingestion of *Hakarl* by the visitor should provoke nothing worse than a rising gorge, but taken on its own it is a confusing experience, a little heart of darkness. It is a *memento mori*, a reminder for the tourist of how the vagaries of the elements have hammered ingenuity down into the lives of those who survived on that desolate cyst of borrowed land, called Iceland.

A final word on water resources and fish (this is all of antiquarian interest, now, after all): in the hotsprings of Laugar the thermal water spouts out and runs over the colder layers of a glacial stream swirling below, in which current swim shoals of hungry trout (there is not much in the way of insect life for them, in such a confluence, but they have somehow learned not to complain). Hook one of these by lowering your lure into the cool hypolimnion, and you will find that as you draw it up towards the surface it is boiled at the end of your line. I have always maintained that angling was a foolish sport, but Iceland is the only country where you can put a fish into your creel, ready-cooked.

It was hardly surprising that a people who used to live on the carapace of a natural catastrophe should have been so thoroughly superstitious a race. They believed in a line of invisible humans called the Huldufolk, who inhabited secret places that you would visit only at your peril. The Hidden Folk were thought to be the direct descendants of the unwashed children of Eve, whom she would not show to God when He required an inspection of the Orchard; she produced her clean infants, but hid the others under a bush (or perhaps it was the apple tree). The Almighty saw through this deception, and in His famous wisdom decreed, 'That which is hidden from Me shall forever be hidden from Man.' Since that day, these tall figures with their black hair and grey clothes have lived like mortals, but have the power to turn themselves and their property invisible. If something was lost on the island of Iceland, it was explained by the fact that the Hidden Folk had picked it up for themselves (but what if you lost a person? What was the explanation if members of your family disappeared?). These spectral residents were held to be responsible for any island disasters, the result of infringements upon their secret territories. They were visible to their sublunary cousins only in dreams, or as sudden daylight avatars to small children roving the landscape alone. The Hidden Folk were taken very seriously indeed, by a race that realized the terrain with which it was blessed had precious few places where a person might hide and survive, if discovery was deemed to be in any way undesirable.

But the moral about hygiene, underlying this myth, does not appear to have taken root.

Take the sheepdogs – every homestead had one, a variety of Spitz which was especially adept at seeing off foxes during the lambing season. Crucial in this way, but also doubling up as a kitchen aide – because the tongue of a farm dog was thought to be sterile (its system being purged with laxatives every month), and so these animals were conscripted to lick clean the dishes and cups and plates after a meal. It is true that they were not required to cleanse the nether-regions of babies, but this belief that dogs' tongues were dependably pure must have resulted in certain numbers of the Icelandic population suffering from infestation with lethal parasites. Against this possibility must be set the fact that the dogs served another, quite unrelated function: they would raise their hackles and growl, several days before a volcanic eruption.

They did so in 1783, when the notorious Laki craters opened up along a 20-mile fissure and began spewing out ash and lava equivalent, over a period of six months, to the total mass of Mont Blanc. Sunsets around the world were affected all summer, and a blue haze hung over the island, causing the crops to fail. On Sunday 20 July the hamlet of Kirkjubaejarklauster was threatened by a slow trail of rubble and lava the height of a house, and the pastor, Jon Steingrimsson, summoned the villagers into his turf chapel and preached against the terrible climate a polemic that entered history as 'The Fire Sermon'. When the faithful emerged, the lava had halted for ever in its tracks.

It was always accepted that areas of Iceland came and went, that its topography was never more than provisional. Consider the fate of the Great Auk. These penguin-like birds, that stood man-high, were hunted during the last century until the few survivors took refuge on the little isle of Eldey, in 1844. Their stock dwindled, but they continued to breed, and it looked as if they would escape the extermination suffered by the dodo or the Australian burrow-parrot or the North American passenger pigeon. But the subterranean chemistry of the area flared up in 1873 and the whole colony exploded, with no survivors.

By the same token, the arena of Iceland was also hot on geological initiative. On 14 November 1963 the island of Surtsey arose smoking out of the sea by the Westmann Islands, like some ash-grey deity. And in 1966 another islet of black tephra reared up beside it, disappearing again after a couple of months. It was always on the cards that this clutch of islands was a blueprint for Atlantis, or a harbinger of what might yet occur.

Past and present collide, their currents rip uneasily around the coast, generating strange weather. In 1996, Iceland was connected umbilically to the British republic when a 600-mile network of submarine cable that fed 2000 mg of electricity into the new National Grid was laid across the ocean floor to Scotland. For a time it looked as if this geothermal drain was going to work miracles, and enrich the economies of both islands. But then the sheepdogs raised their hackles, and began to bark.

This February there were fresh eruptions on Hekla, and during the course of two weeks the island split and started to go into the throes of a hideous labour. Instruments recorded unprecedented seismic activity, alarming fluctuations in both the level and temperature of the sea around the northern coast. The majority of Iceland's quarter-million population was evacuated. There was no one who remembered how to deliver a Fire Sermon.

When it came, it was the opposite of the heavens opening. Iceland sank entirely, and down with it went all the youngest parts of European history. The French have a phrase, *la couleur du temps*, which alludes to the colour of the weather, the signs of the times. The obliteration of Iceland has provoked a millennial shiver, as if some canary had died down a coalmine. We've been fiddling around with Dame Nature for too long, and someone up there (or is it down?) has finally flipped the switch and juiced us – a quick tug on the tectonic plates, to show just how easily the whole house of cards could come down. Iceland may only be the tip of the . . . but we should have thought about this long ago.

At any rate, it's too late for Ultima Thule, which ancient explorers regarded as the end of the world. Now you can't go there at all. Eels haunt its valleys, and the homesteads are blanketed with kelp. The geysers have been stifled, the testimony of the ice is dissolving, the fosses no longer arc down the crags, and the church bells clong in the conflicting currents as the submarine weather goes round and round. Maybe the Huldufolk were enraged at the energy being sapped from their homeland, and detonated the island. They are well and truly hidden now, in the crop of the ocean, where not even the little children can see them.

SIX

The first time I ever came to Switzerland, I hated it. We did not often take holidays abroad when I was little, and there were certainly no yachts or villas or anything exotic like that. My mother used to say this was because my father had at one time travelled so much on business, but in fact they tended to go away on their own while I was at school, and thus avoid the trials involved in that contradiction in terms, a family holiday.

On those rare occasions when we did venture off *en famille*, it was evident just how ill-suited we were to living together at very close quarters – Spellbrook was sufficiently large to accommodate a number of separate bolt-holes, but when we resided in a hotel there was an enforced and alarming approximation of familial symbiosis.

I was nine, and Cosmo five, when they took us to learn how to ski. We spent a week at a castellated hotel in Crans-sur-Sierre, and by the time we left I was fully confirmed in my hatred for Alpine sports – a sentiment which lives in me to this day. It was almost as bad as riding, except that I never learned to go fast enough on snow to be similarly frightened, in fact I do not recall having made it down the nursery slopes even once without wobbling sideways into the hill. This was frustrating, in the same way that being unable to score a goal with a football seemed beyond me, but at least I could understand the point of soccer: skiing down a little run, and then being dragged up with one of those precarious soup-plates shuddering between your thighs, only to repeat the process, struck me as only a slightly less dull way of passing one's precious time than being forced to swim incessantly up and down the length of a pool. I was no good at it, naturally, and what frightened me was not the prospect of fractured limbs but the daily ignominy of being the only boy, of any nationality, in the class who could not master even the rudiments of balance and posture after the first few days.

Cosmo got off much more lightly, because he was allowed to spend much of his time tobogganing with my mother who, having been brought up in Burma, had never learned to ski, and now felt she was too fragile to begin. My father, who was fairly accomplished, had no intention of being confined to the piste just above the car park while his son and heir made a fool of himself in public. 'And besides, Rich will benefit from being with other boys of his own age and with the chance to improve his French,' as my mother put it, propaganda-wise over break-fast, when it was explained that I would be spending a week of my school holidays joining yet another school of sorts, and definitely not building snowmen or anything frivolous like that.

'But I don't *like* skiing,' I told my father.

'You're being insolent and absurd. You have never tried it. If I were you, I would not plan to go through life with an attitude such as that. It will get you precisely nowhere. It is symptomatic of a prematurely closed mind. Do I make myself clear? Well then. Enough.'

'What I mean is, I don't *need* to learn; I can just follow you.'

'When you have acquired the necessary skills, we shall cer-tainly ski together. But for the time being you will learn from a professional, and benefit from the company of others in a similar position. You know nothing about it, whereas I do. Nor am I intending to discuss this any further. If you take the trouble to apply yourself, you will soon begin to enjoy the sport. You may take my word for it.'

On New Year's Eve there was a buffet supper in the hotel, and, for the first time in my life I was allowed to stay up for an hour and join my parents. I have never quite fathomed the complexities of Swiss cuisine, but there was a kind of long meatloaf on offer, and as the chef cut a little slice for my proffered plate, he suddenly let out a roar of triumph, and began clapping his hands above his head, and the other guests gradually fell silent as he announced (in French, but it all became horribly clear, before too long) that he had found the almond.

There was, indeed, a nut peeping out of the meat on my plate. A few moments later the manager of the hotel was shaking me by the hand, had placed a golden cardboard crown upon my head, and was leading me through the crowd, to a vantage-point from which he could deliver a speech. It transpired that I was, by virtue of this nut, the *Prince de la Neige* for the evening, and was required to cut a mountainous iced cake, dotted with small plastic figures slaloming down its sugar, and then, by tradition, I was to select a lady to be crowned my snow-maiden for the festivities. By this time I felt my face must be melting with self-consciousness. I really had no choice. To great applause, *le petit milord anglais* stepped three paces away from the table and presented the tinfoil sceptre to his own mother. We had our picture taken, she hugged me and seemed delighted, my father explained to the manager that it would shortly be time for my bed, and so the evening and the year closèd in excruciating fashion. We never again went skiing *en famille*, but I continue to harbour an antipathy to snow, and a considerable suspicion of anything to do with almonds.

It might, therefore, seem perverse that I have come to rest in Schwyz – the kernel, shall we say, of Old Europe. But there is more to this place than fondue parties and steaming couples discussing black runs as they lounge in their *salopettes* and sip *Glühwein*. I am glad, now, that I followed my father's advice and gave it a chance. Despite the show of hospitality it stages for the visitor, this is surely the most secretive country on earth, the archetypal hideaway. The patronizing tourist sees – and always has seen – virtually nothing of the hidden life it affords its inhabitants, the quiet survivalists, the folk who seem grey and earnest and ignorant of pleasures such as laughter, oral sex, chitchat. You may take my word for it. I am no longer the person I once was: I am a Swiss.

Since the heyday of the Romantics (compare and contrast the early Continental and later English exponents, with particu-

lar reference to *one* or *two* authors or artists) this neurotic little
agglomeration of smallholdings has been a feature on the short-
range tourist's map. The mountains! The sunrises! The opportunities for poorly trimmed poetical wallpaper depicting scenes
that the versifier, poleaxed by ozone, imagined were the meta-
phora of his youth. The sheer variety of the land, the soaring
and the sinking, the shadows and reflections and the herd-bells
at evening. Yes, indeed, we have those still, it was agreed by
referendum. Very little happens here by chance: the eminent
horologist, the fuckwit skier, the chocolate epicure, the trekker
after *antiquités*, and the merchant banker all manage to return
home gratified by what has been on offer. A remarkable
country; much underrated; wonderful to visit, but I wouldn't
want to live there; worth taking a bit of trouble to explore,
off the beaten track; tricky people to do business with, no
imagination; dead in the evening, out of season; you could eat
off the floor, and one night we did; we were at school together;
wonder what it's like in summer; very polite; expensive, of
course; the thing is, they're totally reliable. Fantastic people, in
their way.

And I see their point. Goddamn Switzerland, my foster
country that first reduced me to the ranks and then made me fall
in love like some fugitive legionnaire. Inscrutable, xenophobic,
curmudgeonly, perfectionist, reactionary, it accepted my
deposit, and opened my account. Granted me sky-fall when
most I needed it. Here I am lost among the local prejudices;
German, Italian, French, Romansch. It is impossible to charac-
terize us by language. You would scarcely believe the degrees
of snobbery and dogma at work within this parochial milieu:
judgements are based on almost infinitesimal gradations in geography, with people from one canton regarding those from the
next as incompetent foreigners. To us, there exists a class system
taken from the map. This renders Swiss society pretty much
invisible to any visitor, and proves a tremendous advantage to
anyone who manages to penetrate it – as I think I have been
lucky enough to do – by the peculiar process of osmosis that
swaps money for silence.

I had plenty of trouble with the Schweizerdeutsch to begin with, but Magda has been giving me lessons (she is a better student than I am, however). The language helps me blend into the landscape, articulates my new identity. I am becoming like the polar bear who survives by the simple expedient of putting one forepaw over its nose, and advancing on its quarry across the ice: at some stage in its evolution it worked out that by covering the only part of itself that is black, this renders it almost invisible. I no longer feel like a stranger in a strange land.

We used to visit the Isle of Wight every August, for a fortnight, where we stayed at the Royal Squadron Hotel, in Bembridge. There were plenty of nautical people for my father (though during the second week he would leave to go grouse-shooting in Scotland), and my mother had a friend who lived there, whom she had known since her days at Cheltenham. Cosmo and I used to share a room, and it was during these holidays, when we had no choice but to do everything together, that we had the most fun. I explained to my brother that I was the General in charge of all expeditions, and appointed him my lieutenant, with prospects of promotion for unswerving obedience. This regularized our relationship to my satisfaction, and since Cosmo always preferred things to be clear-cut, he seemed to accept the situation.

Nanny would escort us to the beach every day after breakfast, climbing up the stepped lane behind the hotel, and down between the back gardens of the yacht-club folk; the verges were foaming with cow-parsley, tangled with goosegrass from which we made bracelets and circlets. I used to like popping the fuchsia buds that dangled enticingly over the walls, and Nanny, already hot and bothered in her sensible cardigan, would say, 'And just what do you think you are up to, young man? Those flowers do not belong to us, do they?' – adding (for this was the main point), 'They are probably full of horrid little insects.' Once she reached the beach, Nanny Mottram looked relieved, because here there were duckboards and beach-huts, deckchairs and fellow professionals, and she could settle down while we entertained ourselves in full view at all times, and there was little need for much locomotion on her part until my mother arrived around lunch-time, at which point Nanny would participate industriously in whatever hole we were excavating, or pool we were dredging for crustacea.

There was a dark green tea-hut at the left extremity of the sand, that sold Penguins and Eccles cakes and Spangles and potato crisps with the salt in a blue paper twist, and tall-necked bottles of Hubbly-Bubbly in fiery red and lurid green flavours. This emporium was controlled by Mrs Black, a termagant with a large kettle and a pronounced dislike of children. She had little patience as we craned on tiptoe to deliberate how best to spend our shilling, and would say, 'Next, then,' after thirty seconds, should there be a queue behind us, and refuse to acknowledge our presence until we were the only customers before her wooden counter. If an adult was with us, she would ignore us altogether, and hand the goods directly to Nanny or my mother, rather than performing as such characters are supposed to do, when drawn from Central Casting, and leaning over to hand the 99 cone or the glass of Idris to the child who had requested it. I used to scare Cosmo at night telling him stories about Mrs Black – how she had once boiled a baby in that kettle of hers, how she was a witch (after whom sandwiches had been named), you must never look her in the eye, or she would climb in through your bedroom window at midnight, and similar tales that he implored me to assure him could not be true.

Mr Black was a stooping, phthisic-looking man, with black brilliantined hair, and a Woodbine pinched between thumb and forefinger, cupped in his palm. His duties included allocation and security of the huts, swabbing the duckboards, supervision of rowing-boat hire, and winking craftily at the nannies. Whenever my father descended to inspect arrangements at the beach, immaculate in his white drill trousers, a naval sweater around his shoulders, Mr Black (who had, I think, served in the Merchant Navy, but was no fool when he spotted the prospect of a tip) would march along the duckboards and present himself, with a salute, outside our beach-hut. 'All shipshape and satisfactory, Your Graces?' he might ask, and my mother would treat him to a long, silent smile ('Such a helpful little man, despite that string vest') while my father would reply, 'Yes, thank you, Black. Keep a close eye on them for me, won't you?' pressing a folded fiver into the man's approaching, and deliberately Woodbine-free, palm.

Since elsewhere it was such a rare occurrence, I have to say that my father was fun to be with during those few days each year at the seaside. He would take Cosmo and me on his shoulders, in turns, and run into the water until it was up to his chest – this meant going a long way out across the flat Solent beach, and then he'd rock from side to side, and cry up, 'Feeling sea-sick yet?' though he never actually laughed aloud at his version of antics. At low tide we would go with him in search of razor-fish, pouring salt down their little volcanoes on the sand-flats, and grabbing them as they popped up, thinking the tide had returned and all was safe. He would obtain two of Mr Black's flat-bottomed miniature boats, and lash one behind the other with a painter, and tow us around for hours on end, moving much faster than the children who were trying to row themselves, and whose fathers were too tall to fit into the boats. On the beaches of Bembridge I saw my father as a real maritime hero – instructing us in the tying of nautical knots, inspecting the state of the tide, supervising our shrimping technique – and although he was always on the move and never to be found frequenting a deckchair, I think he was responding to the proximity of the sea with a certain tense pleasure, the vestiges, perhaps, of what had been a youthful affinity.

It was in our bathroom at the Royal Squadron that Cosmo and I saw the big house-spider. It was in the basin when Cosmo got up one morning to pee, and he came and fetched me: we both peered fearfully at this intruder, and then I ordered my lieutenant to turn on the tap. He refused, saying it might jump out at him, or start swimming. He said I was the General, and would have to fetch Nanny. Instead, I turned on the hot tap, and stood back.

The water was cool at first, and the creature began scrabbling at the curves of the bowl to escape it, but even with the plug-hole open the volume was such that the level rose and it started to float precariously, paddling its wiry legs and breaking through the surface film; as the water entering the sink became warm, and then hot, the legs buckled, and the spider's star-shape contracted into a rolling tumbleweed. I shut off the flow, and the body whirled and swivelled in the typhoon funnel as the water spiralled down the plug-hole, round and round, until it sank on to the metal cross-bars between which its body was too big to be driven. The tips of two legs felt their way, like creepers out of the damp hole. The ball quivered and shook. At that moment I was aware that Cosmo was no longer at my side, and I turned round, and saw my father in his silk dressing-gown, leaning against the frame of the bathroom door. His face was white, and he looked as if he was going to be sick. My brother was staring at him anxiously as he turned away and walked very slowly across the passage, and into his bedroom.

I poked the emerging spider down the waste with the handle of my toothbrush, and ran scalding water down the sink. The steam smelt briefly of singed hair, and then it was gone.

We did not see my father again that day, but my mother and Gilbey explained at bedtime that he had been feeling sick, and that was why he was heading for the bathroom. But then she confused the issue by saying, 'It's quite common, you know – he just doesn't like spiders. Do try to be dear boys, and not mention it again. He gets so dreadfully upset, just at the thought of them.'

I really don't think she ever knew.

There exist almost a million different species of insect in this world, but the spider – with her eight legs – is not one of them. It was to escape from the arachnids that insects first evolved wings.

Spider blood is pale blue, and the heart is a long tube; they have book-lungs like concertinas, and eight eyes. Most are as short-sighted as babies, but they navigate by vibration. When surprised, many species respond by thrusting forward their front legs – do not be alarmed by this posture of apparent menace: it is only their way of laughing. They are sensitive to noise, and some seem to respond to music, and they are not always silent themselves. On occasions they make a stridulating sound by brushing their jaws with their pedipalps – do not take fright, if you should hear this near your pillow in the dark: it is merely a spider cleaning her teeth, after feeding.

The female can prove especially strong. The so-called 'bird-eaters' from Panama can measure up to 10 inches across the leg-span, and big specimens dropped into killing bottles have been known to plunge around for hours in the poison. The rain-forest *Lasiodora* attains a weight of a quarter of a pound avoirdupois – the same as a substantial hamburger. They have proved oddly popular as pets, and quite often there is a scare when one escapes. Do not worry if this happens in your neighbourhood: the owners will assure everyone that these loved ones need high temperatures to survive, which of course they will not find in the artificially heated suburban house, behind the pelmet of your dressed curtains, in the bedroom. (It would be as well to investigate quite cautiously any unusual rasping noises from such an area, just in case.)

They took a survey of a field in Sussex, one summer, and found it held two-and-a-quarter million spiders – per acre, that is. A meadow with a hundred million mandibles. In Britain every year these arthropods consume a total number of insects collectively heavier than the entire bodyweight of the human population of the Republic. But we do not normally appreciate just how many there are, because they prefer to run at night. They do not sleep. The male of the long-legged household species *Tegenaria atrica* leaves his ragged web at sunset, and goes in search of a mate. He descends the short curtain beside the window, undrawn for the summer's heat, and feels his way on to the sill. He creeps over the angle of the wood, and arrives at a cool surface, where he drinks in water. He advances, slides down the enamelled side of the basin, and exhausts himself trying to gain a purchase on this slippery slope (he could never, of course, make his way up through the plug-hole). When the sun rises and glares off the white glaze, it renders him snow-blind. He cannot jump or swim, and is powerless against the boy who wants to display bravado to a younger brother, and proceeds to drown, and crush and burn, a trapped spinner.

But they are there in their millions, in places you would not normally care to look. And at night they will continue to dance over your food, explore discarded clothing, and finger the faces of your sleeping children.

The night before we broke up for the school holidays – and the destructive finality of that phrase quietly embodied all our fiercest longings – the dorms at Stockhill would be perfervid with anticipation. Trunks stacked, shelves and baskets cleared, overnight bags ready for the final impedimenta, we felt inviolate, unable to sleep, a little band of freedom-fighters who had just heard the broadcast about a successful revolution. Our defiance was quite puerile, naturally: 'No more Latin, no more French, no more sitting on the hard, hard bench.' Then Mr Gardner would materialize in the doorway, and say, 'Ha. I suppose you're all at it again. There's always next term, remember that,' but the very idea was unimaginably distant, like some unnamed star.

For me the happiest prospect that the holidays held was nothing to do with trips to the seaside, but the excitement of returning to Spellbrook. It was usually Flynn who came to collect me, and my homecoming was an event that provoked a happy sequence of hugs and promises and plans from our staff, admiration at how tall I had grown, praise for how well they had heard I was doing (I may not have been much cop at games, but at least I was in the scholarship stream.) Heady-making fuss and attention. A right royal welcome. The familiar joy of an Aertex shirt and jeans, and one of Iris's cottage pies sent up for Nanny to serve ('She likes to think it's a favourite of yours, pet, and we mustn't go upsetting her, what with all her problems'), and the quiet after communal clatter and clamour, the peace of our estate.

It might not be until nearer evening that I saw either of my parents, depending on how busy they were. My father had enjoyed his time at the Hill, and could not recall any such fuss attending the event of breaking up, and my mother was by this stage too wedded to her morning-room to be interrupted from her preoccupations before our bath-time, when a good siesta would have done its work, and her eyes were bright and could involve the reappearance of a boy almost bursting with relief at having arrived home.

I can no longer tell whether it was really the case that those summer holidays I seemed to race through at Spellbrook when I was ten or eleven, just before my father died, were the best few seasons of my life, or if this is a mirage imparted by retrospect (with all its distorting lenses), and an image made fond by nostalgia, and the strabismic effect of thousands of bottles of Scotch whisky. I have no wish to mimic Dylan Thomas, and dish up a vision of 'Fern Hill' that is misleading, and conceals an ill relative in a shambolic homestead, but if I conceived of my own Hill, the school, in terms of a February day beleaguered with rugby, its correlative would be a day in early July at Spellbrook, with the landscape a braggart fat with chlorophyll, the hedgerows swelling from their stake-and-bind, and Charlie Sanga quietly guiding me through the under-growth, with my first dog, Nabob, at my heels.

Nabob was a black-and-white springer, and the worst gun-dog I ever had. He was chronically disobedient, but I adored him, and tried very hard to cover up for his occupational inad-equacies. He would hunt way ahead of the beaters, and tended to maul game. For one of his breed, he had an unusually hard mouth, and was only allowed to chase runners that had been tried by the more trusty dogs in the field. But one of the great advantages that Nabob enjoyed was that Charlie loved him, and for all his recklessness, his refusal to apply nose to scent, there were times when he retrieved birds that the other dogs had passed over, though you had to get the bird from him pretty smartish, in case he decided to start eating it.

I knew for a fact that Charlie was able to track down crippled birds before my spaniel, but he often let Nabob per-form the retrieve, where his rivals had failed, and this more than redeemed the reputation of my erratic but enthusiastic little dog, and did me no harm, as Nabob offered up the fruits of his service to me, his putative master, his equivalent General.

Charlie lived alone in the Keeper's Cottage by the kennels, where he maintained an immaculate vegetable garden and several hives of honey-bees. So far as I know, there was never a woman in his life. The interior of his home was orderly but austere; he had no pictures on the walls, very little furniture, and kept his fire burning even in high summer. Whatever the season, he spent most of his day outside – swathed in a herring-bone greatcoat, with a woollen balaclava in winter, or barefoot in shorts during the summer months, striding the fields with his stick and his golden retrievers, the Keeper, the guardian, of Spellbrook.

He never took a holiday, although on more than one occasion my father certainly offered to buy him air tickets so he could revisit his family in Kenya, but he politely declined. He did not seem curious to explore Britain, either, though for ten seasons he travelled north to load for my father in the grouse-butts on Sir Mark Maxwell's estate near Blairgowrie. By the time he had been Head Keeper for a couple of years, Charlie was already quite renowned among the shooting fraternity of the south. There had been an article about him in the *Field*, and wherever guns were chatting about shoots over the sloe-gin or the last of the stilton there would be someone who might say, 'Is it true that they've got a black man in charge on the Londons' estate?' – but on his first visit to Scotland Charlie was still quite a young man, and most of those who worked for Maxwell had never seen a black man in their lives. It was inevitable that he was at the receiving end of caustic humour on arrival, and the conservative Highland keepers initially regarded him with great suspicion, especially since Charlie towered over them, and did not drink alcohol. There were remarks about His Lordship opening a safari park, and some ribald references to the bush, but apparently Charlie remained unprovoked by this, and bided his time.

It was the tradition on that shoot that on 11 August (the day before the start of the grouse season) a tournament was staged between the guests at the lodge and the team of keepers, competing at clay pigeons. There was much sharing of drams, betting, and scarcely veiled rivalry on that day because the keepers always considered themselves the better marksmen (most of them had never even fired at a red grouse on the wing, but they did practise regularly at clays), and of course honour was at the stake. That first year, before they had the measure of his abilities, Charlie was approached on the morning of the event by MacKinnon, the Head Keeper, and asked dubiously whether or not he could handle a shot-gun. It was an insult compounded by the fact that the weapon MacKinnon was proposing to loan him for the day was a fowling-piece with tightly choked barrels designed for long shots at geese and ducks, and utterly unsuitable for the quick swing and wide pattern needed to shatter clays. 'The boys reckoned you'd be happy with it,' he said, as Charlie accepted the heavy weapon, 'because it's the nearest thing we can get to an elephant gun.'

When he 'smoked' the first twelve targets they sent scud-
ding over him, and thereby moved to first position in the field,
Charlie Sanga received more in the way of congratulations from
the house-guests than from his own team, but as the morning
wore on, and at each separate stand – rabbit and partridge
targets, crossing pairs, springing teal, the pheasants off the high
tower – his scores began to push his team ahead, the attitude
to the 'big black' changed. There were murmurs of approval
and encouragement as he took up position for his turn, and at
the penultimate stand MacKinnon made what was intended as
a reconciliatory joke about Charlie having cartridges specially
loaded with black powder. With the keepers' team comfortably
ahead, a certain amount of overfamiliarity was creeping into
the comments they were making in stage whispers about the
performance of their 'gentlemen' by the time both teams arrived
at the final event, which was the most taxing of all – the 'flush',
in which two guns fired as rapidly as possible at a randomly
scattered stream of targets skimmed over them from two different traps. Even a really proficient shot would be unlikely to hit
more than eight of these in the brief flurry: Charlie excelled
himself by breaking twelve, and shattering the last with a stone
from his sling, which brought a roar of admiration from the
crowd. He never attempted this feat again, but told me it was
not really that difficult because Yaaku boys were trained from
the age of four to hunt sand-grouse as they came flighting in to
the waterholes at dusk. Sir Mark requested Charlie to donate
the sling to the lodge, where it now hangs framed in the gun-
room beside the rest of the sporting memorabilia.

At an age when I had only just stopped thinking that lions
were male and tigers female, Charlie was telling me about the
silver-throated lizard that spat sparks if you stroked it with a
stick, was teaching me how to make spear-shafts from ash wood
and how to burn on to them the patterns that would ensure the
blade went true to its mark. He showed me how to shoot my
bow, explaining that the Yaaku hunter stops his heart for two
beats before he lets fly, and that a dying creature seems to pant
for breath because its soul has a steep climb up the House of

Death. He taught me how to track deer, sneak up on predators, stave off a shower of rain by tying back the weather with little strings of grass, mimic the feeding-chuckles of certain ducks, and make waterbottles out of rabbit-skin. I doubt I could manage any of these things now; they only seemed to work when I was in his company as a child. Charlie's spells were interactive – you had to have faith in his powers. When I grew older, I regret to say that I lost sight of this, and began to imagine a different world, one where I had discovered some knowledge for myself, and I lost the clue to his magic for ever.

'One day Njau the hunter goes in search of meat, far from the village, a part of the forest he never been before. And through the trees he hears a little voice, very beautiful, singing: Man bring bad fortune on himself. Things do not force themselves on him. And when he go very carefully up to the clearing, there is a tortoise playing her *lidungu* – like a lute, very beautiful and small. And Njau invite her to come back with him and share his hut, so every day he can hear her sing and play music, and she will agree only if he promise to keep this a secret. And Njau gives her his promise.

'But soon he gets impatient, and wants to tell others in the tribe of his great discovery. And the Chief hear these rumours of what Njau claim, and has him appear before the fire to explain: and then they all laugh at him, and make him very angry, and he swear he will bring her next evening to prove it is true about his tortoise, or else the Elders may put him to the sword for breaking his honour.

'So next evening Njau bring her and her lute and set them down before the Elders of the tribe, and hours pass by, but no song. No music. The hunter whispers and says, "Kobe, kobe," to his pet, but she stay silent. His people stand around him, angry at his lies, and as the last sunray disappear, the Chief chop off his head with a *panga*. At once, the animal begins to play and sing: Man bring bad fortune on himself. Things do not force themselves on him. And the tribe cry, "What have we done, what have we done to Njau the hunter?"

'The little tortoise speaks then, "He brought it on himself.

He break his promise, and give my secret to the world. Now I go to the forest, and no man will ever hear my music again.' "

When I was ten, I was playing with my soldiers in the tree-house by the lake when I saw a boy, curiously dressed in a brightly coloured track-suit, lying on his stomach on the Chinese bridge way below me, with his arm stretched down towards the water, as if straining to reach something. He looked much younger than me, and I did not recognize him; I could not think what he was doing there suddenly, right in front of our house.

Nanny had taken Cosmo into Guildford that afternoon for his haircut, and I was in the charge of Flynn, who was stretched out on the bench at the foot of the tree, asleep. I ran down the path, round the magnolia, and when I reached the edge of the lake I called out to the strange boy. He sprang up in alarm, looked around as if confused by his surroundings (perhaps he could not tell from which direction my voice had come, across the water), began stepping backwards and, as he did so, slipped and fell between the central struts of the parapet, and disappeared into the water below.

I ran up the bank, shouting uselessly for him, crossed the bridge and looked everywhere, but there was no sign. I went and roused Flynn, who was most alarmed that he had dozed off, and together we stared urgently into the greenish water of the lake, but we could see nothing.

The police were called, and they dragged both ends of the lake, later sending down two frogmen, at my father's insistence. There was no body in the lake, no sign of footprints other than my own, no child reported missing in the area. The following day my father summoned me to his library and upbraided me for concocting stories, trying to attract attention to myself, and for wasting the local constabulary's valuable time.

I stuck to my story, but this only made things worse. It remained a mystery to me for another twenty-five years.

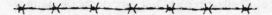

The summer before my father died, they made me a monitor at Stockhill, and I proudly collected my starry tie from Mr Vaughan on the first morning of what was to be my last term there, before going on to Eton. By now Cosmo had also joined the school, and we had all bidden a sad farewell to Nanny Mottram who had retired to a flat in Frinton in 1968. I was about to become a teenager. I was about to fall from grace, and then become a Duke. There were tangled times ahead.

In the calendar of schoolboy heroes it was not the names of those painted for posterity on the oak boards hanging in the Library that excited our wonder – those who had won scholarships, or, even better, as some would have it, played in the First Eleven for their public schools: the real heroes were those who had attempted a Great Escape. In the oral history of the Hill the names of Spencer and Cotterell, Timms and Mansel ma., were resonant with past glory – they had escaped the school grounds within living memory, and made it to Egham, or Sunninghill, or (in the case of Timms) to the refuge of his godmother's house in the village, some time during the Fifties. Since then, it had been quite difficult to break out. But this was the express intention of Chandupura, who had trifled sufficiently with the eccentric restrictions imposed upon him at the Hill. He had a kingdom awaiting him in India, and there was precious little the Stockhill staff could do to persuade him that it might be worth staying the course, though he was careful not to appear rebellious, and kept his plans to himself. Well, almost.

Chandy was not exactly treated like other boys, and I suppose I can see why. His widowed mother had donated a magnificent new cricket pavilion to the school, and he was the undisputed fast-bowler at the Hill. When he was the first pupil ever to be caught smoking, this munificence was, I am sure, taken into consideration in deciding his punishment. The ceremony of dedication to his late father's memory was the occasion of a school holiday, and the pavilion was officially opened by the Indian Ambassador, with Chandy's mother surrounded by a retinue of attendants in turbans and silken tunics, and his three elder sisters in the background. The Vaughans, having sat through this like some High Commissioner and his wife, could hardly have countenanced anything more severe than detention when Chandy was spotted with his packet of Rothmans in the area called 'Above the Nets' (the sprawl of ditches and gorse behind the cricket nets, where boys went to lurk, and 'oiks' from the other side of the railway-line used to fire air-gun pellets at the uniformed snobs who played in the folds and the ditches). But Chandy wanted out, and because he was such a hero, I agreed to his plan. I was not distinguishing myself in any other way, and I suppose I aspired to becoming the stuff of legends (we had absorbed dangerous levels of heroic nonsense from some of those forbidden Commando comics, I'm afraid). I found the Hill monotonous and repetitive, too, and such was the glamour of Chandupura's friendship that I stupidly agreed with him that we would make a bid together for a Great Escape.

When the weather was good, the boys from the senior dorms would be allowed to go swimming in the evenings, instead of taking a bath. This entailed running downstairs naked and crossing the gravel of the drive, and the lawn of the Private Side, and directly out to the pool. There would usually be thirty minutes of plunging around before bedtime, with Chris Lawson in attendance. Chandy masterminded it all. Earlier that day we both deposited weekend clothes in a roll of towelling, beneath the *cupressus leylandii* that concealed the pool from the public road. At the appointed hour for scampering off to swim, Chandy and I, in our respective dorms, took a little too long to prepare ourselves, and left the building slightly behind the eager crew. We headed straight for the main gates (which we knew would be locked) and then bolted to the right, where our cache of clothes was concealed. We shrugged on our jeans and jumpers and crept along the perimeter wall, searching for the spots we had been reliably informed were not crested with wire. There was barbed wire along the whole wall, set up to deter invaders, no doubt, but that was not how it seemed to the two of us as we attempted this final obstacle that intervened between the Hill and the liberty we envisaged, beyond.

The plan was quite simple: we would walk the two miles to the nearest station and catch a train to London. (Chandy had, in contravention of the school rules, more than £50 in cash about his person.) We would make our way to his mother's apartment in Mayfair, and stay the night. Quite what I imagined would then happen to me, I do not recall. I suspect that I had not dared to think beyond the immediate euphoria of leaving the Hill; Chandy was planning to fly home to Delhi, which was hardly an option for me. In the event I was spared this dilemma, because what I had not taken into consideration was the fact that Chandy was much more agile than myself, and while he was soon over the wall, and calling softly that the way was clear, I was struggling to extricate my sweater from the double line of wire I was straddling on my stomach.

'Take it off, and jump,' said Chandy. But by this time I was in trouble, for both my sleeves were entangled and would not pull free; wriggling backwards on my knees, with the wire perilously between my legs, I attempted to drag the sweater off over my head, but in doing so I lost my balance and fell back into the school grounds. The wire had torn through my denim, and given me a nasty gash up my left shin, and I had twisted the other ankle so that it felt agony even to stand up. There was no chance of ascending the wall a second time. Forgetting the need for subterfuge in my discomfort, I shouted over to Chandy that I had hurt myself, and he'd have to run for it on his own, which he did straight away. As I limped and stumbled up the slope towards the school I was intercepted by Mr

Lawson, who had been on swimming duty, and my escapade was over.

They picked up Chandy on the platform, and that was the end of our friendship. I had committed the unforgivable schoolboy crime by sneaking on him, though I have no doubt they would have spotted his absence before too long, even if I had held my peace. Still, he might just have had time to catch a train, had I been less craven in the face of the authorities, but by then I was fearful of punishment, and so I betrayed him, and received the contempt I deserved.

The following day I stood on the dais in the dining-room after grace, and handed my monitor's tie over to the Headmaster. Chandy (who had never been considered suitable monitorial material in the first place) received twenty hours of evening detentions. They would have expelled us, I suppose, but in those days it might not have been good publicity to sack a Prince and a Marquess simultaneously for trying to run away from what was supposed to be a fashionably good institution.

My father was livid, and wrote me a letter informing me I had disgraced the entire family, and tarnished several generations of its good reputation at Stockhill, moving on to anatomize my ingratitude, irresponsibility, and persistent childishness. He said I had shamed him personally, and for that he could not forgive me. It was typically considerate of him.

SEVEN

A SHORT HISTORY
OF
BARBED WIRE

It began with the search for an artificial thornbush.

On the morning of 12 October 1492, a look-out on the *Pinta* sighted land, and Cristoforo Colombo 'discovered' the New World. This was almost five hundred years after the Icelanders, of course, but he probably knew this perfectly well; he had sailed to Iceland himself in 1477, but the Catholic authorities suppressed this information since they would have lost their legal claim to the New World if it had been suggested that he had heard the history of the Vikings and Vineland.

On 2 January 1494, Columbus landed the first cattle and horses on Hispaniola, from where they were taken by Spanish pioneers all over the Americas. Secure in his knowledge of God's Providence, the intrepid sailor hauled a cargo of native slaves back to Iberia, by way of fair exchange.

His legacy of horn and hoof flourished, however, and for several centuries the 'mustang' cattle were regarded as wild public property to be hunted in a free-for-all across the open ranges of the Great Plains. The settlers competed for them with the native Indians, against whom they were soon waging wars. The buffalo that once travelled in herds 10 miles square, and outnumbered the human population of the planet, were at the same time being slaughtered in such numbers that by 1900 they had been reduced to eight hundred bewildered specimens. The hunters ignored the older 'moss-backs', whose tough hides were difficult to strip, and concentrated on the young for their precious leather. The carcass would be abandoned, with just the tongue cut out, to be eaten with whiskey, for supper. As a result of shooting, logging, damming and burning there perished some of the great seasonal migrations of natural history – the bison, the salmon and the passenger pigeon.

Husbandry was clearly needed, and the ranching system was first adopted in the Northern Plains in the 1840s, becoming established over the next forty years in the heartlands of Texas, Arizona and New Mexico. During the heyday of the cattle barons, hundreds of riders might be employed for several months during the seasonal round-up of longhorn cattle, trail-driving the herds north to where the markets lay, and later to the nearest rail-heads. These riders, of course, were cowboys.

Like many things in history, the image of the quarrelsome cowpuncher, bow-legged and pistol-packing, subsisting on 'slow elk' and sonofabitch stew, is an amalgam of myth and fact. The Anglo cowboys of dime novel fame did not spring fully armed out of the skull of the Texan dirt. Their complex pedigree embraced the Hispanic (roaming Texas since the end of the seventeenth century), the Mexican *vaquero*, the Venezuelan *Illanero*, and even the peaceful *paniolo* of Hawaii, who wore flowers around his neck. There were black cowboys, female cowboys, Indian cowboys. It was a mixed culture, its members united by a common contempt for agriculture, and any forms of work to be done on foot. It was the unemployed who caused most of the legendary trouble. As the corporate ranches grew in size (often through land frauds and the illegal appropriation of public domains), the cowmen imposed tight regulations on their employees, and there was little room for unruly mavericks; ranching and droving was big business, highly organized, and riders had to develop special skills like horse-breaking, castration and branding, if they were to be offered work. Very few risked unnecessary physical injury in the pursuit of thrills: the best a lame cowboy could hope for was the unenviable job of camp cook, but once he was unfit for the saddle he would more often find himself destitute.

Some of the myths about the 'wildness' of the West were perpetuated by ranchers themselves, who had a vested interest in the land having a reputation for being inhospitable and difficult to settle. They stressed its desert qualities to combat the notion amongst the burgeoning population of the East that it was an under-explored Utopia, the frontiers of which merely needed pushing further back, until the real extent of the continent was known. After the end of the Civil War, a new migratory phenomenon began in earnest as pioneering settlers began to push West and stake their claims to build homesteads on unoccupied Government land – they knew when they had reached the cusp of the Great Plains, somewhere just west of the 98th meridian, because the rainfall was so unpredictable that the banks would not grant them a homestead loan. The cowmen, who despised tillage, watched with alarm as these sod-busting newcomers began, against all the odds, to make incursions on the range land they regarded as their natural preserve.

Herd law in the East put the onus on stockmen to contain their cattle, and the earlier settlers had plenty of timber from the forests they were clearing to construct wooden rail fences and houses, as well as to furnish them with fuel. When you crossed into the West, however, it was the responsibility of the settler to ensure that beasts were excluded from the crops; but there was scarcely any wood, and very little stone of the type manageable for making walls. In Nebraska they tried clay ridges, in Illinois they ditched, but these methods did not keep out the steers. Crops were devastated, morale was lowered by rumour, and for a while – to the delight of the ranchers – it looked as if fencing was going to prove an insuperable problem, and the flow of migrants began to dwindle.

There was much experimentation with hedge-fences – willows, mesquite, cherokee rose and thorn locust were all tried (that evocative tumbleweed you see bouncing across the High Plains in the movies is in fact an imported Russian thistle). Where these did take, they offered shade, but also caused perilous snowdrifts; they harboured pests, exhausted the soil, were not movable, and were a great risk of prairie fires. In the 1870s there was a vogue for planting Osage orange, with dealers making a fortune by selling seeds at $25 a bushel, claiming this hedge (from which the Indians traditionally made their bows) grew 'horse-high, bull-strong, and pig-tight'. They omitted to add that it took four long years to mature, required constant pruning, and cast a huge shadow. None of these growths proved satisfactory, and in the end it was the Industrial Revolution that supplied an answer where Nature apparently could not.

In the increasingly urgent quest for a solution that would prove highly lucrative if adopted by the 'nesters' of the West, experiments had been made with plain wire. Following the invention of the telegraph, steel wire was being widely manufactured, and miles of it were employed as fencing during the 1860s, but it was ineffective: steers were not deterred by it, and used it for rubbing. It was easy for them to squeeze their heads through and graze crops, and its low-grade galvanized construction meant that it constantly sagged or snapped in the fluctuating seasonal temperatures, no matter how strategically the stakes were spaced. What was needed was an artificial thornbush.

Barbed wire was invented in 1857, by a Swiss ironworker called John Grenningen who lived by the river in Austin, Texas, and was enraged at the frequency with which cattle coming down to drink broke his fences and damaged his fruit trees. So he attached jagged metal strips to the posts, which severely injured many animals, and so incensed his neighbours that they tried to have him evicted. In the end he was murdered in 1862.

Barbed wire was invented in 1860, by a blacksmith called Christian E. Shone who lived in Brooklyn, Iowa, and experimented with bending some of his horseshoe nails around lengths of strong, plain wire. The samples were considered to be too heavy and vicious, and were abandoned.

Barbed wire was invented in July 1860, by a French metalworker called Leonce Eugene Grassin-Baledons, who was granted a patent for his *fil de fer herissie* – a strand of twisted metal with 'bristles' or 'prickles' attached.

Barbed wire was invented in 1861, by a boy of ten called Adrian C. Latta who lived in Friendship, New York, when he twisted some barbs by hand around the lowest wire section of a garden fence, to keep out the farmer's hogs. This fence remained intact for fifteen years, but he never did anything further about his idea. (Einstein, when asked what was the first thing he did when he had a good idea, replied: 'I don't really know. I've only ever had one.')

Barbed wire was invented in 1873 – and at this stage history stops repeating itself, and once again puts its best foot forward – when a farmer exhibited 'a fence with sharp projections on it' at the De Kalb County Fair, Illinois. The idea appealed quite independently to three people who saw it, each of whom went away and embarked on separate modifications that were to make a lot of money for their lawyers in the years to follow. One of these keen-eyed farmers was Joseph Glidden, who began crimping barbs on to wire in his kitchen, using his wife's coffee-mill. He had Lucinda's approval for this because she wanted to keep stray pigs out of her garden. Glidden went on to devise a twisting and stretching machine in a bid to beat his competitors, and on 24 November 1874 his wire ('The Winner') was awarded US Patent Number 157124. It was an invention that transformed the economy of North America, generated a massive industry of its own, and had a pronounced effect on the history of subsequent warfare.

Glidden's two immediate, and very different, competitors who left that County Fair inspired by what they had seen were Isaac Leonard Ellwood, a young hardware merchant, and a German lumberman called Jacob Haish. While Ellwood conceded that Glidden's product was superior to any of his own attempts, and formed a partnership with him (The Barb Fence Company), the flamboyant Haish preferred never to acknowledge any prior designs in the field, and served interference papers on his rivals. Two modest industries thus grew up acrimoniously side by side in a flurry of legal paperwork.

In February 1876, Charles Washburn of the firm Washburn and Moen, Mass., decided to visit the County in person to investigate this steady demand for plain wire from his company. He soon caught wind of the new twisting business, and paid a call on Haish, inviting him to name his price for selling an interest in his cottage industry. Haish quoted the sum of $200,000, whereupon Washburn repaired to Glidden, who agreed to $60,000 plus a royalty, and promptly retired. Washburn and Ellwood became partners, and embarked on what was to prove, literally, to be a money-spinning enterprise.

Not everyone was happy with this invention, however. As hundreds of miles of 'bob wire' began to be erected, some ranchers realized that the settlers were now fencing them out, preventing access to vital water-holes, and causing damage to their steers. In Texas and Wyoming 'Wire Wars' were soon raging between herdsmen of the traditional open range and the newly secure homesteaders. There were fierce disputes over territorial rights, and the ethics of the new thorny fencing. The Indians referred to it as 'the devil's rope', because it cut across their own ancestral webs of migration, impeding their hunts and moonlit manoeuvres. Later, it was to enclose their reservations, and their tribal graveyards.

But many stockmen recognized the advantages of the wire as a flexible instrument for consolidating their property, minimizing the incidence of strays and thefts, and allowing the proper regulation of breeding. It meant they could enclose huge areas of land to rival the *latifundiae* of the southern part of the continent, and by the 1880s there were extravagant plans such as the XIT ranch in Texas (so called because it involved ten counties) that was to use 1500 miles of wire to enclose three million acres, and 50,000 cattle. The days of the open range had gone forever.

Those early salesmen initially met with apathy and incomprehension over the product, however. There had been claims and gimmicks like this before, and many of the ranchers from the Southern states were scornful of it as some Yankee device. This was all changed by 'Colonel Ike' Ellwood in 1876, when, in a moment of inspiration crucial to his future fortunes, he hired a brash, inexperienced young salesman named John Warne Gates and settled him in San Antonio, Texas.

Gates was a gambler and a showman, and he realized that 'Ole Santone' was an important centre for cattlemen; if he could convert them here, the word would soon spread. He somehow persuaded the city officials to let him erect in the Military Plaza a corral rigged with barbed wire, which he trumpeted as being 'Light as air. Stronger than whiskey. Cheaper than dirt.' In front of an audience of incredulous Texans, he then had sixty wild longhorns driven in (some claim he arranged for cattle especially selected as docile) and had men with torches spur on the beasts to try and break free. Time and again they charged the wire, and then they simply refused.

That night, Gates sold hundreds of miles of the stuff. It became so much in demand that soon they were selling it directly off the railways, and cutting out the need for dealers. That year alone, there were sold across the country some 2,840,000 pounds of barbed wire, which by 1880 had risen to an annual total of over eighty and a half million pounds.

Pretty soon, everyone jumped on the bandwagon, and writs for infringement of patents were beng served with great regularity, since there was clearly such a hungry market for the devil's hatband. Indeed, some of the varieties were evidence of an almost diabolical ingenuity. There was cut and span, caduceus, spiral barb, kink, coil, arch and crimp barb. There was a single and double strand. It was painted, japanned, copperized or varnished with linseed. There was diamond chain and link-mesh, gull-wing, pigtail, triangle, zig-zag, shock-absorber and snake's-tongue, with tattered-leaf discs, and wheels and spinners attached.

Havenhill's Arrowpoint, Dodge's Spurwheel, Blake's Body Grip, Duffy-Schroeder's Grooved Diamond, Sjostrom's Saucer Barb, Shellaberger's Spaced Loops, Waco Twist – they sound like weird breakfast cereals, but these were the real names behind how the West was won.

Two men cashed in on this boom, and amassed even larger fortunes than the inventors themselves. 'Bet-A-Million' Gates was one, setting up his own, unlicensed factory in St Louis in 1878. The patentees whose ideas he was copying were unable to serve subpoena papers on him, because every night he floated his machinery over the Missouri in a barge, so that next day he was in the state of Illinois. Thus was born the term 'moonshining', but the man who was nicknamed The Monarch of Moonshine Wire was a Philadelphian called Michael T. Clay.

My ancestor knew little about metallurgy and industrial manufacture, but he had been an attorney by training and could see a method of exploiting the confused situation about who was licensed to produce what particular design of wire. He realized that the cattlemen were not so much choosy about the exact shape of the barb as concerned to get their miles of it as cheaply as possible, so he set about applying for dozens of different patents that were only marginal variations on existing designs, and while these were pending he proceeded with production in a dozen different factories across the Midwest. When a patent was refused, he merely closed down the relevant factory for a while until he had filed for a new design, and in this way he managed to sell hundreds of thousands of dollars' worth of wire by undercutting the prices of the licensed manufacturers.

By 1880, his activities had so exasperated the Ellwood Corporation that they offered to buy him out. Recalling the story of Haish, he named and received a sum of $400,000 that February – just three months before a court in Chicago passed a ruling which would have made him liable to retrospective payments and damages, which would surely have reduced him to bankruptcy. As it was, he invested his new capital in railroad stock, and later took out an interest in a cannery company in Chicago. Unlike Gates, who went on to oil, Clay preferred to concentrate his holdings in these new areas, having benefited once from a freakish moment in industrial history, and (fortunately for us) he was not a congenital gambler.

But what was good for Clay's interests spelled the end of the line for the cowboy. Fencing prevented the overland trail, and the proliferation of the railway network meant less demand for marshalling cattle to market. Windmills were introduced and made access to water easier: if he was to survive, the cowboy had to adapt to fence maintenance, mowing for winter hay, the operation of pumps, and the alien experience of working on foot. He might still call himself a cowboy, but he had been reduced to a ranch-hand, almost indistinguishable from other agricultural employees. Some of the old hands went North, and worked the tamer plains of Alberta; others followed the now economically outdated longhorns and joined travelling rodeos, and thence a few made it into the cinema.

In 1887, Buffalo Bill Cody brought his Wild West Show to London, complete with two hundred participants, and three hundred head of livestock, to coincide with the Golden Jubilee of Queen Victoria. Michael T. Clay took a house in London that year for the Season, and brought with him his wife Ruth, and his daughters Anna and Martha. They attended Bill Cody's pantomime, and later that night went on to a fancy-dress ball at Londonderry House, where the profits from the demise of the American cowboy were destined to revive the fortunes of the landless Dukes of London.

Following its introduction to Leicestershire by the Fifth Earl Spencer in 1880, barbed wire was to effect a more profound change on traditional fox-hunting society than anything before the arrival of the internal combustion engine. A court order had previously proclaimed for the first time that hunts did 'not have unrestricted access' over the length and breadth of the English countryside, and farmers began to demand compensation for damages to their hedgerows and wooden fences. Barbed wire represented one-tenth of the cost of such barriers, and was rapidly adopted as a serious hazard to horses where the hunts in question ignored the new regulations. Letters were written to the *Telegraph*, and the cry of ''Ware Wire' came to symbolize the serious curtailment of the freedom and abandon enjoyed for centuries by the galloping classes, in their thin red line across the countryside.

When my great-grandfather Harry was serving in his blood-red tunic in the war against the Boers, barbed wire was pressed into service, not to keep out cattle, but to keep people in. One of Kitchener's distinctions was that he invented the concentration camp: in the Cape Colony under his command in 1901 he erected a line of blockhouses and surrounded it with the wire the Boer soldiers had used in their defences. Imprisoned therein were some 120,000 women and children from the farms he had razed. Of these, 20,000 were to die of neglect or disease before the guerrillas (outnumbered five-fold by the Imperial forces) capitulated to the imposition of British sovereignty at the Treaty of Vreeniging.

When barbed wire made its first appearance in Iceland, just after the Boer War, it was one of the revolutionary events in the island's culture. Before its arrival there had never been an effective barrier method for the demarcation of territory – timber was almost non-existent, and the landscape too tortuous and unstable for the systematic construction of walls. Boundaries had to be marked by lone boulders and obscure ditches, some of them unchanged since the time of the Sagas. But the Icelanders took this extremely expensive foreign import to their hearts, and there was a mania for festooning it across the primordial farmland. The Althing passed a law decreeing that it was inviolate, and fines of 10 krónur were imposed on anyone caught climbing over these costly new fences. Children used to leap over them for a dare, count up the fines they would have incurred if caught, and fantasize about what they could buy with all that money, if only there had been anything but dried fish and tea and snuff and knitted woollens in the shops.

As history progresses into the present century, the refinements become more efficient and hideous. It was the weblike wirefields of the Great War that lead directly to the invention of the tank. There were the Nazi camps. The Japanese developed the use of underwater barbed wire to blockade harbours, a grim peril for frogmen. In Korea, the United States produced concertina wire – a single roll of high tensile sprung steel which opened out instantly to expose 14,000 barbs along its length. There was the Berlin Wall, with its killing strip. The electric fence that used to separate the old South Africa from Mozambique earlier this decade was charged to deliver a lethal jolt of 11 kilowatts, but few people ever made it even through the outlying layers of razor-wire that surrounded it; once you enter a thicket of this stuff, you cannot go back. It is like being tumbled in a cement-mixer with a million small scimitars.

With only the security of his wife's flower-patch in mind, Mr Glidden could not have had the slightest inkling, as he toiled over the coffee-grinder on the threshold of his contented retirement, of how many lives were to be taken by the tearing, slicing and impaling of humans trapped in his terrifying funnel-webs of coiled steel.

During the almost ubiquitous escalation of armed criminal activity across the states of Europe during the last five years, exclusion deterrents have understandably become much in demand, especially since electronic systems requiring liveware response (detection followed by investigation) have proved so inefficient. Expensive though they are, there are at least two varieties of wire that are extremely popular for the protection of property. Both have a ghastly but teleologic beauty. They are not universally available, but here in Switzerland they can be purchased under licence, and we are taught how to handle them correctly as part of our military instruction. The first is Banderilla Wire, which injects minute barbs deep under the skin upon the lightest contact, like the leg-bristles of certain arboreal spiders, and these require treatment within several hours to prevent paralysis of the surrounding muscle. Swiss regulations stipulate that this wire may only be installed at a height above ground level of 4 metres, and each household authorized to erect it must carry the standard B-Box antidote chest, access to which must be granted for any Swiss national so requesting it, provided that he or she consents to the police being summoned at the same time.

The APW – or Anti-Personnel Wire – which we are trained

to lay by the militia is a more elaborate affair, and is rarely seen adorning private property. The internal circumference of its coils (which must be carefully positioned) transmits an electronic circuit that causes the wire to snap closed whenever this is broken, like a handcuff, like some mythical *vagina dentata*, that seizes the intruder and simultaneously triggers an alarm. It is used quite extensively around military installations, and will lacerate the flesh even through Grade VI protective armour. None of us really likes working with it, especially since its constrictive effects are usually impressed upon the militia by a demonstration that involves a baseball bat being sliced in two.

Like many other corporate premises, the buildings of the Institute here in Schwyz are sealed off at night by the system developed by Bruno Plimmer, and known as Laser Wire. No wire is actually involved, of course; no wire in the sense of perimeter band. A beam of light oscillating at high frequency in an arc that mutates every 0.55 seconds across the target area has only to be interrupted by a moving object emitting source-heat equivalent to a human weighing anything over 84 pounds (there have to be tolerances built in to allow for the remote possibility of stray children) and a floating holographic sensor will appear, warning you that you have forty-five seconds to produce a deflective authorization card (this is all in the *Citizens' Manual*), failing which the system will trigger a beam of incapacitating light.

With the invention of barbed wire, the whole idea of free movement was crowned with thorns. If we live today under a state of siege, it is because we are running out of space: there are too many of us, the laws in respect of property ownership have, in most places, irretrievably broken down, and we are running out of time. Unless a latter-day Colombo discovers that Mars is a more congenial place than had hitherto been suggested, there will be no New Worlds for us to settle and claim, fence and till, and the areas we have already annexed are being reclaimed by the seas and the weather: the dishes of dust that were the Great Plains, the atolls that housed small civilizations in the Pacific, the swamped marshlands of Asia Minor. But perhaps we are destined for some submarine reincarnation, another Age of Atlantis, where the weather makes monsters of us all, and we sink into the deep trenches with our new sets of fin and gill. It is possible that this is what we deserve, for we have not been good homesteaders, and our husbandry of available land has been only too ingenious. We have erected barriers and imposed borders, protected this and conserved that, but in the end our collective position is indefensible. We have strangled ourselves with the devil's rope of our inventions.

In the meantime, if you should find yourself straying from your usual zone – inquisitive or lost, drunkenly defiant or primed with investigative altruism – and you enter, for whatever motive, a cul-de-sac or other restricted area, and an indigo hologram wobbles to address you out of the dark, forget your mission. Whatever it may have been, look once for confirmation at the hovering light, and throw to the winds of the darkness your original intention. Forget the precepts you may have learned about our federal society preserving its traditions of freedom, those arguments about the collective need to keep the faith. When it comes down to it, when it comes down to the matter of individuality, they never existed.

Turn, and run. Turn your back on all you have been told about history.

And run like fuck.

EIGHT

My first day at Eton, I felt like a bit-part actor drafted into a movie at short notice and before having had the chance to glance at the script. I was awoken by a stout woman I had never seen before, who entered my room, drew back the curtains, and said, 'Good morning, Mister Waterstock. It's time to get up.' I stared at her from my pillow. The little room had become scented overnight by the cache of Spellbrook Seedlings I had in a box under the bed. 'I'm Mrs Ransome, your Boy's Maid,' she explained. The first in what was literally a cast of thousands.

In the washroom were two bleary-eyed men shaving. One of them was bigger than my father. They ignored me, and continued grunting into the mirrors. While I was brushing my teeth, a slightly younger man came in and asked if anyone had some spare studs. 'Fuck off, Stewart,' said one shaver. 'The same fucking shambles every half,' said his lathery companion. A script really would have been useful, along with a glossary. ('There are some exceptionally talented boys in this House,' my father had assured me, before leaving me the previous evening.)

My new uniform was hanging funereally on the back of my door – black tail-coat, waistcoat and striped trousers, tailored for me by Denham and Goddard. Doors thudded closed and the ceiling shook, as I struggled with my stiff collar and the vestigial little strip of white cotton that made up my tie. It felt less like a prison than the Hill had done – already I had the impression of joining some strange regiment.

There was a knock on the door, and at last it was someone I recognized: Miss Herrick, the Dame, had come to take me down to breakfast. I remembered to address her as Ma'am, though this did seem a little incongruous; kindly as she no doubt was, Miss Herrick was not overtly feminine. She had a bass voice, wore tie-up suede shoes, and was (so far as one could see) almost entirely flat-chested. There were to be no buxom school matrons here, to remind one fondly of nannies – I was escorted down to my first meal by the Regimental Sergeant-Major.

Out into the tide of boys in the streets, sweeping toward the chapels, I was suddenly flotsam nudging around a great swirl of a community about which I knew little beyond the fact that my father had been a notable success here before the war, and that it was costing him a lot of money to send me in his footsteps. The most bewildering aspect was the sheer scale of the place; it was like a little town of its own, and during those first few weeks you had to get yourself geographically organized and gauge carefully the exact time required for travelling from place to place. This was a new, and very real, anxiety. There was a blue booklet called the *Fixtures* – a kind of diary into which you copied your timetable, and noted appointments – and you were continually tugging it from your pocket just to check you were on course for the right part of the school, a cool fear under the tight collar if you realized you had confused your destinations with only minutes to spare. But all this kept you too busy to despair, although there was from the beginning that peculiarly unpleasant sensation of being lonely in a crowd.

Which is the more ominous preface to a disquisition – a man maintaining he was unhappy at school, or one who recalls schooldays as idyllic? I can't claim that I hated my five years at Eton: what I think I hated was being a teenager, and my navigation through this inescapable region of turbulence was not exactly assisted by the man in overall charge of my well-being. Your experience of this huge school was largely dictated by the House you found yourself in; your House was your regiment, with its own colours and cups and staff, and it was designated by the initials of your Housemaster, and had no permanent identification with the building where it was currently encamped, though that building had a postal address by which it was known to the outside world. Thus, the house which comprised my barracks was called Mussiter's, but my House was RET after my wonderful Housemaster, Dr Robin Tappen, from whose imaginative gifts I derived so much benefit during the typhoon years of my adolescence.

To be fair to my father (aha, what's this? Do my eyes deceive me?), Tappen had not been his original choice, but such were the vagaries of the House List system when he put down my name shortly after birth that you could not guarantee the master you chose would actually be at the school when your son was admitted, thirteen years later. The rising star in 1956 among the younger 'beaks' at Eton was said to be a certain P. L. Webber, and he had accepted my infant name for his 1969 List, but had left to take up the post of headmaster somewhere else, the year before I arrived. By all accounts he was widely missed by those boys who had been in the House during his time: a low-slung, easy-going historian with a reputation for sorting out muddles without them reaching the ear of the Head Master; a family man who kept a good cellar and preferred golf to any more strenuous athletics – this paragon had been lured elsewhere, and in his place had materialized a changeling, a man who belonged to the grey dawn.

Dr Tappen would have been about thirty-seven when I put in an appearance for my first Half – just a few years younger than my mother, though I was still not old enough to be able to distinguish with much confidence between adult generations. To me he seemed merely to be of housemasterly age, an impression confirmed by his receding red hair, his prematurely avuncular tweeds, and his parsimonious habits. He was a classicist, regarded by his colleagues as 'in possession of a fine mind', though amongst his boys the word was that his sense of humour had been surgically removed at Gonville and Caius, Cambridge.

Although many of the Houses had been renovated in recent years, Mussiter's had not yet come to the top of the list. It therefore retained some of its Regency features, particularly in the areas of heating and sanitation. There were four baths available on the Boys' Side (which meant you were unlikely to go clean from the playing-fields to afternoon school, sharing these facilities with forty-seven other boys), four indoor bogs (the regulation outdoor block was deemed out of bounds after curfew, or Lock Up) and a pervasive interior chill that was acceptable in summer, but which deepened during winter until it seemed to be colder in than out. The ancient building was none the less the home of fauna that probably were direct linear descendants of the original intake of vermin, just as were some of the boys. At night, the scuffed linoleum of the passageways became the haunt of large spiders, and quite often you would hear a scuffling in your corner, and surprise a mouse in the beam of your torch. The rooms had no central heating, but three times a week you could collect a small scuttle of coal with which to make a fire in your individual grate during specific hours of the evening. There was just about sufficient for a small flame lasting perhaps three hours with careful husbandry, so that on alternate nights you just worked in bed, with your clothes on, longing for a return of the tradition in Gladstone's day, when the Dame would administer a little cognac on cold nights.

It might be argued that the human brain actually functions better at below room temperature, and that learning to budget one's resources was an integral part of the education for Life, and even, perhaps, that knowing how to keep a fire going could possibly save one's skin in later years. It was certainly a challenge. We were spared the business of cleaning the hearth, however, since this fell within the brief of Luis, the House factotum, who also washed the floors and the plates, and cleaned our shoes in his 'boot-hole' near the back door.

One of the chief features of the entire school was that you had your own room, right from your first day (the King's Scholars, or 'tugs', merely had cubicles to start with, but they were different in many respects). This was to foster the principle that you were left to organize your evening time unsupervised and uninterrupted, learning to make your own decisions and establish your own priorities in the face of other temptations (like time-wasting, self-abuse, and Commando comics), and in this respect Eton College promoted independence that made it more like a miniature university than merely a school for boys. This privacy was certainly welcome, perhaps especially to those who wished to make nocturnal assignations of a nature only educational in the broadest possible sense.

As with most things in this rigid hierarchy, you started at the bottom and hoped to work your way up – will you please quieten down, there at the back? I am referring to the system by which you could move to a bigger and better room as you became more senior within the house. In my first Half I was assigned to what was little more than a box-room with a window, but this was my own cabin and the safest place in the ocean. There was a desk provided by the school (a 'burry'), a leather-topped ottoman for keeping clothes, an armchair and curtains made in the fabric of my mother's choice (sadly, a risible pattern of harlequins cavorting in black and white, rather than something more robust like spaniels hunting through brambles, which Kit Hamilton had managed to secure for his trimmings, or, better still, some abstract design in lurid Sixties hues, suggesting my fondness for psychedelia, my precocious penchant for hip, perhaps) and a bed that folded vertically against the wall during the day. I arrived with very little else in the way of decoration, but soon one gathered that your room was a showcase for whatever personality you wished to project, and the walls would be lined in coloured tinfoil, there would be posters of Hendrix, the Doors, Bardot (female images allowed only from the collar-bone up, was the sensible rule of Tappen), Asian floor-cushions, tinted light-bulbs, whatever you could get away with. The rooms tended to start off austere and uncertain, rising towards the end of a boy's first year to safe versions of what was then seen as cool; then there would be provocative elements, brinkmanship to test the authorities (the outcome was never in any doubt: sex and drugs were banned); next, a minimalist phase, with purple crêpe paper, a coptic cross, as a boy teetered on the edge of being promoted to some position of eminence within the school, in which case suddenly everything about the décor became rather more pukka, and the ambience changed, and you'd be treated to rows of school colours, and a shrine dedicated to signed leaving-photographs from friends, and perhaps a Magritte poster, or something suggesting a visit to an Italian gallery, all signifying that the occupant of this large and enviable room was about to leave the school and take his place in the world outside.

You might not have thought it, as the parent peeping through the doorways of these dens on the way to collect a son, but this was the most famous school on earth, and it prided itself in producing the modern equivalent of the Renaissance Man, although the rag-and-bone-shop interiors might have suggested Cro-Magnon was somewhere nearer the mark.

There were three new boys in RET that Half, and you may be sure that none of us found much familiar about our environment, but I was lucky in that one – Kit Hamilton – had been with me at the Hill, and in due course this came to make a considerable difference to my whole experience of the place. For the first three weeks we were excused fagging so that we could learn the jargon and topography of the school, but that was the only concession. In this particular tide-rip, the tradition was sink or swim. At the end of this probationary period, we had to take a Colours Test conducted by the Captain of the House, and there was the threat of beating if we failed. This rite of passage involved us memorizing the colours of all the different school caps (there were dozens of them), plus the names and nicknames of senior members of the staff, such abstruse information as where Queen Anne's flowerpot was to be found (the answer was: Lupton's Tower), what was meant by an Eight Tan (a beating by the members of the senior rowing crew for misbehaviour on the Thames), and what went up Judy's Passage (the answer, again, was: Lupton's Tower). Yes, the foundations of a Renaissance education, beyond a doubt.

Like the surnames of our roll-call at the Hill, these shards of information are still bedded within my memory, as they must have been for decades of chaps in linen suits and cravats, hands a touch unsteady from malaria or *chotah pegs*, who congregated in the consulates and clubs of the old Commonwealth until really quite recently, and were able to recall with pride the resplendent heraldry of their old school, the satisfying knowledge that the colours of the Second Field were still tangerine with a black lion.

You started at the bottom, in F Block, and worked your way up towards A: the letter of the alphabet denoted your age-group within the community, and that was at least some index of progress. When you first arrived, there was no doubt about your position – you were right at the sump of the system. Some boys who had been minor swells at their prep schools found this reversal of fortune rather difficult to cope with at first, but this was not one of the problems that faced me. Stockhill had reduced me to the ranks, and as far as I was concerned, this new and infinitely more complex system was one I was going to study quietly, and with care. It seemed to me there might be a way one could pick through the labyrinth, but it would take time, it would require luck, and it was probably a good idea to go it alone.

The gulf between the men at the top end of the House and the boys who had just arrived was almost unthinkable. It was difficult to imagine that one would ever get there from one's origins. As a new boy, you were straining your imagination so far into a projective future that it was an exercise hardly worth performing: in some cases, you were hoping for starlight without out a telescope. They were far off, these men. You shared a building, but not much of the life under its roof. The Houses were largely self-policing, and Tappen had little to do with the daily discipline that quite effectively organized our behaviour. There was a two-tier system of ennoblement as you got older and became eligible – first, election to the House Debating Society (this meant you could stay up a little later, possess a radio, and opt out of games), and then elevation to the higher echelons of the Library (House prefects, who could have hifi's, fine boys for any infringements of the House rules, stay up fairly late and drink cocoa, and generally swagger around, calling for fags to run errands, and enforcing regulations of their own devising).

Members of Debate never had to indulge in debates, and the Library was a room with a dart-board, but no books. So much for the reliability of names and titles.

When I took my Colours Test, our Captain of the House was a man named Simon Wood – a devastating spinbowler, by general agreement, and the school squash supremo. He was svelte and clean-limbed, and had a slight muscular hunch. We feared and admired his physique, but the great thing about Wood was the fact that he was a Member of Pop.

Now, this is something almost impossible to explain to a non-Etonian (I have always enjoyed the essential desperation involved in that epithet of exclusion, the sense that one is otherwise lost for descriptive terms) but Members of The Eton Society, or Pop, were the Gods of the College, the gilded élite, the self-perpetuating secret police, the blades, Turks, and Jumping Jack Flashes of the community. In return for such onerous duties as checking off names in Lower Chapel and acting as bouncers at rock concerts in School Hall, they were allowed to impose fines at whim, disappear at night without permission, and carry their gamps rolled-up. They sported a brash uniform of spongebag trousers and brocade waistcoats, with flowers in their buttonholes and silk handkerchiefs spilling from their top pockets.

Only the most rebellious or apathetic among the Lower Boys did not dream that one day they might be thus apotheosized, but you had little chance unless you rose to become one of the finer sportsmen in the school. Pop was a smug club for jocks, but this never prevented a number of lounge lizards, *flâneurs*, riff-raff and also-rans, from doing their utmost to curry favour. Direct credit transfers between accounts at Coutts were sometimes arranged, but the munificence of the settlor was rarely successful, and his bribe would be wasted. One desperate aspirant was said to have offered the sexual services of his sister to the Keeper of Racquets during the summer holidays, but I believe the loyal girl acquiesced in vain. Such was the glamour of this popinjay corps that failure to become one of its elect often lingered as a sour memory well into middle age. Not long before I left England, I chanced upon a photograph of a boy who had been my contemporary, and had been disappointed in his desire for Etonian ennoblement: he was best man at a wedding, and was wearing Pop trousers, acting out his schoolboy fantasies.

On the first and last Sundays of each half the members would convene in Pop Room (a bolt-hole to which even the teaching staff were denied access) and hold an election to maintain their numbers. They would then parade the streets, shouting and posturing, as they made their way to the rooms of the chosen, where the new members would have their school dress torn to pieces from their bodies in a ritual signifying the end of the humble chrysalis and the emergence of the bright butterfly – an excuse for hooliganism, in fact. Scuttling in their wake would be the fags of the leavers, clutching coat-hangers laden with waistcoats to sell to the mauled neophytes, nipping in quick on them like hyenas to a carcass after the pride has had its fill.

I need hardly say that I never made it into this august body, as my sporting skills had, if anything, actually declined since my days at Stockhill. It was unfortunate that RET was rather an athletic house, and shirkers were not tolerated. It was compulsory for junior boys to clock up a certain number of hours' exercise per week, to be entered on a chart on the house notice-board. The penalty for fudging a claim was a beating by the Captain of the House, a risk not worth the running. With the possible exception of Fives, there was not a single sport that I positively enjoyed, but this was an irrelevance. The standing of the House was largely judged by the number of school cups displayed along its dining-room tables, and every inmate was expected to pull his weight. This was impressed upon you on your first afternoon, as the Captain of Games hauled you off to the site where the Battle of Waterloo was won, and began rehearsing you for your own little part in the Etonian ritual called The Field Game.

I never did quite master the rules to this pastime, but it was supposed to be an amalgam of soccer and rugger, with the advantages of both. It was certainly very noisy and confusing, but for some reason it was not a game that was ever taken up by those outside the school, despite the conviction of its devotees that it was the greatest ball game ever devised. One drawback to this was that you could not compete gloriously against other schools, but this afforded excellent advantages for the keenest of Old Etonians to revisit the school each winter with scratch teams to take on the best young bloods. The spectacle of Army officers and City financiers kitted out in their old colours and chasing furiously around the pitch, the movie of past greatness flickering before their eyes, was one I found intriguing. It also furnished me with one of the better oaths I have heard: a man in his forties (he was, I think, a Brigadier in the Household Cavalry) was brought low by what he considered a foul tackle, and as he sprang to his feet he bellowed at his enemy, 'May God shit in your mouth!' – no doubt a traditional battle-cry from the days of Waterloo.

Having passed my Colours Test, I was assigned to Anthony Middleton as his personal fag. This entailed me being in attendance in his room after breakfast and before prayers every day, to tidy his room, run errands, or simply sit in silence until he thought up something for me to do. The idea behind this system (if there was one at all) was to teach little Etonians the concepts of service and interdependence, while allowing younger boys to get to know someone senior in their house. But Middleton was a real hogfucker of a man, and enjoyed a puny sense of power from having a boy at his beck and call (especially, no doubt, a jumped-up snob of a Marquess), and the give-and-take side of the relationship never materialized. He was arrogant and self-regarding, and liked to embarrass me by telling filthy jokes

and then getting me to explain them, mocking my ignorance –
'Christ, don't they teach you the facts of life in your family,
Waterstock? Go down to Jennings's room, and ask him to
explain what a rim job is. God, you're worse than a bloody
prole.' He spent a lot of time monitoring his complexion in the
mirror, and rubbing raw alcohol into his skin. I must say, he
rather frightened me.

Fagging, however, meant I had to acquire in a very short
space of time certain essential skills, such as the way to polish
the buckles of a Gucci loafer using a woman's silk stocking
(sadly, without the woman's leg inside it), how to clean Middleton's razor and tidy his underwear drawer, how to fold his
pyjamas correctly when making his bed in the morning, and
how to sweep the pubes off his base-sheet before stretching it
to immaculate smoothness. Once a week it was also my duty
to prepare and serve tea for all the Library before I could go
and get my own, and here came the business of poaching
unbroken eggs, brewing tea or collecting pheasants that had
been roasted in Rowlands, the school food shop, and had to be
rushed back to the House in their cardboard boxes, with containers of chips and peas, since you'd be in trouble if the food
was not piping hot on arrival. Tea was the most important meal
of the day, because it was self-catering, and you could actually
sit down to a palatable meal, but if you were tea-fag you'd be
lucky to get time to snaffle a bowl of cereal back in your own
room (where I 'messed' with Kit) before heading off for more
Afternoon School.

One of the reasons why that first half was just about toler-
able was that Kit and I were able to share the bewilderment of
many of these experiences. Even then, he and I were tempera-
mentally quite different – he was extrovert, and inclined to be
cheeky whenever he thought his good looks would bestow
immunity, which proved to be quite often, since the senior boys
clearly thought he was rather good news, and no doubt fancied
him. He also got off to a promising start by being agile with a
football at his feet (he had been Captain of the First Eleven at

the Hill, which was probably why we had not become closer friends up until now) and this gave him an early confidence off the pitch as well. By comparison I was physically a little immature, poorly co-ordinated, and wore a cowed look that had nothing of the effortless superiority one was supposed to be cultivating from the very beginning. To make things worse, I was labelled a 'sap', meaning I was in the top Division of the first-year boys, having passed the Common Entrance exams with really quite high marks – small wonder, then, that I did not feel very high in the popularity stakes in a House such as RET.

The academic work was at least not a source of real anxiety, and I found, rather to my surprise, that the Hill had actually prepared me rather well for most subjects, though I was taking science for the first time. My Order Cards and interim reports suggested both industry and competence, but Dr Tappen was a hard man to please: if something was good, he wanted to know what you were going to do to make it excellent, and he had forgotten how to say 'Well done'. It was not exactly that I had become habituated to fulsome praise either at home or at the Hill, but a smidgin of encouragement once a month might have been a help. If you showed up with a piece of work that had been commended for his signature, he would often quibble about the untidiness of the calligraphy, or cock his head from side to side and hum, 'Well, all right. But it seems to me rather a slight essay for a boy in F One. And of course Cassivellaunus has two ls. Next.'

At the end of the Half we sat for Trials, and when the results were proclaimed at the Reading Over ceremony in School Hall, I was delighted to hear that I had been placed with a First Class. This was not the very top category (scholars and the real intellectuals achieved a Distinction), but it was good enough to afford me some relief that I had beaten several other boys in my div. and the great majority of boys in my year. But it was not a result that drew much approbation from RET, who underlined my poorish Chemistry marks in red ink (to draw my father's attention to them), and told me that he was frankly disappointed I had failed to win a Distinction, and he trusted I would apply myself more assiduously next time round. His covering letter that later accompanied my report spoke of his concern that I was not yet participating fully enough in the diverse opportunities afforded by House life, ticked me off for a couple of instances of unpunctuality, and expressed the hope that I would galvanize my efforts on the playing field and desist from settling for second best. And this was the final bulletin about my progress on which my father had to comment, in his library, a few days before Christmas, where, producing a grey look, tapping of the fingers, he delivered an exhortation to pull up my mental socks and realize that I was becoming a man.

It was one of the last interviews we ever had.

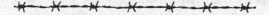

I was not looking when it happened. I was standing at the southern end of the conservatory, with my back to him, talking to Mary Begg, who was complaining of the 'flu. The glass made a terrible noise as its five panes were torn, and then there was a momentary silence. We all turned, and I felt someone grip my shoulders. I remember a mess of screaming, people moving busily, the glimpse of my mother pushing towards him, then falling; Flynn thrusting the others away, turning him gently over, the head at a bad angle, one eye open, left arm beating like a wing against the butler's back. I saw blood on his hand, saw Flynn frowning with intense concentration into his face, heard the batrachian groan as – I don't know, something wrenched its way out of my father's body, making it convulse, causing his left leg to kick out, leaving his body supine and concave in Flynn's arms.

Had it been part of a down-pipe he would probably not have died. These were made from lead, and were soft. But it was a section of the more modern, horizontal iron gutter that had broken off at a flaw, and its tip had been pointed and hard. They took him to the hospital, but my father was dead on arrival. The accident was reported in the national newspapers. My mother was sedated for two days, Charlie cancelled the Boxing Day shoot, and Mr Reid, the family solicitor, paid a call the next day.

As I said, this was how I became the Eighth Duke of London.

It is difficult for me now to be objective about my reaction to my father's death. What I saw was horrifying – a length of sharp metal protruding from the neck, that busy show of blood – but I will come clean, and say that I never did like my father very much, and I now like the idea of him even less. I know that this is disloyal, but loyalty has been consigned to a weird crucible since then. *De mortuis nil nisi bonum*: I am aware that the failings of the dead should never be mentioned, nor do I intend to itemize them here, but since I find myself now adrift on the currents of middle age I do not think any purpose is served by pretending the past was better in this respect. I am sure there were times when we might have had certain discussions, but they did not happen, and that has to be an end of it. I can hardly blame him for being killed by a freak of the weather; that might have carried off any one of our employees standing close to him at the time. The misfortune would have been identical, but not for me. When I lost my father, I had to become someone else. I wasn't ready.

My mother surprised everyone by refusing to go to pieces. She gave a fine performance of stoicism at the funeral ('Eternal Father, strong to save . . . ') and for several months afterwards she looked neat and radiant in her new black clothes. There was an immense amount of paperwork to negotiate, and she spent a lot of time in Durham Walk with Mr Reid and his briefcases. On two visits before the new Half began I had to accompany her and sign documents myself, because although I was a minor I was the principal beneficiary of my father's will, and there were offshore trusts, overseas deposits, two parcels of land in

Martha's Vineyard and some Highland forestry to be dealt with, quite apart from the estate at Spellbrook. I had very little idea of what was going on, except that Mr Reid arranged for a number of bank accounts to be opened at Hoare's in my name, and he introduced me to two other serious men whom I gathered were his fellow trustees. In fact, I was in the process of inheriting a fortune.

Although Robin Tappen had written a letter of condolence to my mother, he was not a believer in paying special attention to individual boys in case it smacked of favouritism (spin-bowlers being the only exception to this rule), and if he was disposed to show any unusual sympathy to a boy of thirteen who had recently lost a father, it was an impulse he suppressed with admirable self-discipline. (In retrospect I can see that he was just a blivet – two pounds of shit in a one-pound bag – but in those days I still harboured a secret hope that adults often knew best.)

And so it was business as usual, except that Mrs Pike sent me back to Eton with a little bag of new Cash's name-tapes to be sewn into my underwear, so that the world and the laundry would know I was now Richard London. I was the only Duke in the school at that time, and I suppose I did stick out a bit, athough there was an African Prince, an Earl, five Lords, a brace of fatherless Baronets with beaky noses, and a generous sprinkling of 'Misters'. The last were not what they seemed, for in the titular system of the school you were designated 'Mr' if you were in real life, as it were, 'The Hon.'. Boys who had no other title – and I hasten to stress that they were slightly in the majority – were merely referred to by their surname, plus the usual taxonomy from Max. to Min. (like some outdoor thermometer) for brothers, and a distinguishing initial for those who shared a common surname but were cousins, or perhaps victims of coincidence. Well, at least people tended to remember my name.

I got teased, of course, and was suspected even more than before of affecting airs and graces. There was an especially pernicious, and mentally most slow, New Zealander in the block above me in RET, a ginger-haired, foul-mannered scroyle of a boy named Paul Sutton, the grobian offspring of an airline pilot and a befreckled woman who used to teeter around the Boys' Side with a mentholated cigarette in her claw whenever she came to visit her little thug of a son, the best bits of whom ran down her leg during the throes of parturition. Sutton's nickname was 'Chopper', and his room, which for a year was next to mine, smelled of cheese (it was probably smegma). He wore the face of his watch on the underside of his fat wrist, its expandable metallic strap permanently stretched so that the flesh peeped through the links. There was reddish, bristly hair in his ears. He knew I had spotted him as an alien from the planet Mucus, but he was older and heavier than me, and he knew how to throw his weight around.

It was Sutton who began the vogue for the cowboy walk. When he saw me in the passage he would whoop, 'Watch out, everyone, here comes the Duke,' and then lumber towards me with an exaggerated bow-legged gait like John Wayne. It was harmless enough stuff in a way, but the relentless tone of mockery became irksome, especially since I had no real antidote or counterblast, and it encouraged the Chopper's cohorts to push me around physically whenever they felt like it, and stage impromptu saloon-bar brawls in my room, circling me with their arms at the ready as if about to draw, piling in with kidney-chops or crotch-holds, emptying cereal down my trousers ('Have some true grit, Duke'), throwing my books out of the window into the yard ('Fucking *sap*'). This lasted for just over a year, and then I was saved by the fact that Sutton failed so many of his O Levels that he was removed to a crammer in London, whence he was rumoured to have graduated with no further qualifications and to have gone into the mobile discotheque business.

When it came to bullying, it all depended on how alert your Housemaster was to the adolescent electricity humming away through the four floors on the far side of his building – and in this respect I think the estimable Dr Tappen had long ago damaged his voltmeter, probably dropping it while pleasuring himself inside the spine of the revised edition of a Liddell and Scott Greek Dictionary. Quite a deal of thuggery took place beneath the roof of Mussiter's and I do not think he was alive to it – at least, not until they almost killed Stephen Kahn. Gallaher may have had his face plastered in shit and Gillette foam because of his pre-Jurassic acne contours, Meakin (or 'Merkin', as his tormentors liked to call him) may have had his pubes shaved forcibly with Gifford Major's cut-throat while under suspicion of stealing, and Suarez (who had 'peached' on Dixon Smith for having an SMP Answers book and got him rusticated) may have been forced to consume a bar of coaltar soap in front of the assembled Library ('Coaltar to match your wog face, Suarez'), but at least none of them had the misfortune to be Jewish.

Innocent as I was – though before long I was rapidly becoming less so – I had not the faintest notion until I became an Etonian that some Englishmen considered Jews to belong to a race apart, still less that many Jews thought so, for other reasons. I entertained only the vaguest, comic-book impressions of World War Two: I had never heard of the Holocaust, and to me the Jews were a people contained within the pages of the Bible, like the Hittites or the Moabites. But it was not long before I became aware of a groundswell of anti-Semitism amongst a small but virulent number of boys – that's all it takes, a little rennet to make a junket. I didn't know what they were talking about, when I first heard myself called a Yid: I assumed it was yet another example of antique jargon that I hadn't yet deciphered – which, in a way, it was. I can remember the occasion quite exactly. Kit and I were messing at tea one day about a fortnight into our first Half, and a normally rather affable boy in C, called Riley, stuck his head round the door and said he had forgotten to buy anything to eat, and could I provide him with a tin of soup, or some eggs. He marched in, and opened my cupboard (which was nearly always full of food, because my mother had the Harrods van deliver provisions to me once a fortnight, to my embarrassment) and selected a can of spaghetti. I told him he could not have it. He asked me if I was a bloody Yid. Kit had to explain that this was a word that meant you were careful of your possessions. It also might be taken to imply you had a largish nose, or liked to keep to yourself, or your parents drove a Jag and did not live in the West End of London, or that you had refused any basic request for assistance from a senior boy. It was, in fact, a general term of opprobrium, an instance of satanic shorthand, that certainly enjoyed a wide currency in our House before the arrival of Stephen Kahn.

It must have been at the beginning of my second year when he joined the leaky vessel that sailed under the colours of RET. Kahn was already sixteen, and had been in High School in New York before his father had been transferred to a banking post in London, and the school authorities had found a place for him at short notice. He was unlucky, as it turned out. He was small, and dark, and a mathematician. On the playing-fields he was even less accomplished than me, but at least he had some excuse – you don't hear much about the Field Game in Manhattan (well, you didn't in those days), and he would not have been anyone's choice for baseball, let alone cricket. Stephen Kahn just wanted to be left to his own devices, to continue work on his calculus, and to be able to sleep at night in a bed on which the House Side had not taken it in turns to piss, after a session of drinking beer in 'Tap'. But he seemed to them like a God-given victim, a puny version of the ram caught in the thicket. It may have started with teasing about his accent ('What is it with this accent thing? Where I come from, everybody speaks like this. Give me a break'), but Kahn had already become a marked man: he did not attend Chapel, he did not eat sausages, he was considered fucking antisocial, even for a Yid. He was rude to the Dame (actually, he was slightly deaf, even to her parade-ground delivery), he was subversive (he decided not to join the Corps, very wisely), he was dirty in his personal habits (yes, we're getting there now), and there were three members of Debate who just did not like the way he looked, and that was enough for them.

Do I blame Robin Tappen for failing to prevent what occurred? Yes, I think I do. It was perfectly clear, even to us younger boys, that Kahn was being ostracized by the others in his year, and a little pre-emptive diplomacy would possibly have deflected some of the pressure. He could have pointed out, for instance, that Stephen had come third in the International Mathematics Olympiad the previous year, and was therefore an intellectual asset for our House to rival any of the tugs in College. He could have advised Foster, then House Captain, and a powerful member of Pop, that Stephen's father was one of the Governing Board of Yale, and thus of more than passing interest to our own Head Master in terms of educational politics. And it might just have crossed his mind, had it not been a precinct almost permanently wired off by more urgent concerns such as the use of the optative in Aeschylus, or the exact disposition of forces during the Jugurthine War, that to have had placed in his charge a small Jewish genius from abroad was an event of such Etonian rarity that it required the breaking out of the contents of the Kid Glove Cupboard (standard issue, surely?). But, it seems, the phenomenon of Stephen Kahn's brief residency did not make that vital little walk into the private intellectual territory of the man known as Tappen, with the following result.

There were three of them, as I said, and they took Stephen Kahn to the bath on the second floor, towards the end of his first Half. At least, this is what I heard about it the next day. They bunged a football sock in his mouth, ran the hot tap for five minutes, and then flung him in. The executioners promptly legged it, but his cries awoke smaller boys in the vicinity, and he was pulled out just in time. His arms and legs had been pinioned with House Colour scarves of knitted wool, knotted tight, tied close and with a real intent to restrain. Apparently, his burns were disgusting; the boys who rescued him spoke of the smell. Stephen Kahn was taken at once to the College Sanatorium, and then to a clinic in London. We never saw him again.

The three boys were expelled – McKay, Selby and Campbell – but the damage it did to the reputation of RET was almost immeasurable. This was, after all, 1970, and the Sixties just beginning to click in. The Summer of Love might have gone the way of all liquids, but its aftermath was just coming up over the horizon in its tie-dyed colours. There was a new kind of dawn, even in the public schools. We had the gear and the kit, although it was contrary to all regulations.

It was quite a revelation when I realized that my voice was breaking, and that I was entering some new zone: there was to be a chemical frenzy in my life, and some heavy emotional weather. In fact, the next couple of years were going to prove a ghastly blur.

When he was ten, Cosmo was deemed by the staff at Stockhill House to be suffering from some kind of learning disability, and it was recommended that my mother engage a tutor to help him continue with his studies during the holidays. My brother was in fact not backward in anything but a social sense; he was withdrawn, and caught up in a world of his own. He was perhaps not very talkative, and seemed to have made few friends, but I think he was shy rather than slow, and was possessed of a mind that refused to assimilate information that did not interest him. He was certainly capable of intense concentration when something attracted him – he was beginning to build up a sizeable philatelic collection, and had also developed a fondness for angling which was just about his only outdoor interst, a solitary vice that involved him sitting for hours on end on the bank of our lake watching the red tip of a quill bob around in search of a dull carp or diminutive roach.

The Pembridge Tutorial Agency finally supplied my mother with a man who came to live at Spellbrook for the first three weeks of every holidays. His name was Mr Meech, and from the start I did not like him. He was squat and balding and had short, squarish fingers and the habit of extending his left hand while discoursing self-importantly on some topic and inspecting his fingernails with a look of perverse admiration. His hobby was the cultivation of cactus, and he announced that his great ambition when he retired (he was fifty-six when he arrived at Spellbrook) was to visit Mexico and observe the mescal plants in their native habitat. With my mother's permission, he arranged that Buxton should accommodate in his greenhouses some of the more precious specimens he brought down from London on the back seat of his Triumph, and he began to raise others from seed acquired by mail order from a firm in Cincinnati. This and rounds of golf occupied his afternoons off, when he was not required to supervise Cosmo in the little school-room that had been set up in my grandfather's old apartment, now made over to construe and the crop cycles of the coffee bean.

When my voice broke and my body began to be tugged around by strange new forces it was 1970, and although chronologically the Sixties were at an end, their spirit was raging to its height. This was an unfortunate coincidence, because as I became progressively disorientated in my oozing and leaking new body, with testosterone causing volcanic upheavals on my epidermis, and nocturnal emissions that filled my umbilical crater like a little cup of glue, there was a whiff of youthful rebellion in the air, even in a place like Eton, and to a sebaceously challenged adolescent it seemed for a couple of years as if this might be The Real Thing. Modelling myself on Kit, who lived in Chelsea and had a brother of twenty who had been to Marrakech and Goa and seen all types of light, I began to complete the process already begun by the monsoons of puberty, and set about transforming my appearance so that none should fear for one moment that I was hidebound by the traditions of society. I'm afraid the results were ludicrous and unprepossessing in the holidays, and frustratingly mild during the Half, because almost everything you needed to make you resemble an American roadie was in contravention of the school rules on dress and hair.

For a start, you were forbidden to wear anything made of denim, which really meant your efforts were dead in the water; your hair was not to cover your ears, or touch your collar, so (short of wearing a wig from the Kensington Market) you could never get it long enough to look properly dishevelled, even by the end of the summer holiday. I adopted a centre parting, let the hair go lank and unwashed (this set off the sauce pizzaiola face a treat), affected a bracelet of elephant's tail-hair, wore a fake Iron Cross on a chain beneath my shirt, developed a hunched posture, refused to meet the eye of most adults during conversation, scuffed my shoes, rubbed my accent very slightly with Cockney, tried to look as if I was eating large quantities of drugs (I had plenty of role models from the photographs in the *NME*), spent my money on flared moleskin loons and tie-dyed grandfather T-shirts, and hung an American flag on my wall next to the poster of Hendrix, the plastic skull, the German helmet bought from Fred Owen's emporium on the High Street, and my pinned copy of the School Timetable.

When my mother saw my room that second year, and put a hand to her clavicle, gasping, 'But, Rich, it's so *ugly*,' I could not have been more delighted.

By the time I was fourteen I was an enthusiastic masturbator (still am, in fact), and like most of my confrères I went around in a state of almost permanent sexual tension, so packed with cocktails from the gonads that we felt on the brink of disaster – like a desperate smuggler detained in transit with a heroin-stuffed condom in his gut. A couple of times a day I would take Rosy Palm and her five daughters on a trip to the eyelid movies, and every night without fail I would enjoy a hand-raised pork-pie before sliding sideways into sleep. In retrospect, I am surprised there wasn't a better organized underground circulation of beaver mags and one-handed literature, but it was quite difficult to obtain (though easy to come·by, of course: by the time you got hold of the image of one of these sirens she would be looking as crumpled and tired as some poor tribal girl from a Foreign Legion bordello).

The visual sources of stimulation were likewise very thin on the ground in our rarefied community, and the very sighting of a female human under, say, the age of fifty was in itself a potential mnemonic trophy. We became as keen-eyed as twitchers who have heard the rumour that a Codfish Island fernbird is flitting somewhere through the Fens. Those who starred in my early movies included the wives of three Housemasters, the teenage daughter of the pottery tutor, two housekeepers from the bachelor beaks' colonies, one of the secretaries who worked in School Office and whom I had cast up when by chance I spotted her wearing hot-pants in Windsor High Street one afternoon, with Kit as my witness, and the dark-haired lab assistant from the Science Schools, who bicycled to work down Keate's Lane each morning, and sometimes did so in zippered black boots, and the occasional local schoolgirl from Dorney or Eton Wick who came into the House to serve supper at weekends, causing hungry stares. But best of all was Prue, the Assistant Librarian, who was blonde and fat-breasted, and whose nylon thighs swished through the straining silence as she shepherded her books around the stacks – if you were strategically placed, you could inhale the thin slipstream of her perfume as she passed. Somehow or other you had to top up your masturbatory master-battery to keep you juiced during the weekdays, but Sundays usually brought a transfusion as mothers and sisters appeared in the streets (Chapel was even better, as it gave you much longer to fix your mental film) and temporarily unlocked the doors of the universe as you arced into the new footage, cleaving clenched Kleenex to marinated glans.

There was a great deal of talk about women, especially from the most senior men, many of whom had real experience, and who would sometimes invite their girlfriends down to the school, to show them off. There were muttered myths about the opportunities to 'do it', if only one had free access to the outside world – there was an actress in Fulham, a wine bar in Chelsea where older women were known to congregate for the express purpose of relieving teenaged boys of their virginity, somebody's cousin from St Mary's, Ascot was good for a try during the exeat – these lies were perhaps necessary fictions, but, on the slightest attempt to prove them, their tissue collapsed like the glued lapels of some Take Six suit in the rain.

Despite swiving them vigorously in my imagination, I was awkward and halting with girls in Real Life, and I don't suppose my appearance at that stage was much of an advantage. In fact, having no sister or female cousin, it was pretty hard to meet girls even in the holidays unless you hung around London a lot, like Kit did. I went to the odd local party – fumbling barbecues with cider-cup cut furtively with vodka, loud rock music in family cellars – but in the circles through which I was making my desultory, pustular progress at the age of fifteen, the most you could dream of would be to get your hand on the blouse of some demi-vierge from a convent school, and there was never much chance (or was that *danger*?) of going the whole hog. A bit of tongue sushi, and you felt you had acquitted yourself with great distinction, and this gave you plenty of freedom for gross exaggeration when retailing your triumph to your male friends.

I practically vomited with excitement and apprehension the night I got Veronica Clutton-Brown alone on her parents' sofa in Tite Street, and ran my right hand up her skirt before she crossed her legs and twisted away. ('Was it damp?' Kit had demanded, and I lied and said, 'God, yeah,' like I was describing my experiences in Vietnam.) But there would have been no chance there anyway, as I discovered years later, because it was part of the Clutton-Brown family tradition that all daughters were deflowered on their sixteenth birthdays by their own fathers, and Veronica was still only fifteen, so it was understandable that she was saving herself.

There were always the other boys, anyway. It is often

suggested that at such single-sex residential public schools sodomy is an inescapable part of the curriculum, but so far as I remember there were never any cases of anal buggery – most of the time it was just a question of mutual manufriction or intercrural frottage. As a little Etonian you might become the love object of a senior boy's crush, and he might make a pass at you or try to 'queer you up' in your room, but the rules to this courtship game were well defined, and physical coercion was something I heard of on only one occasion. If you were caught 'having it off' with another boy, there would be big trouble for both of you, so you had really to desire one another to take the risk. There were rumours surrounding certain boys being promiscuous 'tarts', but on the whole these were more likely to be pretty and unobtainable flirts who became the subject of frustrated fantasies.

Before my voice broke and my skin erupted I received the odd nocturnal visit from those higher up in the House as the hopefuls did their rounds, but I turned down their proposals long before they got over-excited. I did spend part of one night in Kit's bed, however, and came happily over his stomach, but it was not an experiment we repeated, though I must say he had quite a good body. For a couple of years after that I had to stick to the movies, because my acne was so hideous that not even a blind boy would have laid a hand on such a papuliferous suitor, but by the time my last year hove into view that little nightmare was beginning to recede, and I did succeed in a couple of trysts with a boy called Oliver Philips who was a fetching South African blond. I groped optimistically through his pyjamas as he emerged from the ground-floor bathroom one evening, while I was waiting my turn to go in – we were soon both behind the door, which was the only one that had a lock, and I remember he surprised me by being very skilful for a fourteen-year-old whose skin was still downy and soft behind the jawbones, oh God, yes, very nimble with his fingers, and whispering 'Keep quiet, keep quiet,' (as clearly now as if it were only yesterday).

There were stories about certain members of the staff, inevitably, but while I suspect some of them may have enjoyed affairs together, I very much doubt they got anywhere physically with any of the pupils. They were just uranist window-shoppers, with the odd pansy thrown in, but no one smelled remotely dangerous, least of all Johnny Lyle, the beak most famous for being queer. Known among the boys as 'Vile Lyle', or, variously, 'Rubber John', he was an Old Etonian himself and had returned to teach and stayed for thirty years. He was reputed to have inherited a lot of money from a queer uncle (how speculation built up, fragment by fragment, like a cairn over his whole reputation) and to possess an estate in Somerset where he kept a boyfriend. There were jokes about Winston his dalmatian, to whom Lyle was said to be unnaturally devoted, and he was generally held to be the incarnation of homosexual lechery, inclined to invite boys to his rooms for extra trigonometry, beaming sideways at known tarts in the street between divisions, and making provocative remarks. He was certainly fond of extravagant vocabulary and simpering innuendo. I recall him looking up from the sums he was scribbling in felt pen on the overhead projector, and catching me pulling faces and winking across the room at a colleger called Townsend. 'London,' he drawled, 'if you do not desist from nictication during my divisions you will excite the opprobrium of the Head Master, and, since persistent winking is bad for you, it is conceivable you may go blind. I now see why your grasp of calculus is positively gelogenic, since you prefer to look at the subject with only one eye at any given time. If you consider that, because you are a mere Duke, you can afford, unlike the formicating *hoi polloi*, to ignore that which fails to entertain you, then it confirms my belief that shortly we will be living under a kakistocracy, a position which I personally would find intensely uncomfortable.' He played up to his image, and he could put the verbals on you all right, but I don't think Rubber John ever tried to get inside a boy's Y-fronts: he was just one of those necessary demons that help any community to focus its particular anxieties.

It must have been almost exactly half-way through my time at Eton that I was briefly convinced I had contracted cancer of the bowel from eating too much strawberry yoghurt. Although the food at RET was considerably better than what we had been offered at the Hill, your diet still needed supplementing with regular visits to one of the 'sock' shops where you could buy plates of chips, hot pies, cake, ice-cream and chocolate, or splash out on a Brown Cow, egg on a raft, or Strawberry Mess. This was real food that gave you an alimentary fix, and not the corned beef pudding and tinned-pear crumble doled out by Mrs Ball, our smirking and jaundiced House cook (yet every night from the same stinking pandaemonium of a kitchen she would issue with a trolley for the Private Side that bore wonders such as rack of lamb and lemon syllabub). One summer afternoon when the weather had fortunately washed away the need to play cricket, I went to sock in Jack's, the shop near the Fives Courts, and they had on sale a new type of lolly made of frozen yoghurt that I found so delicious I consumed five of them in succession, along with a sausage roll and a pint of raspberry fizz. The next day I began to pass blood copiously from my backside and decided with the instant clarity that demented teenagers often possess that I was afflicted with a fatal growth brought on overnight by my indulgence. There in the white-washed gloom of the communal bog, peering into the bowl where it looked as if an axe-murderer had been practising on a couple of baby armadillos, I realized I was going to die.

The obvious thing to have done would have been to explain my symptoms to Miss Herrick, but I was too embarrassed; however, I did think I should seek a second opinion, so I spent all afternoon in the medical section of the School Library (usually visited only by those in diligent search of details about sexual perversity) and was somewhat relieved to discover it was more likely that I was a precocious sufferer from incipient haemorrhoids. (St Fiacre be blessed; it was a tube of Anusol I needed, not surgery.) Ludicrous as my adolescent panic seems now, that moment was real when a secret fear surfaced and made me feel alone, just a brick's depth away from the boy in the adjacent cubicle who was quite content with the state of his intestinal tract, and was contemplating the prospect of a game of tennis or a tin of Coke, and I was staring into a worn Shank's bowl that seemed, from the livid splash and slash of my own blood, to be presaging my death as surely as the constellar swirls and configurations of tea-leaves in the curve of a bogus gypsy woman's cup, at the end of some seaside pier.

It was on an afternoon during August of that year, when he was eleven, that I passed the door of my brother's bedroom and heard him crying. He was lying on the bed with his face to the wall, naked except for his shirt. The eiderdown was thrown back, and his top-sheet was feathered with blood.

I went over to him, but he had clamped his arms over his head, biceps pressing into his ears, and he did not reply to any of my questions. I ran down to the basement to fetch Flynn.

By the time the story was coaxed from Cosmo, Mr Meech had long since gone. My mother was treated for shock, but in truth I don't think the reality of the assault ever properly impressed itself upon her. She would clasp Cosmo and pat him with her thin hands, beating him lightly on the back as if to drive something malevolent from his body. She would hum rhythmically over his head, her eyes tightly closed. I have no idea what she was seeing with those rapid eye movements in the bright, red theatre behind her lids, for she never once spoke directly to me of the event, except to say (with what always sounded like a curtain-line), 'Oh, Rich, Rich – you must look after your precious little brother.'

The police hunted for Mr Meech, of course, but the trail was cold. Nanny Mottram came out of retirement to take Cosmo to Bembridge for three weeks' recuperation (although, quite understandably, he never did quite recover), and I returned to school. Perhaps my father had been right, and I had become a nasty, selfish, ungrateful person, because despite what my brother was suffering my main concern was any possible consequences to myself if news of the incident reached the ears of other boys in the House. Terse and sullen, braced against the first sniggers or jibes, I waited for something to circulate on the pernicious grapevine. But there was nothing, nor was there any allusion to the event from RET himself (someone in the family must have thought to tell him, surely – but now I realize that my mother was the only person who could have done so, and that must have proved beyond her). And so it became the first family secret to be locked away from others, or so I imagined.

Having spent two years being a conspicuous lout, I began a process of reformation that September as I embarked on my A Level programme. Despite having cultivated an image of being a Philistine and a slubberdegullion, I had maintained good progress with the academic work, and was to specialize in English, History and Geography (the latter not considered by the soi-disant intellectuals in the school to be a proper subject). My first really good stroke of fortune was that David Elliott – DSLE – had agreed to act as my Modern Tutor and supervise my work. A young, nervy Oxford graduate with round, steel-rimmed spectacles and a long thin nose, he had an unpredictable temper and exacting standards, and was already something of a cult for his controversial productions of *Macbeth* and *Waiting for Godot*, and also because he had actually published two books of his own (a cultural history of Cairo, and a novel called *Women and Children*). He was one of those dissenters that the school sometimes managed to attract – vociferously critical of the outmoded syllabus, intolerant of the copious deadwood on the staff, and apparently without the traditional ambition to become a Housemaster. He was therefore regarded with suspicion by the likes of RET ('Are you really sure Mr Elliott is your *style* of tutor, in the long run?'), which was another major criterion in his favour. In fact, he became my lifeline.

David Elliott lived in a house up in Willowbrook with his wife Jennie and their baby daughter, Fran. Two evenings a week his pupils would go up to his home for an hour of 'Private Business', during which he would conduct some extra-curricular education. Apart from the fact that he introduced us to the work of Bellow and Larkin (much too modern to feature on any mainstream course), gave slide-shows and talks about Italian painting, organized readings of contemporary plays, and was prepared to discuss rock music, these visits were our only opportunity to spend a little time in what felt like a real home. Tense and chain-smoking he may have been, curled up in his swivel chair, cat on lap, legs tucked under him, but David Elliott's evening sessions were a delicious antidote to the formality that seemed to pervade the rest of the community. He had that gift of making things sound as if they really mattered, as if they were related to the world outside, and this was a new experience for me. He was intellectually rigorous, and he took words seriously; sloppy, nihilistic replies of the type I had become accustomed to making were subjected to vehement challenging – 'What do you *mean*, you don't see the point of this scene? Do you think Pinter sat down and made a list of *points* he wanted to include during the course of the next few pages? I'm asking you, Richard, is that the way you think it works, writers trying to make a *point*?' Well, he could be quite scary and personal at times, once becoming so exasperated that he dismissed all five of us and went around his study banging his palm down on to piles of books and calling us all upper-class morons, but at least this was inspirational behaviour. I confess he became my hero.

His wife Jennie taught the flute in the Music Schools, and had a penchant for cheesecloth shirts and sandals. She was small, with a button nose and dark hair worn in a crop. Very often she would ask us into the kitchen for something to eat before we left, and chat with us about our families – never Eton business – while she produced a quiche or a fruit salad. It was Jennie Elliott who gave me my first glass of wine, quite against the rules, just before Christmas. If she saw you in the High Street, she would stop and talk, rather than nod and trundle on by with her buggy. At that time in my life she was the only woman who did not make me feel like a freak when I had a conversation with her, and for that feat of empathy, apart from everything else, I have remained grateful.

Although it was virtually a requirement of all beaks that they should contribute something to the athletic aspect of school life, DSLE seemed to get away with little more than cycling up the tow-path occasionally while coaching a House Bumping Four through a megaphone. I certainly never saw him with a pair of boots on, and Wimbledon didn't interest him. But he was instrumental in teasing me out of the sulk into which I had sunk on the subject of all games, by pointing out that I had just become defeatist. It was his suggestion that I try to find some sporting activity that enjoyed a minority following, and concentrate exclusively on that, in an attempt to disprove my now ingrained belief that I would never be good at anything apart from work. I thus took up rifle-shooting (a sport which was normally dominated by members of the Corps who were keen to pursue a military career when they left) and discovered that, with regular practice in the range above the Gym, I was quite good at it. I never quite mastered Charlie Sanga's trick of stopping the heart, but he did help me during the holidays with lessons using his roe-deer rifle, and his encouragement gave me confidence – which was what my life had been lacking for several years, but it now looked as if things were going to change for the better.

I remember my penultimate Fourth of June with particular clarity because it was the first time my mother and I were invited to Dr Tappen's drinks party for senior boys and their families. My mother was wearing one of her hats, an elaborate floral construction that looked more edible than elegant to me, though of course my disapproval had less to do with aesthetics and more to do with the fact that *no one* else's mother wore hats with such Ascot dimensions. But RET seemed delighted at having an even partially animated Duchess attend his 'little gathering', and she and Gilbey were evidently enjoying the excruciatingly stilted occasion. I introduced her to David Elliott, with whom she discussed theatrical history ('Such an interesting young man, Rich. And he seems to have your best interests at heart, though I'm not surprised, no, not surprised at all'). Miss Herrick ('Rather a strange woman, Rich, but sad, too, don't you feel?') regaled her with a comprehensive description of the plans for the new Central Feeding Complex. Bobby MacDougall's parents had the benefit of Her Grace's memories of Edinburgh, Kit's Dad got an unexpected kiss because she mistook him for someone else, and Luis (who had donned a white jacket especially borrowed for the day, and was wandering far from his accustomed boot-hole, staring seriously at his trayful of glasses) was a little taken aback when the Duchess offered to shake him by the hand ('He's that charming man who helps you with the fires, isn't he?') and he had to pass his tray to the Dame, wipe his palm on his trousers, and then perform a bow that would not have disgraced one of Chandupura's punkah-wallahs.

Later, Flynn would drive us up to Agar's in the Bentley (we had become quite posh in the automobile department since my mother gave up driving herself around, on doctor's orders), and a full picnic would be laid out, with fluted goblets for her champagne ('Are you allowed some, Rich, I never can remember?'), and periodically she would apply a pair of mother-of-pearl opera glasses to her eyes, and scan the cricketers, and enquire when it would be my turn to play ('Possibly next year, Mother'), and I would steal glances at my watch and wonder if she would make it through the Procession of Boats before succumbing to a little nap lasting two hours.

But the great event of that Fourth was when Dr Tappen called for silence during his party on the lawn, and amazed our world by announcing that he was engaged to be married, that he had hoped to be able to introduce us to his fiancée that day, but she had been detained at the hospital, and that the nuptials were to occur during the summer holidays, because neither he nor his bride-to-be believed in standing on ceremony (a good one, that) and they wanted to be able to live together at Mussiter's as soon as possible (God save us all). Assuming this was not just some brain-fevered delusion on the part of our revered tutor, we imagined at best some stumpy nurse, or possibly a cleaning-lady from the hospital who might have become the unwitting target for Cupid's fickle bow, and we waited eagerly to behold the countenance of one who could distract Robin Tappen from his perusal of the latest history of the *Peisistratidae* and drag him down into the reeking *Cloaca Maxima* of matrimony.

She was tall, with short brown hair, a generous mouth (oh, how we thought about that) and what looked as if they must be very long legs. 'Legs that start last Tuesday, and go all the way up to Nirvana,' guessed MacDougall, who was a surrealist and a polymath, and smelled accordingly. She wasn't quite as good-looking as some of the new boys, but Janet Tappen's presence transformed our lives. She wore long skirts that swirled deliciously with paisley pleats, and little Peruvian jackets knitted in vivid colours, and leather boots, and big earrings of hooped gold, and strips of Indian silk around her head. She was older than her husband, but it looked the other way round; she was in fact forty-two, with a grown-up son by her first marriage. Robin and Janet never had any children from their union, and the joke was that he was still waiting for his sexual relations to arrive. We were just aflame with jealousy, that was all. To think that she was sleeping in the same building. But in the event we got to see very little of her, because she worked quite independently as a doctor in Slough.

Exactly what could have persuaded her into an alliance with her chosen doctor of letters, none of us could divine. As far as we could tell (and at that stage we did not appreciate that we knew next to nothing about such matters) they hardly saw each other as a couple. What was his secret? Was he so well hung that he had to climb up the trees to escape women, after all?

Could it be that his years of dry study had yielded the lost formula after which all men hanker? Did our eyes deceive us, or was there not an Amazon by the impossible name of Tappen walking down Common Lane to post a letter, or sitting with her papers on the lawn during a clement afternoon in the autumn, or (Jesus God, keep a tight one on it, you're in your pyjamas) knocking on your door once a month, and coming in to talk to you for five minutes, stretching her miraculous hands out towards the fire dying in your grate, and saying, throaty (watch the tall throat from which these words for you arise), 'I like this room. You've made it very comfortable. And it looks so much better since you removed that poster, and the silly skull.'

She became the new burning-point for dozens of pairs of eager eyes, imprinting her picture for our memory-banks, for later delectation. In fact, she must have become one of the most masturbated-over women in the entire country.

During my last year at Eton I suppose I learned more than I had during all the previous years of my expensive education put together. I had found in the study of English a subject that seemed really congenial, and in David Elliott there was at least one grown-up who was not obsessed by Etonian concerns – in fact, I would say that it was due to his particular mixture of academic precision and extra-curricular informality that I began, for the first time in my teenage life, to enjoy a little self-confidence. Having been elected to Library, I learned for the first time the taste of petty power, and found it worryingly agreeable; having decided to smarten up my act within the House, I realized the value of creating good impressions if you want to be left to your own devices; and I took the first quick steps down my road towards becoming a drinker. In the High Street was the old Christopher Tap Club, a kind of private pub for senior boys – an appropriate oxymoron, perhaps, for a private community calling itself a public school. You were allowed to consume two pints of beer per day in Tap, and Mrs Moulton, the agreeable landlady, kept a weather eye open for boys silly enough to think they could fool her with multiple rounds, or drinks fetched by those who were sticking to beverages (the idea of going there for a soft drink was as bizarre as nipping down to the Moti Mahal and having chicken and chips, but some boys regarded it as the social crucible of the school, and hung around there making contacts and trying to purchase popularity); I developed a taste for draught Guinness, but a couple of pints was never quite sufficient to give me a proper click, and I found Tap noisy and crowded. Kit and I had already decided that if you were going to get drunk you wanted to do it in select company, sitting down in comfort: late at night in the House Library was the obvious solution, but the problem was how to secure the necessary liquids.

We agreed that a bottle of vodka would be the best buy, since in those days we believed the *canard* about it not registering on your breath. There was no chance of us buying that in Windsor, because you were only allowed over the bridge in full School Dress (the tourists liked this spectacle, and you learned some new terms of abuse from young locals passing you in their cars) and no off-licence was going to risk serving you in that uniform. The only other possibility was Slough, which you had to get special permission to visit by bike, and where you could wear 'change', or civvies – a boy in Etonian uniform would have lasted about ten minutes in Slough before being tarred and feathered, or such was the received wisdom. Bobby MacDougall went to Slough every other Friday as part of the Social Services scheme run by the school – he helped paint old ladies' kitchens, did some gardening, that sort of stuff – and he reckoned he could fit two half-bottles into his saddle-bag. This would be more than enough for the four of us in Library, we solemnly guessed. Like an idiot, Bobby just stuffed the bottles in his pouch with only tissue-paper round them, and when he got back to the bike-shed he found one of them had smashed in transit; he grabbed the carrier-bag and began legging it up the staircase to the relative sanctuary of the Library but on the second landing he encountered Miss Herrick.

'What on earth have you got in that bag, MacDougall?' she

demanded (it was a plain plastic carrier, thank God). 'It sounds like broken glass. I do hope you're not running around my corridors with a bagful of dangerous litter.'

Bobby clutched the neck of the bag tightly, and explained that it was a bottle of paint-stripper from the Social Services, and he was just going to dispose of it. She let him go, and that night we split the remaining half between the four of us, and were well buzzed within half an hour, mixing it with Quosh tropical fruit cordial and lemonade. But Bobby said it was more than his life was worth to risk it again, and we'd have to come up with some other source of supply.

It was Kit Hamilton who suggested approaching Consuelo, the Spanish maid recently recruited by Mrs Ball to stand in for Luis's wife, who was expecting their first baby. Consuelo was a widow from Barcelona, and she lived in the downstairs annexe. She had green eyes, a faint moustache, and long, straight hair; she always dressed in black, although her disposition was far from gloomy, and there was a gleam of gold from her mouth when she laughed. I doubt she was much more than thirty-five, but her hands were those of an older woman, reddened from years of manual work.

Kit asked her to bring a bottle of vodka back from Windsor when next she had an afternoon off; she agreed, he gave her our money, and arranged to collect the contraband from her after RET had done his evening rounds. And so the following Saturday night we sent Kit down (with a box of chocolates as a thank-you present, to cement the partnership) while the rest of us waited eagerly in the Library, with our Quosh and tins of mixers.

After half an hour, Peter Moss said, 'Something's wrong.' He was House Captain, and had the most to lose. 'He's been caught. Must have been. It would be better if we got out of here. Kit won't peach. Let's get the fuck out.' Bobby agreed: he'd had enough scares trying to get this vodka scam off the ground already, and it was tough shit if Kit was the one to land on the carpet. The two of them went to bed. I wondered if I should go and look for him, or see if he had taken refuge in his room – it was now after ten-thirty and there seemed little sense in holding the fort. Then the door swung open, and there was Kit with the bottle in his hand.

'Kit, thank Christ. It worked OK?'

He smiled. 'Yes. It worked.' He put the bottle in the sock-cupboard, and obscured it behind a cereal packet.

'Where the fuck have you been? The others thought . . . '

'I did it. It finally happened.'

'What is all this – what's wrong?'

'Consuelo. I had Consuelo. I just poked her, in her room.'

I could hardly believe it as he told me how she'd been so pleased with her present, she'd offered him a glass of wine, he'd begun to flirt a bit and pay her compliments, and then, sensing there was little to lose, he'd asked if he could kiss her goodnight, and minutes later he had scored between the posts.

'What was she like?'

'Fantastic. It was all over in minutes.'

'Christ.'

'You should have a go yourself.'

'Oh, my God.'

'Next week, you should fix it up. You're randy, aren't you? It's a push-over. Incredible, right here under our noses. Jesus, I'm tired.'

I was pretty nervous about the whole idea, but Kit assured me it was worth a try. He was certainly keen for more, but he thought he'd better cool it before going for a replay. We would take it in turns, the four of us, and let on to no one else; take a nice little present, and maybe save money by reducing our order to a half-bottle, since alcohol was no longer the chief purpose of the operation. Oh yes, within a couple of days Kit had got it all planned.

'And you must have a johnny,' he instructed me, 'she wouldn't let me in without. I always keep one in my wallet. You'll have to get some, too.'

'Since when have you been buying johnnies? Where did you get them, anyway?'

'Don't be a cretin, Rich – you go to Bell's in the High

Street. Just ask for Durex. You can't poke a woman without a rubber.'

'But isn't she a Catholic? I mean, she's Spanish – surely they don't . . . '

'You need a johnny. Do you want me to come with you?'

So Kit took me to Mr Bell's chemist shop (not the College Pharmacy, of course, where you traded in chits for Germolene and Euthymol) and when the place was empty of other customers, we asked for the precious condoms, and he placed a packet wearily on the glass counter. With the earnestness of experts posing a trenchant question about the provenance of a piece of antique porcelain, we asked him, were they lubricated? In a whisper, as if acknowledging that this was a matter of utmost matrimonial importance to us, he said, 'Gentlemen, they are *all* lubricated. Every single one. I assure you. If you discover anything less than satisfactory about their quality, you have only to return them to me.' I paid, and we fled. Later, Kit admitted that he had actually been given his rubber by his older brother, and, like me, had never been into Bell's before in his life.

At eight-thirty the following Saturday evening I was launched from the Library with a variety of lewd hand-signals, and made my way down to the staff annexe, with a little bottle of 'April Shower' eau de toilette gift-wrapped in my pocket. I had signed out on the pretext of attending a shooting practice in the Gym, and I would not be missed for an hour. This was only going to take minutes, I reminded myself, as I tapped on the widow's door.

The room was warm, and smelled of citrus – there was a big bowl of lemons on the dresser, like a still-life. Consuelo put a finger to her lips, and closed the door. She was wearing a black blouse, but I could see the shoulder-straps of her black bra beneath it. I gave her the perfume, and she sat on her bed and opened it, while I stood like some traffic warden waiting for the regulation minutes to elapse before slapping a ticket on a vehicle, hands behind my back, a steaming great erection threatening the architecture of my grey flannel trousers. Consuelo dabbed some of the scent on to the inside of her left wrist, and offered it to me; I held her finger-tips, and her elbow, and sniffed. 'Very nice,' I said, 'I hope you like it.'

'Very kind, you thank them,' said Consuelo. 'You like a drink?'

I sat on her bed with a tumbler of wine, and thought: if I don't get out of here, I'm going to die. I hunched over my glass, staring at her rug. Watermills began to churn within my ears. My vision swam a little yellow, from the lemons.

'Last week, your friend Kit come – he tell you stories about me, yes?'

And then I realized: he'd set me up, the bastard. He never did the deed. I'd get him for that, but now all I had to do was knock back the wine, take the vodka, and regain my safety.

'Kit a sweetie. Real gentle. He stay with me for a time, and kiss me the goodnight. When you finish drink, you like to kiss, also, is alright. You nice man, also, London.'

Her mouth tasted peppery, and I could feel the little hairs on her upper lip against mine, as I drank in her tongue. She lay back on the bed, and I collapsed on to her skirt, one hand scrabbling at her knee; I pushed up with my elbows, and received a mouthful of black hair; I grasped her ear with my lips, felt her fingers work down beneath my belt. She pushed me off, and began to undress herself. I was staring at her, as I tugged at my own clothes, the thick hair beneath her arms, the great purplish nipples, the dimples around her hips – 'You make safe,' she ordered, dropping the shuck of her tights to the floor, and I dived for the foil oval in my trouser pocket, tore into it with the urgency of a man in the bush needing the antidote to some bite, and hurriedly rolled it on, forgetting to squeeze the teat, because this was the first time I had seen active service, this was the Big Moment, snap the rim down against the base of my burning offering, don't look where he's headed, get hold of one of those breasts (concentrate, now; you haven't sucked on one of these for ages, a slightly bitter taste, the odd bristly hair, there's one hand scraping at the nape of your neck, and a good deal of grunting from both parties), and then fur meets fur, with guidance on one hand and startled excitement on the other, and it's too much, it's better than the dreams, the movies, it's like being involved in a complex episode of geological history, I *am* the earth moving, we *are*, we are.

I shot the yoghurt pretty promptly, and went small within her. The rubber constricted my rapid flaccidity like a chrysalis. I lay on Consuelo's chest, and wondered what to say, as she hauled me uselessly into herself by grabbing my buttocks. I had turned into a hermit-crab: I was good for nothing. After a while, she relaxed her grip, and gave out the first of those sighs that I have since become horribly used to hearing – an exhalation of disappointment which follows the sexual exertion of so many Englishmen in bed. And I made things worse by saying 'Thank you' (always, always, a mistake), before dressing and leaving with the smuggled bottle, and getting back to the Library, shorn of my heterosexual virginity, but unsure about my feelings, to be met with the prurient enquiries of my comrades, and the need to tell them about something which had suddenly become too personal, too extraordinary, to explain.

They blamed me when Bobby tried his luck the next week, and Consuelo told him she wasn't going shopping any more. 'What the hell did you do to her, Rich?' they complained. Even Kit couldn't manage another visit, and I'm afraid the truth of the matter was that Consuelo guessed what we were trying to engineer and got bored with it. Yes, she became bored with the prospect of people like me, who afforded her no pleasure, and she pulled the plug on it, before Kit's careful system ever took effect. Luis and his wife had a baby girl in October 1973, and Consuelo left the House shortly thereafter, and married a building contractor from Earleigh. She was probably more busy in her private life than even the RET Library could have imagined.

When the male becomes mature, and has completed his moults, he gives up spinning, and wanders in search of a mate. The female is almost always more massive (in one species, she will be a thousand times his size) but he cannot rely on her eyesight when he enters her hammock; he advances with a lifeline attached, and plays her abode like an instrument, for fear he arouses quite a different appetite in the object of his amorous intentions.

The spider reproduces by artificial insemination. He weaves a small pad of special silk, and squirts his sperm on to it; he sucks this mass up with his pedipalps and approaches his mate with the intention of thrusting these into her abdomen. He needs to adopt a number of ingenious courtship postures before attempting this risky penetration, and even then he may only ensure his safety by jamming his mandibles between the female jaws.

Although there is rarely anything to compare with the ballet of butterflies or the crickets' serenading violin, some arachnids have developed mating rituals that do not just depend on stealth and speed. The wolf-spiders execute a semaphoric dance, and the striped male jumping-spider *Pisaura mirabilis* does indeed give a wonderful performance, since he brings his lady love the present of an insect trussed in silk – he relies on her hunger preoccupying her whilst she unwraps this gift, and he consummates his mission. Some males try to deceive their mate by first draining the insect of its nutrients, but this can prove a fatal mistake as she is capable of devouring him after (or even during) the act of procreation.

Pisaura is known as the nursery-web spider, because of the flocculent tent the mother constructs to protect her eggs as they hatch in the woodlands, but she is a fickle nurse, and frequently eats some of her children, too.

With one species of crab-spider, the male is inclined to adopt another approach altogether during his sexual forays. The diminutive *Xysticus cristatus* sidles up to the female in apparently submissive fashion, and drums against her abdomen with his feathery forearms; she takes this to be the caresses of foreplay, but he suddenly spurts a viscid web over her, enrobing her in a silken bridal veil from which she is briefly unable to move, and beneath which, upside-down, he crawls in his attempt at fertilization. This makes the spider the only other creature in the world that regularly resorts to rape.

Perhaps by some system of iatrohydraulics my cerebellum had been cleansed of accumulated jism when I lost my virginity, allowing me to see the world in technicolour – whatever the reason, I managed a final adolescent moult before it was too late, and began to make something of the opportunities the school offered, during my final three Halves. A little success was coming my way, and instead of souring it, I decided to enjoy any recognition which was offered. I was awarded my Shooting Eight, and finally won the right to wear a coloured blazer during that summer. I accumulated just enough Distinctions to be promoted to the Sixth Form Select (the academic elite of senior boys, most of them scholars); I continued to benefit from David Elliott's tutorials, and it looked as if – depending on my results at A Level – I would be staying on to sit the Oxford Entrance exams for a place to read English. Kit got his Field, and in the spring he was elected to Pop; he assured me that he would try to promote my candidacy at each election, but I had left it too late to become really prominent within the school, and had few other friends who were members. The exams came and went (I almost burst my brain with cramming for the History papers, and seriously contemplated throwing myself from my window on to Dr Tappen's driveway, the night before the S-Level) and then it was the last Sunday of the Summer Half, and I just made it to the hallowed Short List, but the band of clothes-rippers never visited Mussiter's that day, and Kit (my best hope as an advocate) was leaving the school the following week. I had not anticipated my degree of disappointment.

Here then, twenty-five years later, is the list of those vile and contemptible boys who disbarred me from high office, for perfectly justifiable reasons, and prevented me from the public pleasure of sporting a leopardskin waistcoat (present occupations in brackets): Millard (attorney), Walker (military), Pugh (farmer), de Vere (insolvent publisher), Ryland (estate agent), Lee (military), Parry-Smith (whereabouts unknown), Houghton Major (financier, Japan), Cox (Special Forces), Strickland (politico), Greene (journalist), Brookenden (expat. viniculturist, California), Herne (recording industry), Berry (sculptor, Norway), Bowen (civil servant), Briggs-Bayley (unemployed), and Hamilton (deceased). Bloody conspirators, the lot of them (actually, some of them really were, and at least two now hold senior office in the Republic – Jamie Bowen is Superintendent of Public Works and Robert Strickland is of course Northern Minister in charge of a province where unemployment is running at 79 per cent). No, of course I've never forgiven them, the bastards.

At the end of the summer, RET summoned me to his study, and delivered the following, charismatic pronouncement: 'Ah, Richard, there you are. I am able to delay no longer in declaring who is to be my next Captain of House, and so I can tell you that, against my better judgement in some regards, I have decided to appoint you, always assuming that you consider yourself capable of doing the job and devoting sufficient time to its multiple demands. You may interrupt me, if you wish. I confess I have had reservations about certain of your attitudes toward this House in the past, especially when I felt you were resistant to the entire principle of team spirit – without which, as you will appreciate, our task here would be rendered practically impossible. But you have attained some seniority within the school this year, and I believe that when you leave here you are going to require some previous experience of leadership as you take your place in society and begin to face the responsibilities which will attach to your estate and standing, and so it seems to me it would be quite wrong if I were to pass you over at this juncture. Now, what have you got to say?'

'Thank you, sir. I will try to do my very best for you and the whole House,' I replied, already relishing the confrontational opportunities this new position would furnish. And I did my best to be a thorn in his side, to engineer disputes and challenge the pettier of his intransigent regulations, and, like the father of a chapel, I developed a sense of the power of numbers, and how false is that precept that it's not worth fighting unless you stand to benefit from victory. In all of this, I'm sure I did not disappoint his secret expectations, and while I'm not certain my refusal to act as the little Quisling he desired really benefited the other boys in his House, I am confident that the experience was a happy one for me.

As was the other, final memory of the building called Mussiter's.

One day shortly after Long Leave I sustained a nasty injury to my right thigh, when it was raked and torn by studs during an energetic scrimmage I had been unable to avoid during an inter-House Field match. The dressing needed changing, and Miss Herrick was away on compassionate leave because her brother had been involved in a car crash somewhere near Exeter, and when I turned up at evening surgery, who should be covering for her but the other Dr Tappen, the real one, the one who knew about bodies rather than the Julio-Claudian family tree, the willowy woman who wandered through our fervent fantasies, and she asked me – no! She instructed me to lie down on the couch, and push my trousers below my knees, and snip, she went, snip, snip. 'I need to cut away this dressing. Keep still, now.'

Oh, yes, I said, Yes, but I couldn't, it wouldn't. 'I can't get the scissors in properly, unless you remain absolutely motionless. It's dangerous. Do you understand me? Are you listening, in fact?' I felt one arm of her cool forfex slide between gauze and skin, and then closed my eyes. 'London,' she said sharply, 'what on earth are you doing? Have you taken leave of your senses?' (I can only suppose that sort of old-world, B-movie phraseology came to her lips through a year's exposure to her husband's dreary idiolect, but right then Robin Tappen was not on my mind.) I fear I was unable to stop myself. I had Viscount Bellibone out from his Chilprufe boxer-shorts and was brandishing him at her face as she bent over – if I could, I would have torn him out by his roots and thrust him towards her crimped pink mouth, as perhaps she could now tell from my bursting face. 'I think,' she said quietly, though her words boomed and ricocheted around the speluncar recesses of my distant universe, 'that you should go straight up to your room,' but I saw that her eyes were brown and shining, and I heard my clotted voice say 'please'.

Janet did not speak any more, but began – quite roughly – to bring me off. She never released me from the disapproving web of her gaze. When it was finished, she wiped her hand on my shirt, grasping and wringing it as some mechanic might handle his habitual rag. 'You children can be perfectly disgusting,' she told me, and then she left the room.

I adored her from that day on, but nothing further ever took place between us; and when, a few weeks later, it was time for me to leave the school, I gave her husband a case of claret, and said goodbye, and shook her by the hand (the last time we touched), and even then she hardly gave a smile.

A few years after they retired to Dorset, Janet diagnosed her own breast cancer. I gather that Dr Tappen still survives, getting on for seventy, no doubt following the cricket and wearing his Panama and puzzling over the ways in which the military events in the new Britain were mimicking certain aspects of classical history, and parading the erudition he attempted to instil into hundreds of boys who have since forgotten that the aorist tense ever even existed.

And I wonder if he regrets not having had a proper family of his own.

NINE

In the spring of 1975, while Kit and I were driving our Volkswagen across America, Interpol arrested Meech and three of his friends in Amsterdam, after infiltrating a paedophile ring. He had been living under the name of Peter Johnson. He was extradited, charged with indecent assault, aggravated assault on a minor, and seven contraventions of the Obscene Publications Act, and tried *sub judice* to protect the identities of those informants to whom the police had guaranteed immunity. This was just as well for our own family. Cosmo was still a pupil at Bedales, and despite being allowed to give evidence protected by a screen from view of the accused, he found he could hardly speak when the judge gently invited him to repeat his earlier statement that refuted Meech's brazen defence that the Spellbrook assault was a fabrication, and that my brother had been making advances of a sexual nature which Meech had rebuffed, and that Cosmo's injuries were self-inflicted attempts to exact revenge.

Timothy Meech was convicted on all charges, and turned out to have an established record of offences against minors – something it had not occurred to the Pembridge Tutorial Agency to check. He was sentenced to nine years' imprisonment, with the judge's recommendation that he serve his full time without parole.

We returned from the States in July, and I determined to use the few months before going up to Oxford by turning myself into a Dirty Young Man on the deb circuit. I bought myself a rag-top Alfa Romeo (convertibles are so happily reminiscent of old-fashioned prams), joined the Françoise nightclub off Sloane Square, went to Sweeney's in Beauchamp Place to get a chunky-layered haircut, bought shirts from Harvie and

Hudson, trousers from Blades, three double-breasted suits by Tommy Nutter, a range of Gucci footwear, cashmeres from Piero de Monzi and Dunhill accessories (there, I think that's enough in the way of shorthand brand-names: you get the picture). I then began a Season of sharking for England, with a foil-wrapped love puppet in my snakeskin wallet at all times.

It wasn't too difficult getting invitations from all those socially aspiring Mums (some of them not too bad-looking, either, superbabes in Ferragamo pumps and origami dresses: quite tasty) who were giving drinks parties and receptions and dances to launch their daughters' social lives – my title proved to be a very useful four-letter word, a tetragrammaton that opened doors, and perhaps certain thighs, like a runic spell. When planning one of these parties, the hostess might avail herself of a list specially compiled by the ubiquitous Social Editor of *Tatler*, containing the names of tried and tested young bloods who were deemed suitable escorts, and were presumably considered Safe in Taxis: I believe my name was inscribed in green ink at the top of this list at one time, and I certainly was able to accept three cocktail parties each week, plus a house-party or ball any weekend I chose. It was fun for a while. There was a relatively small caucus of men involved – maybe twenty or so of us were committed regulars – and we soon cultivated the foppish languor that seemed to make the girls relax, and a snobbish insouciance that is the hallmark of the incipient poodlefaker.

The drinks parties at Searcy's, or maybe at the In and Out, or the Dorchester, or Knightsbridge Barracks, were practically indistinguishable, and collectively a pretty good approximation of canapé hell; you cruised through the reefs of silken girls with their borrowed jewellery and Belville Sassoon frocks, trying to keep the tip of your fin below the shallow surface of the conversation so as not to cause alarm too early on in the evening, but always on the move, nosing here and there, showing your teeth as a cheek was presented. I took up smoking as a pose, initially, with rather expensive Imperial Sobranie lungfuckers that had a built-in, authentically Russian, hollow filter of card-board, believing that this gave me an extra, exotic little sartorial signature – but it was absolutely crucial not to appear to be trying too hard to be impressive. Arrogance was what you had to exude, and (strange to say) this I did not find too difficult. I played a part I had never consciously tried before, and became a supercilious young grandee. It was an interesting experience.

Much social tattle has found its way into print about the ethos of these 'coming-out' events, and most of it was true. Some of the girls were Little Miss Muffets, already inhabiting a hopelessly idealistic world of finishing-school leisure and romantic delusions reflected from the Fifties that their mothers so fondly remembered; there was a great deal of shrieking and giggling of the type later made familiar to a wider public by the antics of the younger Royals, a general inability to tolerate alcohol, and a level of flirtatiousness that often belied innocence of the simple fact that most of the men were only affecting charm in the hope of later parking their Tonka Truck in a new garage.

For the men a combination of suave demeanour and saurian looks was probably the best advantage, and I can't pretend I was much more than passable in this department – but I did have two unfair aces: I was reputed to be immensely rich, and therefore able to treat girls to venues more sumptuous than the inexpensive Fulham restaurants frequented by my competitors, and I also had free run of our house in Durham Walk when my mother was not in town. Once I could get a girl away from the crowd, and back there on her own, I was in with a good chance of a series of night baseball.

I would like to recall that this happened with almost monot-onous regularity, but there were perhaps six or seven such successes during that summer (all right, I can only swear to six). At the time it seemed like a lot. Number Three Durham Walk was a pad with all the appurtenances requisite for seductions and recreational sex – I don't mean it had water-beds and a heated swimming-pool, but there was an L-shaped drawing room where I had rheostats fitted to dim the lights, a couple of good big sofas, a capacious drinks cabinet including a concealed fridge that meant you never had to break off for more champagne, and my Bang and Olufsen (one more brand-name, though we don't want to sound like some shopping-and-fucking novel, I agree) from which to waft Roxy Music, Abba, Bowie, or Captain Beefheart, depending on my diagnosis of how far down the line we had reached. So it might be an arm around the waist going upstairs, a tulip glass of fizz on the sofa (a riff of flattering chin music, here, to make Sophie, Annabelle, Miranda, Rachel, laugh – crucial), then a little dance (energetic, disconnected freestyle if exhibitionism still required, or nice and slow if the going looks firm), gentle lobe-work, left hand on nape, whisper, right hand on coccyx and still moving, full oral hydraulics, right hand round and ascending to left breast (sometimes resulting in the breakdown of negotiations), explicit groin frottage, and then – twice on the carpet, once against the wall, otherwise in the dark blue bedroom that had been my father's – reassuring murmurs during the tricky button phase, unhooking, get your own shirt off, never hunt fur pie in tie-up shoes, the big slide – and a cyclone at the base of my spine, the heavens are going to open, an electric crack across the universe, and there, God, the *Flachenblitz* – reverse lightning.

Followed by a delicious little depression over London, eye-lids drooping, zigzag smile. Heroic sleep. (Ah! The old days; the weather was surely so much better, then. The luck, the stamina of youth.)

Although the random samplings from my fieldwork during this period were not as extensive as I would have liked, the available data did suggest a couple of things about debs and Belgravia girls in general: they were fairly reluctant to blow your cookies, and several of them had a pronounced preference for being penetrated *a tergo* (something to do with a childhood spent with ponies, I shouldn't wonder). So most of the time it was plain vanilla sex, though once I was treated to a bonus 'Ninety-nine' from a girl called Maria Watson, a big babe with a blatant mouth and rather heavy hips. She wasn't strictly a deb, but I'd met her when I was billeted with her family for a dance in Wiltshire, and she looked quite lickerous, so I asked her for a date when next she came to town.

We went for dinner in Trader Vic's, below the Park Lane Hilton – it used to be a good place if you didn't want to run into anyone else you knew – and the meal went most promisingly, with a little external thigh-contact as early as the second Fogcutter cocktail. I got the first kiss in as we descended to the underground car-park, and she bit me on the cheek, for good measure. After a bit of fooling around on the sofa (Derek and the Dominoes, this time – Maria was no delicate socialite, she was about to go to Durham to read Law) I reckoned the time was right to try a hand under her velvet skirt and up the coast of her tights, but was surprised when she grunted into my mouth, and pulled me away. 'No, I can't. It's, you know, the wrong time of the . . . ' I frowned at her in disappointment. 'But don't be sad,' she went on, 'there is something . . . we'll find a way. But you'd better bring a towel.'

When we made it to the bedroom, I vaguely realized I wasn't going to make it up her kumquat but that some kind of satisfaction was evidently in the offing. Her breasts were fetchingly pale and veined, and we began with some intermammary excitation for Viscount Bellibone, and then I shuffled further along the sheets so I was kneeling in her armpits, and introduced him for lunch. This being the first time I had been in such a position, I fear he hardly made it through the hors d'oeuvre, but at that point Maria, with her mouth full (alright, quarter-full) of my very best butter, rolled me on to my back and began to feed my own stickiness back over His Lordship before he could collapse, like a mother bird regurgitating food into the beak of some straining chick. Thus naturally lubricated, I was bundled off the bed as she assumed a foetal position on the towels, then guided me up Hershey Highway – another first for me, and I was just warming to my theme when she took hold of my right hand, which had been chafing her nipple, made a pistol shape of it (the forefinger the barrel, with thumb for hammer) and, grasping my wrist, thrust it into the back of her throat. After a couple of tries, she succeeded in making herself vomit, which had a convulsive effect upon her sphincter – I came again at once, and she shuddered and spat and coughed, and then lay panting.

This minor tactic of the bedroom is apparently called The Wolfbag, and I have never since had it suggested to me by a girl from Wiltshire, or from anywhere else. I imagine it may be of Middle Eastern origin, a second cousin to the once popular practice of sodomizing a large goose and slamming its neck shut in a drawer at the *moment critique*, thus raising its body temperature and causing a similar constriction of the cloacal muscles around the root of the intruded member. Whatever its exotic pedigree, I suggest you remember Maria's caution about the need for proximate towels, especially if you have recently shared a Hawaiian prawn curry, Mimosa fried rice, and coconut ice-cream.

Ordinarily, as I said, these encounters were just a matter of a single-scoop cornet, and then lights out, with the possibility of sloppy seconds in the half-light of sleep – but I'm afraid my attitude was such that they were never more than one-night wonders. Except in the case of Colty Lipton, who was my first real girlfriend.

Anna Lipton was only seventeen when we met at a house-party near Wantage; she had riffling chestnut hair, bronze irises and slender legs that had already earned her the nickname 'Colty'. Her parents were separated, and her Dutch mother lived with a lover in Pelham Crescent, while her father (whom I only met once, and he seemed like a burnished shit) had decamped to Antibes with the mother of one of Colty's school friends. It may be rich, coming from me, but I think her parental background had made her more than a little insecure. When in London, she did not feel safe in areas where she could not sense the heartbeat of Harrods. Our relationship (Jeez, that word) lasted all of a glorious six weeks; she was very elegant, and tender, and young – as she herself might have put it, 'awfully sweet' – and although I don't say, even with the sentimental strabismus of hindsight, that I loved her, she was the first girl who came close to the cellared deep-freeze of my heart.

We had those weeks of fun, however, and it was not merely physical. I found her addictively attractive, despite her penchant for corduroy knee-breeches, but even as I exploited her trust in me that this was not simply a casual affair (I was quite convincing, quite convinced, for a while) I was aware that there were entire dimensions of feeling I was not able to explore. I wasn't ready to play it straight – I was only eighteen myself – and what I needed was a bit of 'give', some room for shape-shifting, a little elasticity in the emotional material. Colty had a monorail mentality which might have served us well as a curving course in later life (yes, I do sometimes think of that) but was ultimately spooky to me as a teenager who was not exactly searching for a Duchess. Perhaps I am being unfair (again, yes), but whenever it came to making decisions like going away for a weekend, or fixing a four-way date, I had a little spectre of me in a cardigan, with a pipe clenched between my teeth in front of the fireplace (a prejudiced projection, I know, but a common one for many males), and some kind of immature voice groaned 'This cannot be right,' instilling that feeling that you might get as a househunter who thinks the first property he sees is ideal and therefore *there must be something wrong with it*. What am I saying – that I wish it had worked out between us? No, probably not. But it may not be coincidence that Magda has a similar, and rare, efflorescence of coppery hair.

No, Colty Lipton and I were never designed for a union made in heaven, without breaking the celestial Trade Descriptions Act. 'Richie,' she would mumble, on the yoke of my shoulder, 'we are so lucky to have found each other. Hold me. Just hold me. I'll always be here for you.' No, no – she became a known quantity, goods that had somehow settled in transit: what she wanted was for time to stand blissfully still. She was stuck in amber. It was surely time to get out. Colty was suffering from a Protean deficiency. She would not change, in the way that I felt I must. Just before I went up to New College we had dinner together at Bianchi's and I told her I thought we were through. I have not cried openly in a restaurant since then (I exclude inebriate weeping in bars), and that occasion must rank as one of my all-time six worst adult evenings. I dropped her back at Pelham Crescent, and returned home to drink a stupid amount of Johnnie Walker on my own, writing her a letter that I later regretted (I churlishly claimed that my mother deemed us an unsuitable match), and convincing myself most prematurely that an affair might be all right, but a relationship was quite out of the question. In truth, I had not learned very much from the curve of those few months in the rarified gyres of the capital.

On my second afternoon at New College I made the acquaintance of Marlin Sullivan when he rapped on my door and, entering unbidden, demanded the loan of a drawing-pin. I was somewhat apprehensively sorting away the volumes of Victorian poetry I had just purchased at Blackwells from my course lists, already wondering whether it had been prudent to ignore the advice to read some of these texts in advance during my nine months' 'gap', and my mind was briefly anxious about matters academic. I turned to be confronted by a tall man with long golden curls, and a ruby-coloured stud in each ear-lobe; he was wearing a pair of mirrored aviator glasses, and from the neck up he resembled some surf bum from Bondi, or a guitarist from a headbanger's band. By contrast, his Thirties-style baggy-kneed double-breasted grey suit, striped silk tie, and black wing-tip brogues suggested a nightclub crooner from the age of Jack Buchanan. He did not introduce himself, then, or indeed ever.

'I'm afraid I don't have one,' I replied, 'but I've got some Blu-Tack.'

'Well, forget it,' said Marlin, with a wave as if swatting away an insect, 'you can't smoke dope off that.'

It was not a very auspicious beginning, but over the next few weeks I got to know him a little better, because the College Aesthete occupied the room opposite mine at the top of the staircase. He was Second Year Modern Languages Exhibitioner whose peculiar sartorial flair and allegedly bisexual lifestyle were already the subject of undergraduate gossip in certain circles, and he was considered a leading light in the Experimental Theatre Company, the fashionable rival to OUDS. I can date our friendship from an evening during my second week, when I was unlocking my door after dinner in Hall, and he appeared on the landing in what looked like a pair of harem pants, and asked me what time it was. I told him nine o'clock, and he enquired if I had anything to drink. We stayed up until three, by which time my meagre stock of Château Palmer was exhausted and we were reduced to drinking neat Pimms. It was clear that Marlin was a crazy, exactly the sort of person I had hoped to encounter at Oxford, and I found his bleak sense of humour peculiarly congenial. He came from a strict Catholic family in Norfolk, and had been educated at Ampleforth; his real Christian name was Nicholas, but one of the masters there (who had served as a military chaplain) remembered that all squaddies by the name of Sullivan were called 'Spike', and the nickname stuck throughout his schooldays, so that when he was expelled (for unspecified misdemeanours about which I could only speculate) and consigned to a tutorial college by his parents, Nicholas Sullivan chose to adopt a lexically logical variation on his previous sobriquet, and – via Marlin-spike – arrived at a new tag that he adopted by deed-poll, thus turning his back on his baptismal name, and satisfactorily antagonizing his family.

The morning that followed our first bout, I had such a hangover that my hair ached at the crown. There was a small bonfire in the back of my throat, and the pressure on my facial musculature was such that I felt I was 30 feet underwater, so that I moved tentatively through what remained of the forenoon like a diver exploring some submarine wreckage. It was to be an experience repeated on many occasions – the conviction, upon awaking, that my cerebral cortex had been replaced by an especially pernicious subspecies of tropical jellyfish – and in fact, if it had not been for my fortuitous association with Marlin I don't think I would have enjoyed my first year at university at all.

I wasn't very impressed by Oxford, not by Town or Gown. It is blasé, I know, but I had been used to venerable architecture and the pursuit of excellence for some years already, and it was difficult to see what all the fuss was about. As an undergraduate experience, I would say that I found it initially depressing – the manic activity of all those Freshers joining societies, scrabbling at the lower rungs, dropping round to one another's rooms to quaff coffee as if it had just been invented, and discussing the candidates for the forthcoming JCR elections or anatomizing the relationships formed between Mary and Paul, Julie and Frank. I have always abominated the taste of coffee, anyway, and no percolator ever got up a head of steam breathing heavily in the fireplace of my rooms. I found it difficult to admire the enthusiasm with which so many seemed to embrace a life that involved wearing a College scarf and fake-coney-fringed parka, anxiety about *The Dream of the Rood*, protracted debates concerning student politics. Arrogant? Elitist? Yes, I suppose I was: but the self-importance of all this activity, the lobbying and canvassing, the voting, vetoeing, and blacking, the petitions, broadsides, and constant *organizing* of opinion left me cold.

Being a Duke, and thus without any aspiration to political office, either within New College or at the ludicrous, down-at-heel Oxford Union, I freely admit that I was in no sense representative of my fellow undergraduates, but that did not exercise my conscience then, and it does not worry me now. I still regard most of the subsidized student activity as a self-indulgent waste of public funding – a view which was then considered politically incorrect, in modern parlance, but has since been justified by historical developments. It is now quite different, getting into Oxford University – if anything they've made it even more elitist, and of course, you've got to do your National Service first – and there's none of the *laissez-faire* which used to allow students like me to attend only two compulsory tutorials a week. Like the entire country, it has become more regimented. I don't think it would have suited me at all.

I did not work too strenuously during my first year, and I'm afraid my scholarship enjoyed minimal progress. My tutor was Christopher Jenkins, an orotund poet with a beard who had published a monograph on Spenserian prosody, and a Life of Dryden. He was unimpressed with most of my early writing, and I antagonized him by turning up for a discussion on Arnold and Clough still attired in my dinner-jacket. Twice a term I made a concerted effort to turn in something I thought was really good, and it was to his credit that he continued to be encouraging on those occasions, and didn't just give up on me entirely. He was a complicated, highly articulate teacher, though, and I still find I refer to notes I took during those tutorials even now that I am a teacher of sorts myself; he was particularly good on stylistics and irony, although like so many analysts of irony he did not seem to have much of a sense of humour himself. He lived with a grim little hazel-haired woman up the Banbury Road, and on the few occasions when I saw them together it did not seem likely that the physiognomy of either would be etched with laughter-lines in later life. (Of course, it's just conceivable that they were both endowed with perfectly serviceable senses of humour which allowed them to roar with laughter at a ridiculous and juvenile-minded under-graduate whose sensibilities had been dulled by the closeted circumstances of his life, and the vapidity of those with whom he consorted.)

Except on mornings when there was a tutorial to attend (I went to all the Faculty lectures during my first week, and then gave them up until my final year) I would seldom surface before about ten, pretend a cheery greeting to my scout, Mrs Bass, and fix myself a Bombay gin, with tonic, chunk of lime and ice from my private fridge, and retire to bed with yesterday's newspaper and my first Gauloise of the day. Already feeling considerably worse, I would set off for a brief constitutional to the English Faculty nearby for a general recce – not so much of the books, though I would be armed with typewritten bibliographical sheets to alarm the opposition, as of the other students. Coming from a single-sex school, I had hardly ever encountered scholarly females before, and I found them curiously exciting – so serious and rapt, frowning with concentration at the printed page, head low over their paper as they inscribed notes. I have often experienced a peculiar sexual frisson in libraries, where the tension of intellectual industry is interrupted only by the rasp and sigh of paper being moved, the coughs and snuffles of a dormitory. And although at that time the female undergraduates at Oxford were outnumbered something like five to one by the men, in the English Faculty they uniquely comprised a majority.

Unfortunately, unlike the hopheads, rugger-buggers, party animals and self-regarding poseurs that made up most of the male student population, these girls tended to concentrate on their proper studies, and usually took all the best English degrees, to the delight of the feminist college authorities who argued from their performance in the annual Norrington Table of exam results that more places should be found for female students. These results were only achieved at the expense of much of their social life, and at many of the parties to which I went a female undergraduate was a genuine rarity – A Level and Secretarial Colleges were a more likely place of origin for party-girls, while the Anglepoises beamed above the desktops of St Hilda's and Somerville.

I knew large numbers of male students already, of course, through fellow Old Etonians and their cliquey friends, but the Christchurch socialites who congregated at the Grid Club for steaks and claret at lunch-time were not of much interest to me, and anyway I saw plenty of them at parties in London: instead, I was becoming intrigued by social hinterlands frequented by the aspirational bohemians I was gradually meeting in College, the drinkers and actors and confused poets with whom I was able to associate quite freely by virtue of my friendship with the egregious Marlin, and whose sartorial predilections I soon came to ape, visiting the Oxpens markets every week to buy dramatic cast-off clothing from a stall known as the Retreat From Moscow. I soon got the hang of the crumpled linen jackets, the waistcoats, collarless shirts, long knitted scarves and monkey-boots that were the visual signatures of this amorphous circle and made them look like a bunch of fans at a *Dr Who* convention, and I felt quite content in my new social camouflage, especially since there was still a pair of monogrammed silk pyjamas waiting for me underneath my pillow when I returned from carousing.

There was a club some second-years had founded called the Forty-Rod – they had originally been in receipt of a small JCR subsidy since it was believed that this was actually some form of College angling society, but this was withdrawn when its real purpose became manifest following an unseemly incident involving one of the night porters and a small bag of offal. Forty-Rod was named after the prohibition slang for bootleg bug-juice that was so coarse and strong that it could knock you down at a distance of forty rods, poles or perches, and the club was dedicated to innovative ways of becoming ape-drunk, or watching the ant-races. There were always thirteen members, of which I became one during my second term, and three annual meetings. The first was an all-night session held before Christmas in the private room of the King's Arms: each member had before him a bottle containing the alcohol of his choice (beer was banned for being little better than a soft drink), and a photocopied sheet with the 228 terms for drunkenness listed in Benjamin Franklin's *Drinker's Dictionary*, which were read out one by one, going anti-clockwise round the table, with a toast from your glass after each. Just to make things a little more dangerous, every time a phrase contained the letter 'r' (as in 'It is starlight with him', or 'He makes Virginia fence') you had to pass your bottle one place to your left – thus you might have taken six drinks of bourbon, and suddenly found yourself having two hits of sloe gin, followed by a neat gin and a Van der Hum. Before too long most members were swaying in rhythm with the walls.

While most clubs held their alfresco drinks parties during the summer, Forty-Rod did so in the quad during February, and guests customarily came wearing greatcoats and ski anoraks; here, it was the responsibility of each member to bring supplies of a cocktail of his devising in a jug or capacious shaker, and offer it to guests at random. They then had to try to guess the ingredients, but after the first half-hour everyone was herding the turkeys, and the noise became like the stockpen in an abattoir. That first February I served Pirate's Blood (hot Bovril with dark rum, a good drink for mid-morning 'comforts' when out shooting), and Marlin offered a concoction known as Death Comes for the Archbishop (neat gin, with a few drops of green cooking dye admixed, to impart a hyaline tint), but it was here that I first made the acquaintance of a real grapple-the-rails dubbed The Belton Bracer.

Tony Belton, its deviser, was a New College oddity: he had already served five years in the Greenjackets, and had been given an Army scholarship to spend three years reading history – but instead of playing polo and haring around in a Bullingdon tail-coat, like most of the military types opted to do, he kind of went native and became a rebellious lush (though it was always worth remembering, even in one's cups, that he was a congenial lush who had spent the last five years being trained how to kill people). The recipe for this drink (not strictly a cocktail at all) is very simple: you need a bottle of ordinary blended Scotch and a large tumbler, which you fill to the brim, making it a brimmer, and then you add a few more drops to the meniscus so that the surface of the liquid is actually convex, which transforms it into a bumper. Then, what you have left in the bottle is a Belton Bracer: to refer to a 'large' or 'double' Belton would therefore be a pleonasm, and the term was

accepted by Forty-Rodders at subsequent events to be synony-
mous with any huge measure.

In the summer we would organize a day spent gastronomi-
cally in reverse. At nine in the morning we assembled in dinner-
jackets and began with brandy and cigars, then cheese and
biscuits, pudding, and so on (with the appropriate drinks) until
you ended your day with cereal and a glass of orange juice.
You were usually all right if you made it past midday, but
inevitably there were casualties who could not say 'National
Intelligencer' at elevenses, and had little hope of surviving until
the pale luncheon sherry at two-thirty. Such failures were
tolerated but not ridiculed, since the only way any Forty-Rod
meeting could be prevented from deteriorating into a riot of
breakages and vomit was for a prevailing tone of high seriousness to be maintained. There were no repetitions of pranks such
as the one with the porter and the offal – the club could only
exist so long as it was just within the bounds of acceptability to
the authorities, since it was from the heavily subsidized College
Cellars that our drink derived.

By working for two days, then boiling around and becoming comatose for three more, and spending the rest of the week
in London, I managed a *modus vivendi* during term-time that
was extremely pleasant, but it did require the connivance of
Mrs Bass, because there were residential conditions attached to
remaining *in statu pupillari*, even if much of that time you were
non compos poopoo. I tried to keep her sweet with little presents
and end-of-term bribes, apologizing for my slovenly habits, my
decadent hours, enquiring solicitously about her chilblains and
the general welfare of her family (her husband was a senior
foreman at the Ford Factory, but suffered from respiratory
infections), and anyway I expect she'd seen it all before, and
worse, in her twenty-six years at the College. 'Well, at least
you're not like that Mr Sullivan,' she would say, jerking her
head towards the door, her mouth sinking in disapproval. 'You
never know what or who you're going to find in *his* room, of
a morning. Clothes hung up on the floor, them cigarettes he

makes stubbed out all over – don't think I don't know just what's going on. It's like the Wreck of the 'Esperus, Mr Sullivan's is. You mark my words, he's a bad 'un. Seen plenty of them come and go from here, I can tell you. No, you don't want to go having anything to do with the likes of him, not a nice Duke like you. Your mother wouldn't know what to think.'

Although I rang my mother regularly from Oxford, I never saw her during term unless we happened to coincide at Durham Walk. She seemed to have no curiosity about my new circumstances, and I think she sometimes even forgot I was at university at all. 'Rich, how lovely. What a surprise,' she might say, when I phoned, 'where are you ringing from?'. And then, still perhaps a little confused geographically (in my absence Gilbey had effectively moved in with her at Spellbrook), 'And what is the weather like, down there with you? Has it been nice and hot?'

'Well, yes, Mother, it hasn't been too bad for November, and the heating in College is very modern.'

During the vacations I spent most of my time back at Spellbrook, partly because I needed some respite from the exhaustions delivered by eight weeks of such an indulgent lifestyle, and partly because there were increasingly matters concerning the running of the estate that needed my approval. The trustees had appointed a new manager, a Scot called Ian Cunningham, and he was keen to involve me in his long-term plans as much as possible – and once away from the inferno of wits, blades, bloods, wags, cads, juice-heads, wastrels, crazies, boffins and posturing intellectuals, I was still capable of being alive to the fact that Spellbrook was my home, and was my future home, and I could not ignore it.

But I was beginning to experience a rather schizophrenic division of my years, the pendulum swing between my Spellbrook persona and my behaviour elsewhere being more pronounced now that I was a relatively free and independently mobile agent. At home I was having to grow into a precocious figure of local authority, whether I liked it or not, whereas at Oxford I was enjoying what has proved to be the most irresponsible period of my whole life (so far, so far). Despite my rodomontade about being accepted into undergraduate circles and metropolitan society, I was only nineteen; I was aware that I had a widowed mother, an estranged younger brother still at school, employees who depended on me, indirectly, for their livelihoods (a worryingly large number, if you added them all up, as Ian Cunningham naturally did, and ensured I was aware of the extent of the business I had inherited), and that, as my father had tried to explain when I was little, these aspects of life at Spellbrook did not somehow magically run themselves. But it was quite a wrench to adjust from the pululating and increasingly prehensile existence as an undergraduate to a world of balance-sheets and projected yields.

Nevertheless, I welcomed that exquisite sensation of sinking down somewhere safe, when very tired. Not that I can claim I was fatigued by much hard work, at that stage, but I was metabolically good and knackered. It was wonderfully comforting to be surrounded by people for whom I had such affection – like Flynn (now on his last legs, and his follicles flakier than ever), and the unsinkable Iris (who always made me Shepherd's Pie the first night I was home), and Charlie, who still looked after Nabob for me, and had become the self-appointed custodian of Cosmo during his holidays, and now presided over a shoot that Cunningham had syndicated, to generate extra income. Now that I stood around six foot tall my relationship with Charlie Sanga had subtly changed. We still roamed the estate together with our guns, on occasion, but he was more reserved with me (not because I was his boss, I think, but because there were other things on his mind). He could no longer regard me as a child, because at my age he had begun his own work on our estate; another cycle of apprenticeship was complete, batons had been exchanged, the circuits were being revised.

Charlie was never quite the same after his visit to Kenya. I was quite surprised when he informed me he wanted to return there for a holiday, and I was alarmed that we might never see him again; but he was just away for the month of May, and though he resumed his duties with customary dedication, there was occasionally a look on his face which suggested to me that we would not hold on to him for ever. He became restless and preoccupied, and I now think that he was really homesick.

At the end of my first year at New College I managed a Second in Mods, and Chris Jenkins wrote me a letter saying that if I bothered to commit myself to academic study for the remainder of my time at Oxford, he thought I was capable of achieving a better degree than that, and he hoped I would consider his remarks very carefully, before deciding to settle for second-best, however tempting.

That summer Nanny Mottram died in Frinton, and the Spellbrook contingent comprised 90 per cent of the congregation at her cremation. 'The Mottrams have always held their God in the highest regard,' she had informed me, more than once. I only hope (pray?) that this obdurate respect was finally reciprocated in that moment when she finally turned her face to the wall, and her untreated gastric growth took her away from a world through which she had butted remorselessly, as if through fields of pack-ice, an Arctic solitude where she must have known she would one day stop, and come to rest, her dogged progress never charted, known only to a few, one of the many hidden journeys. But I wish to record it here, because I was fond of my old nanny in her grey helmet, even though I am far away, and my emotional instruments are a little unreliable. I only hope Nanny slid into the good night she so richly deserved, without the pain of passage, without the parody of birth, with a great swirl, instead, into that Infinite Beyond of which she was so confident during her life.

I got a phone call in August from Kit Hamilton, whom I had last seen when he delivered me to JFK airport at the end of our trip together the previous summer. He had stayed on in the States for a couple of months and had then made his way down to Mexico, and the last I heard from him was a postcard from Venezuela informing me he was living with some woman outside Caracas. Now he was back, and full of schemes; he said he had something he wanted to discuss with me, and we arranged to meet for a drink at the Pheasantry on the King's Road. I arrived before him, and ordered a Sol from a bearded waiter. 'Do you want that in the bottle with lime, in a glass, or up your fucking cornhole?' he asked. I looked back at him in disbelief. It was Kit.

'Jesus,' I said, 'what are you doing, working as a waiter?'

'I'm not a bloody waiter, shit-for-brains. I was sitting over there when you came in, and you looked right through me. If I hadn't come up, we'd have been sitting at separate tables all night. So much for the grand reunion. But God, Rich, you look awful – are you spending all your time indoors, or what?'

He was nearly unrecognizable to look at: his hair had been bleached and straightened, and was licked back across his skull, making him look much older; he was heavily tanned, with a close-cropped, ochreous beard, and something had happened to his blue eyes, which now looked like those of a cephalopod. He was also preternaturally thin – his face looked all right because of the thick stubble, but he was wearing Bermuda shorts and I noticed it most about his legs (which, in a previous incarnation, I had had occasion to admire).

'You've lost weight. Are you OK?'

'It was that little spider-woman, Esperanza – sucked the juices from my body, man. Drained me.' He ran the pale tip of his tongue along his rollie, and sealed the skin. 'It was getting too much. Time to make *el disappearo*, while I still had some strength left.' He began to inspect the end of his lungfucker, poking fastidiously at the shreds of tobacco with the stem of a match.

'You sure you haven't been ill?'

'Won't catch anything off me, if that's your worry.' He closed one eye, sucked in some smoke, grunted, and blew. 'So,' said Kit, 'you having trouble finding a Duchess, or what?'

'On the contrary, I'm so busy I'm thinking of taking on an extra man to help cope.'

Kit made a slow smile. 'When does the interview begin?' he said.

We had a good evening of it, in the end, but it wasn't until we were both half-fried that he broached the matter of his business plans. He and his brother had put in a bid for a lease on a clothes shop in the King's Road, not far from where we had been drinking. They had done their sums carefully, he assured me, and what with refurbishment, advertising and the initial stock, they reckoned they needed another 20K before they could open – would I consider making this investment, and coming in as their partner? As well as all the usual stuff like denims and leathers and T-shirts they'd be selling a lot of Latin-American knitwear and tooled leather, cowboy boots and silver accessories – he'd set up the contacts for supply already, but if they were going to fill an order and make a shipment in time to open in two months, the money would have to be wired almost at once. I could see he was in earnest over this project, and I did not want to offend or disappoint him, but even to the naked eye it had the cellular structure of a complete disaster.

'I don't know,' I told him, 'it's a pretty specialized kind of business. These shops along here seem to close down all the time. Besides, you don't know anything about it – you could go bust before you even get your first set of accounts out.'

'Don't be a stupid cunt, Rich. I've thought about that. This place is going to be different, it's going to be the slyest joint in Chelsea. We'll fill it with beautiful women, and get ourselves in the newspapers. Really, I'm just offering you a piece of the action, as my best friend.'

I suppose the Scotch had begun to corrode my judgement. Kit had style, and it was possible he could pull off something like this; we had plenty of social contacts, and could probably get some publicity; if people came into the shop, Kit had sufficient charm to persuade them into spending, surely, just as he was persuading me now, warm with whisky, happy to be in his company once again.

'The trouble is, I can't just come up with that sort of money at short notice. There is a liquidity problem, and the trustees would have to approve; they'd need to see papers and stuff, probably vet the contracts. Honestly, I don't think this is one for me.'

'Richard, don't bullshit me. You probably have more than that in your petty-cash box right here in town. If you don't want to help, just say so – but don't fucking patronize me, after all these years.'

And so it was that we went into partnership as the Rich Kit Company, and at the end of September (just as the lucrative tourist season was over), Kit Hamilton opened the doors of his emporium, The Jean Pool, and waited.

Most weeks during that winter term I left Oxford on Friday morning, and spent a long weekend in London. I would hang out in the shop for a few hours sipping beer, and helping serve the punters if things got busy (which happened surprisingly often, I was pleased to see) and eyeing Kit's sales assistant, Mango, a singer from Clerkenwell, a great tall black girl with big hair and white painted fingernails who spent most of her time on the phone, and wore a ring in her left nostril, which I dearly desired to tug with my tongue-tip ('Don't even think about it,' warned Kit, 'the guy she lives with is a Cypriot in the wholesale trade, and he comes in here at least once a day, carrying a lot of heavy jewellery. You wouldn't stand a snow-ball's.'), and sometimes trying it on with one of the shoppers ('Could you put your address on the back of the cheque, please, along with your telephone number?'), which worked several times for my business partner, apparently, but never for me (I hadn't yet got the confidence, the sheer gall with which you had to irradiate such gambits).

We had both retained our youthful preference for quiet surroundings rather than pubs and crowded bars when indulging in drink, and although Kit sometimes slid off with various girls from other shops in his area to South London clubs and Fitzrovian cafés, this was not what interested us when we hunted together – we wanted the sort of venue where we could be comfortable, keep an eye on the whole scene, and have the chance of a casual encounter, with transport on hand if we needed to get out for any reason. We did not think of ourselves as playboys, but as soldiers of fortune. We wanted to see how little we could get away with. The obvious places were the bar areas of West End hotels, which offered these elements along with the single drawback that their drinks were extremely expensive, but the deal was that I would pick up the tab in return for Kit's undoubted superiority as a tactician.

The first task was easy: we established those hotels frequented as stopovers by the flight crews of overseas airlines, particularly those that had flown overnight, would spend the day sleeping, and emerge refreshed at Happy Hour. The Royal Kensington, the Cumberland, and the Marble Arch Palace were the three we targeted – it would be a simple enough task to make contact with a couple of hostesses here, we reasoned, and the airline girl was the ultimate flying fuck, here tonight, gone tomorrow. But, of course, we had not reckoned with one salient factor, namely that wherever these women stayed across the world there were clutches of local men trying exactly the same thing, believing the fantasy-fuelled myth that they were glamorous and easy – in fact, most of them were quite ordinary out of uniform, and our advances were both blatant and familiar. Our visions of assured pig-piles soon dwindled as it became clear these girls knew how to repel unwanted approaches by sitting in groups, ignoring loiterers, and mixing in a few male members of cabin crews with their numbers. But we persisted with our game for several weeks, and eventually Kit worked his charm on a woman from Continental, who was called Toni and must have been all of forty-five, but that was not the point. According to our agreed contingency plan, once it looked possible that success was in the air for only one of us, I said I had to go and make some calls, and left by taxi. Kit said he was getting bored with the low strike-rate, so we decided to troll the fishing grounds for just two more days before packing it in. This is usually a mistake (it's better to quit while you're behind, than compound your failures), but for once we had a real run of luck, and managed a double-header.

Kit came round to Durham Walk after closing up the shop, and while I primped and preened myself he began razoring out several lines of snow on top of the swivelling mirror in my bathroom. He knew that I was no good with drugs other than alcohol, and he rarely took any extra form of hit when we headed out together, because we had agreed on the need to pace ourselves in tandem (team spirit, you understand, the legacy of school). Tonight it was to be the Armani single-breasted, blue–black silk mixture with a three-button cuff, white Cerruti shirt with snub collar and onyx links, foulard tie by Lanvin, the usual loafers, a dab of Chimaera by da Mattini behind the jawbone, and there, the young plutocrat look – clear skin, tank watch, plenty of cash. Textbook stuff, surely – dressed to spill.

'Well, Kit, what do you think?'

He shook his head, narrowed his eyes. 'Lamb dressed as ram,' he sighed. 'All you're going to get to pull looking like that is your own dick.'

'Eat shit, you fuckhead.'

'Can I make soup of it?'

'Make yourself useful, and order a cab.'

'Yes, sir, Mr London, and may I be permitted to lick the sole of your shoe while we wait? Or anything else about your person that hasn't been licked in recent years – your wish is my – '

'Kit, are we going out, or not? If you feel like going crazy, let's forget it.'

He pointed a finger at me. 'It's a nice evening,' he said, 'let's walk.'

The Dorchester bar didn't look too promising at first: a couple of pro's in black leggings under the main mirror, some *ad hoc* business coteries, and a clutch of Middle Eastern men wearing jackets of shades of snuff and caramel, puffing on banded cigars. Kit was a click or two up, and he sank his sour mash too quickly for my liking, got impatient with the cocktail girlie when she was slow in bringing his refill. I had seen him like this before, of course, but not in such surroundings. He was making social history by being the first punter ever to roll up a ciggie in this particular bar.

'Rating, on the usual scale?' I asked him, as we scanned the room.

He was despondent. 'Medium-cool, dropping to zero. There's nothing for us here. I've had it with these hotels, Rich. They're a sexual cul-de-sac. You must be crazy hanging out here. It's like listening to paint dry.'

We quit the Dorchester, and tried the Marble Arch Palace, but drew another blank. And then, just as we were emerging from the foyer of the Holiday Inn, Edgware Road, we found two girls dawdling under the canopy as they watched the evening rain smack down on the greasy pavement – Kit went through a brief dumbshow of nipping out to inspect the weather in the sky, and getting his shoulders drenched, and as he ducked back in for shelter he frowned apologetically at the girls, shook water from his hair in a long sweep, and we were away.

Gudrun and Dalla were stewardesses from Icelandair, spoke beautiful English, had lovely hands, and were both enthusiastic drinkers; they had been planning an evening out at a wine bar in Covent Garden, but we took them off to eat at Mr Chow instead.

'Oh, this looks a most expensive restaurant,' said Dalla (cropped blonde hair, plump nectarine skirt, silk blouse with a jewelled pin at her throat).

Kit was already leering at her companion (redhead, bit thin, peony lips, white stirrup-pants, very nice). 'I wouldn't worry about that, Cleopatra,' he said, 'this man is seriously rich. His birth sign is Harrods.' He managed the first orchestrated laugh of the evening, and we began smoking cigarettes furiously over the menus. There was a mesh of chatter. This was it.

Later we went for a spell of dancing at Françoise, and it

looked as if Dalla might be prepared to cuddle a little on my shoulder – it was going even better for Kit, who had scarcely left the dance-floor. Most unwisely, I was tucking into the scotch (well, I was young and nervous), and my Icemaiden with her somewhat dumpy physique but, yes, very fetching smile, was matching me with vodka on the rocks. It was becoming dreamy.

There was an acquaintance of mine called Tony Nickerson who used to visit Iceland each July to go salmon-fishing; he assured me the girls were not so much promiscuous as scrupulously polite, and that if you persisted with them into the early hours they would nearly always invite you home for the night. Well, of course one hears such *canards* from all around the world, but I was still inexperienced enough to give this some lingering credence; so even though the girls announced in concert at half-past one that they had to return to their hotel, I insisted on driving them. We agreed to one more drink, the bar was closed, and in a couple of minutes Dalla and I were in a lift on our own, fourth floor, two fingers of duty-free vodka from her bathroom tumbler, a tight Scandinavian kiss (the opposite, curiously, of the old Western Soviet variety, which was molluscoid once you got inside), and we were finally game on.

She disappeared into the bathroom and I loitered by the wardrobe, vaguely wishing I had skipped the vodka, right hand in trouser-pocket fingering my erection, like some *aficionado* appraising his cigar.

I have mentioned my unique experience of the Wolfbag – well, Dalla is the only woman I have met who could perform a trick known as the Judgement of Solomon. After coaxing the Viscount for a little while with her fingers (John Barleycorn had slightly desensitized him during the course of the evening), she bent down and proved herself to be an even more skilled linguist than I had realized, for no sooner had I yelped into the myoclonic jolts of orgasm than she raised her mouth, leaned up over my chest, and expelled a viscid stream of semen simultaneously from each of her nostrils.

When I came to the next morning she was already dressed

for Heathrow. I gave her my real name and number, but of course she never did call me again when she was next in town. (With some girls I used to be treacherous, and give the telephone number of the Tower of London, and my address as 23 Leinster Gardens – a dummy building that is merely a façade concealing the ventilation shafts of the Underground railway: shitty behaviour after a night of passion, unforgivable, paranoid duplicity.) Served me right, I suppose, after all, it was she – and not I – who had something spectacular to offer. I was just beginning to learn about this, just starting to understand.

But I drove home that day with a smile that would have graced a meter-maid who had just been radioed permission to don arm-bands and actually direct some traffic.

The event which saved me from a pitiful life spent chatting at the counters of perfume departments, or hopelessly flirting through glass partitions with tellers in banks, occurred when I visited the Foxton Gallery off Bond Street in the hope of finding a picture that might suit my mother for her birthday. They were holding an exhibition of Modern Primitives, and although I know almost precisely nothing about contemporary painting (I don't even know what I like, it's that bad) they seemed to be remarkably expensive for naïf scenes of sheep in flat fields, and nursery lions auditioning amid improbably jungly foliage. To my eye, the most interesting item in the Foxton was the spectacular Asian woman at the desk, ignoring me as she spoke into the telephone, her head cradling the receiver against the back of the chair, so that the long skin of her neck was exposed and taut above her collar, and her straight black hair plunged over the lip of the chairback like some cataract in negative. I can certainly remember what she was wearing that day: a yellow sweatshirt, scarlet drainpipe jeans, and gold, Pharaonic sandals, with dangly beads along the toe-strap. She was a good deal older than me, but I reckoned it might be worth a try.

After ten minutes of studious perusal, with much consultation of my price list, and standing back to examine each and every canvas from a variety of perspectives as I imagined connoisseurs do, she was still giving phone, and I was on the point of departing when I spotted a ridiculous little oval painting of a hog standing in some hay, and it occurred to me that my mother might actually like something of this sort, and just then I heard the cradle clack beneath the handset, and a voice of liquid chocolate asked me if I wanted any help. The pig set me back £450 (apparently it was by some well-known woman called Hammam), and the vision stuck a red dot on its title-card with her long forefinger – nail clear-varnished, cut square at the end – and as I handed my cheque over to her, and was about to try one of the stock lines such as, 'How much would I have to spend for you to close up, and come to lunch with me?', she smiled, and said, 'Oh, but you used to know my little brother, didn't you?' It was Chandy's sister.

When I went to collect the pig picture the next week, I invited her to lunch, and she accepted, causing a cold wave of nerves to start through my viscera – 'What a jolly kind idea,' she said, in that same languid parody of polite pre-war English that I remember her brother had used. We went to Cecconi's, and although I was footing the bill, it felt throughout the meal as if she was *my* older sister, taking me out on a treat. Bebe was so much more accomplished socially than me, so obviously relaxed in surroundings of adult luxury, that I lost my edge; I made a mess of my asparagus, found the angel-hair pasta awkward to organize against my spoon, and began to get drunk on the Vernaccia, since I had ordered a bottle before asking her what she would like, and she did not drink alcohol (this is costing me a fortune, just recalling the meal). I spent much of the time looking at my food, because when I looked Bebe in the eyes, I felt scared that I might never see her again.

I asked what Chandy was up to, and she said, 'Oh, you know, he's ruling the old kingdom. Keeping himself busy. Rather like you, I imagine. But he's become so involved in politics, it isn't true. I do worry about him, Richard – so much responsibility, and Papa was never there to guide him.' It seemed like one of the longest and fullest lunches I had enjoyed in my whole life, and in retrospect I think this was because it was not curdled by lust, willingness, and forward planning: Bebe was so clearly unattainable that I just felt I wanted not to disappoint her by proving to be poor company, and this was a new experience for me, and in the end I think it was that desire which cut away my lingering adolescent self-centredness, and jolted me into realizing that I needed to make an effort if I was going to grow up.

Because Bebe rang me a fortnight later and asked me to join a party she was organizing to go to the theatre, and although I must have been the youngest of her friends by maybe eight years she treated me no differently from the others, and when I found myself at dinner talking to one of her contemporaries from Harvard, for the first time in my life I felt I was holding my own in a world where it was possible to be an intelligent hedonist rather than a maundering socialite. With a modicum of input, I could galvanize all the opportunities and privileges that had been part of my good fortune – I had tried the role of *homo ludens*, I had affected the Prince Hal roisterer, and it did not sit well with my temperament, however enjoyable the evenings with Kit or the company of Marlin. During the months that I saw Bebe and her circle of London friends I took some fresh bearings, pulled myself together a little, worshipped her, and became mindful of what she said about her brother: 'Papa was never there to guide him.'

We went out together quite often, sometimes *à deux* but as frequently in a group, and although she might hold on to my arm as we left an opera or arrived at a party, Bebe only ever kissed me on the cheek, for it was an unspoken understanding that we were not going to become physically involved. I'm not saying the thought did not cross what then passed for my mind with alarming regularity, but there are ways of telling with such things, and I was simply grateful to be in her company. She teased me about my appearance in a way that girls of my age never did: 'Oh, Richard, I must say that you look – well, absolutely hilarious in that blazer.' She used me shamelessly as a foil, when the inevitable predators closed in at parties ('Have you met my boyfriend, he's much more interesting than me?') And she told me, as I drove her home to Pimlico, that everything would be all right for us, and one day I would see how things worked out, how they appeared to go round and round without getting anywhere, but in the end most people found their lives spiralled to a point they could recognize as a final beginning, a spot drilled in the dirt where you set your crops and staked out a claim. Because you had travelled so far, and because there is only so much time.

I had already planned to share digs with Angus Fraser (the English scholar of our year), and my new determination to attempt academic distinction was on-stream, when Bebe told me she was leaving for New York. There was a job at Sotheby's, and it would be senseless not to accept. A farewell dinner was arranged at Langan's Brasserie, and most of us went on to Annabel's, where I was the only one to get Scotched up amongst all the religious soft-drinkers, and therefore the only one who wept openly, and embarrassed the assembled company. On the dance-floor I embraced Bebe, and told her I loved her, which was not such a lie as it must have sounded. She said, 'Take me away from this, and pour me a cold drink, Rich, because it's all too much, and one simply has to move on.' We repaired to Durham Walk, and the foolishness in my mind was very nearly made incarnate when she took my hand in the hall, and said, 'Let's go straight to bed. I feel so tired.'

Bebe undresses herself, and slips into bed next to me, wearing only her ankle bracelet with its tiny gold bell. I am rolling my pink love-puppet on under the sheet, my back turned, and she puts her chin over my shoulder, a velutinous cheek against mine, and says, 'Don't bother with that, Richard. I'm a good Muslim girl, you know, and I have to save a tiny part of myself for a husband.' I turn and kiss her several times on the lips, which taste of orange juice, and then gently slice them apart with my tongue. She rolls the Viscount between her palms, like someone kindling fire with a stick in a log. I browse on her breasts, the nipples like burnt umber. 'Just for one night,' breathes Bebe in my ear, then reverses her position so that her dark bouquet is at my mouth, and her bell is tingling beyond my head, I am cupping her cabochon heels, where the evening's stilettos have rubbed away at each calyx, and she treats me to slow choral sex, humming and strumming as she works her mouth, and I lick and nuzzle, unsure exactly how far I can safely sink my tongue – now she has me wrapped in her hair, and is playing me like an instrument, her hands twisting and drawing her tresses around and across me as I strain, trussed in a cat's cradle of dark silk, she blows a zephyrine breath on to his lordship's crown and my sperm fountains like a geyser into the heaven of her hair.

I begged her to give me her ankle-bracelet as a memento, and I still have it – here in this humidor beside my desk, where Magda would never find it. Bebe left for New York at the end of August, two days before my twenty-first birthday; we exchanged letters for the best part of a year, but then she became engaged to a Pakistani banker and they went to live in Hyderabad. Last time I heard from her, just before I left England, they had four children.

So, on 1 September that year, when technically I came of age, Bebe (who had done more than anyone else to help me grow up) was not present at the party my mother gave for two hundred guests at Spellbrook. I had begged her not to make it a black-tie affair, and we agreed on fancy dress instead, with Hollywood the theme – this prospect delighted the Duchess, of course, and on the night she transformed herself into a spectacular, if slightly unsteady, Scarlett O'Hara, while I opted for Bela Lugosi as Dracula – which afforded me the excuse to apply my mouth to the necks of many of the girls. The guest-list was extremely variegated: my mother invited half, which included a number of middle-aged theatrical folk with whom she worked in the Variety Club, plus some of the local County set who were, if anything, even more flamboyantly attired. My friends were a volatile mixture of Oxford (Tony Belton as Ben Hur, with an impressive pair of hairy legs, and the recently graduated Marlin, who arrived in full make-up as the Werewolf of London, complete with widow's peak and gutta-percha dentition), London misfits (Kit brought Mango, and her leopardskin ensemble caused a bit of a stir, since they came as Tarzan and Jane), and some of the more succulent debs with whom I had kept in touch.

Though I say so myself, it was one of the best parties I have ever attended. There was an enormous green and white marquee on the front lawn, connected to the drawing-room by a tunnel of twisted apple-branches strung with lights; the lake was surrounded with flambeaux, and as I cut my cake there began a ten-minute display of fireworks over the water. We had a cabaret and a jazz band by the main dance-floor, while in the tented courtyard there was Pulsin' Pete's disco from Oxford, and a New Wave band called Nuclear Winter which Marlin had found for me in Manchester, where he was in Rep. I drank carefully to start with, enjoying my *droit de seigneur* by dancing with any woman I chose. I got into a delicious clinch with Mango during 'Imagine', executed a kind of foxtrot with my mother, and even did the pogo stick with Chris Jenkins' consort, Barbara, who appeared to have come as a Munchkin, though on that occasion I was too polite to ask. By four in the morning, when breakfast was being served, I was starting to scotch it up with a vengeance, and at five I wove my way up to bed, alone, having made an inevitable and unsuccessful pass at Mango, and so ended my first official day as an adult in a state of alcoholic exhaustion which has since become something of a trademark.

At the start of my final university year, I began to study books in earnest, though I realized at once that I had almost left it too late. Living with Angus was a tremendous boon, because he was highly self-disciplined about his daily routine, and together we organized our lives around work during the weekdays, only socializing on Saturdays, going to libraries and lectures in each other's company, and adhering to a strict regime. We were renting a small house in Mount Street down by the canal, away from most of the other student digs, and it was remarkably easy to isolate ourselves when it mattered, because people very rarely dropped by to disturb us, which was the greatest source of distraction when living in college. Angus was expected to take a First, and he was streets ahead of me academically; but he was a generous man, and helped me with advice about background reading, lent me books and even notes, and generally raised the tone of our discourse. With his example, I learned how to make the best use of my time, how to work the library systems efficiently, when and where one could cut corners, and (this was probably most important) how to get on with our mutual tutor.

When I told Chris that I thought I'd try to concentrate on work in the hope of a degree maybe good enough to lead on to postgraduate study, he made some glib poetical remark along the lines of, 'It's hard for an old rake to turn over a new leaf,' and understandably he needed some convincing. 'You must realize that you have to fit two years' reading into the next six months – and you will be up against other candidates of greater intellectual ability than you, who took the trouble to plan their commitments from the day they arrived. It is now very late in the day, and you will probably be disappointed. But if you are serious, we can make a start at once.' And so began what amounted to a total immersion course in English Language and Literature that really made my frontal lobe sweat for the first time in several years. I gave up alcohol except at weekends, and filled my evenings with the Origins of the English Novel, the Age of the Enlightenment ('the shortest damn age in history', as the *New Yorker* once called it), and the Augustan Muse. For my special papers I chose to concentrate on Dryden and Pope, with Swift and his Circle, partly because Chris was an expert in these fields, partly because all the background material required made these unpopular choices with most undergraduates, but chiefly because the complex wit of these authors genuinely appealed to me. Even reading them under such pressurized circumstances, I found them enjoyable – and the dryasdust scholarship they seemed to have generated merely made their study more amusing.

Along with the reading programme drawn up for me by Chris, I devised an ancillary tactic which was to discombobulate the opposition – the usual suspects who had studied religiously in the Upper Reading Room for three years, won all manner of prizes, and were now tipped for First Class Honours provided they did not make themselves brain-feverish with information overload in the meantime. This was precisely the impression I wanted to create for my prime target, a physically stout and mentally outstanding scholar from St Hughs, a kind of negativa-Zuleika, who had beaten all comers in Mods, was writing an optional dissertation (for those students extraordinarily keen to impress the examiners) on Painting in the Later Russian Novel, and who spoke three languages fluently in addition to word perfect academic English. The name of this paragon was Mary MacNeil, and my plan was to bring her by degrees to despair – hardly the conduct of a gentleman, I admit, but it made me feel better, and the Prince of Darkness was a Gentleman.

My initial attempts to distract her involved leaving notes on her desk, inviting her to coffee, tea, or the movie of her choice. I tried, as subtly as I could, so as to escape suspicion of satire (these Augustans were starting to exercise a wicked influence), to suggest that I was enamoured of her: not that I expected her to be impressed by this, but I imagined she might find it unsettling. As any female scholar will tell you, there are few things that interrupt the proper concentration on research in a library more surely than the undesired attentions of a neigh-bouring male. This did not have the intended effect, however, and if anything Mary conceived an embryonic pity for me; she engaged me in scrupulously polite conversation, sympatheti-cally enquiring, from behind her daily rampart of critical bio-graphies, on how my revision was going, as if my brain could not strictly speaking be considered a vital organ.

Phase two was to work on her own perception of her sanity, to make her apprehensive that her waters of memory were no longer pellucid but becoming cloudy with the colloidal suspension of too many minute, Gradgrindian facts. Every week I would scour the catalogues of Bodley and take the details of two or three obscure titles as irrelevant as possible to Mary's immediate studies, filling out an application slip in her name, using a big round script not dissimilar to her own (of which I had dredged scrumpled samples from the bin). The subjects of these volumes might range from quasars to equine dentistry, taking in (on one especially serendipitous day) six recherché sexual tracts from a Parisian press of the 1890s, a Traveller's Guide to Tuvalu, a History of the British Coal Industry, and a really elementary Student's Introduction to the Victorian novel. When these orders arrived she would seize them and peer crossly at their spines before marking them off the librarian's desk. Whether or not she ever feared she was becoming fifteen annas short of a rupee, I do not know, but it certainly did not put her off her stride when it came to Finals, for she was awarded a Formal First (they just stand up and applaud, when you enter for your viva), and she is now a professor at Yale. Ah, well. It was worth a try.

My own experience was predictably not so smooth, and by the time those exams were actually upon me I was loopy with anxiety; had it not been for the steady reassurance from Angus that I had covered more than enough ground to be confident, I doubt I would have made it into Schools at all. There were two suicides that summer among final year students, and the atmosphere seemed charged with despair even where I sat every night with my reams of stubborn quotations, my little index-cards of dates, critical phrases, accumulated *aperçus*. I survived, but even now I have dreams that it is the night before Finals, I still have a fortnight's revision to do, I have prepared for the wrong paper, I have only finished one essay in three hours, or I have failed my degree entirely – I do think this acute memory has made me more sympathetic towards my own students as they approach their exams, but they face nothing so traumatic as that these days, as we have found ways of assessing qualities other than memorial capacity and stamina. I let my students take in to most of their exams as many books and papers as they can carry; it reduces stress, but they know that if they have to spend much time looking things up they run the risk of short, unsatisfactory replies to my splendid invitations such as 'Examine the interplay of religion and economics in the fictions of Defoe', or 'What contribution did punctuation make to the scientific prose of Dr Arbuthnot?' (only kidding about that one, but you get the idea).

I was summoned for a viva, and the Chairman of the Examiners instructed me to relax. I sat on a chair before a long table covered with green baize, ranged along the far side of which were maybe a dozen dons in academic robes, my scripts spread out in front of them. They interrogated me charmingly for what seemed like five minutes, but was in fact almost half an hour. Had I meant what I had written about *Pericles* enjoying a quintessentially comic structure? Would I care to expand on my contention that Nashe was writing in the light of the Humanist tradition? Could I furnish some examples of Dr Johnson's English verse being demonstrably influenced by the style of eighteenth-century hymnals? I reeled out of the building convinced that I would be lucky to scrape a Second, spent a week getting shickered at a variety of parties, and then kissed goodbye to the dreaming spires, the shivering aspens, and Bodley's crowded dome, for ever. Angus and I cleared out of Mount Street, and with a few regrets I finally went down from Oxford.

When the results were posted, they had given me a First. I promptly did two things; I rang Berry Brothers in St James's and ordered four crates of burgundy to be delivered to Chris and Barbara in the Banbury Road, with a card that read simply, 'Wonders will never cease. With love from Richard', and then I treated myself to something I had long coveted, and purchased at auction an Aston Martin DB6 Mark II, finished in British Racing Green. Like Bebe's bracelet, I still have that, too, hidden away here twenty years on, an object of lasting pride, beautiful salvage.

That summer, Flynn retired after thirty-one years' service at Spellbroook. We held a small party for him, and I presented him with two tickets for the world cruise he had always coveted (he took his old military mate, Billy Gosling, and they sent me cards from every port of call), a compact Citroën and a colour television. He also had the life-occupancy of a flat the trustees bought in Blackpool, and he revisited Spellbrook on several occasions, walking with a stick, his rough dignity unimpaired, berating Philip (his much younger, and overtly effeminate replacement) for alterations made to pantry storage, reminiscing about the boyhood of His Grace – 'I tell you, Philip, Cook used to mash up all his food before he'd eat it' – inspecting the horses with Begg at our new Equestrian Centre, slipping back during tea and cake to the time when he paunched the German submariner, and acquired that trophy compass. It was with great delight that I welcomed Finny back to our home, because by returning he strengthened my own sense of belonging. We would gather in the Staff Sitting-room, and the unquenchable Mrs Pike would subject him to a severe grilling about his domestic arrangements, Charlie Sanga would drop by at dusk and be informed that the hare population was only a vestige of its former numbers, and I would hug Finny for all I was worth before he went off to sleep – in my grandfather's old room, where so often in the past he had been on hand to help a blind man towards the bathroom, or administer the morning shave, or read to him from the newspaper.

Flynn the butler was still going strong when I left the country, pushing ninety but proceeding at his own pace, as always. I never did discover if he had a fobwatch at the end of that chain across his waistcoat.

There belongs a coda, and a sad footnote to this period of my life. In the June of 1978, just as I was winding down the dust-devils towards Finals, I was informed that The Jean Pool was closing, and the Rich Kit Company was going out of business. I have no wish to sound callous, especially in view of what subsequently happened to him, but by that stage I realized that I was leaving the rarefied atmosphere of Kit Hamilton's fantasy world, and I did not want a satellite escort of his type as I re-established contact with Planet Earth; he was going to require breathing apparatus, and I was no longer prepared to risk sharing a mouthpiece. He approached me with a number of hare-brained schemes (importing American cars, setting up a private bed-and-breakfast service for overseas businessmen), but I turned him down. It was not a question of mo⸱ y – I have always been lucky enough to indulge my whims, on that score – but the fact that he was now sinking into a coke culture that isolated us from each other both socially and mentally. Again, I do not want to sound judgmental, but he was in with the sort of guys I no longer found appetizing.

Kit was finally a victim of the long arm of coincidence. Somehow or other, he raised the capital to open a dry-cleaner's in Mayfair (not such a bad idea, except here again he had no professional experience) – Hamilton's Executive Valeting, he called it. One evening, he knocked a motorbike courier off his machine as he reversed his TVR into a parking space outside his home, and the police were summoned. In the boot of his car they discovered a cache of soiled female clothing, some of it stained with blood, three pairs of stiletto shoes, and a moleskin thigh-boot. Kit explained the nature of his business, claimed he was taking them to a specialist cleaner and repair shop, respectively, but he was detained for questioning: although he could prove that the clothes were not stolen, that he had receipts for every item, and even when forensic reports indicated that the bloodstains were menstrual, some version of the story found its way into the newspapers. 'Peer's Nephew in Clothing Scandal', 'Ex-Public Schoolboy Found with Kinky Underwear' – you know the sort of thing. I have no doubt that he had developed the habit of carting such raiment home, and dressing up in it for his personal delight before despatching it the next day to be cleansed of presented, as well as additional, pollutions, but it was a bad way to go. He was Press-gang-banged for a week, the traffic offence melted into the background, and Kit Hamilton left the country.

He went to Kenya, where a second cousin operated a charter

business with Big Game Fishing boats out of Malindi. Kit crewed there for almost two years and then, one morning, he went swimming on his own off the beach, and his body was never recovered.

TEN

My father subscribed to what you might call the treadmill, or tumble-dryer view of history: this suggests that nothing you try to do makes any difference to your destiny, or succeeds in getting you anywhere. It is a breed of fatalism that stops short of being defeatist by adding that this is still not a reason to stop trying to impose some shape on your life – the caged canary converting millet-seed into music must still escape, if his barred door is left open, but canaries have been imprisoned for centuries and must not expect any such chances. (He might have added that the odd one does escape, only to find itself floundering along a dark mineshaft.)

Such a view is nowadays quite unfashionable, since we court interconnection between all things – you know, the philosophy that a butterfly beating its wings in Brazil is contributing to a chain of events that leads to a tornado in Somalia – and while my family history inclines me towards my father's view on this particular matter, I cannot help feeling that a little individual effort to make connections between facts and words may serve by its very process of synthesis and accretion, in however modest a way, to counteract the disintegration and entropy in evidence elsewhere in the world. If enough of us knit as the great sleeve unravels, if enough of us paint while the rest of the bridge rusts, if we bring something (however small, however rarely) to the tip as others scavenge and rummage and remove, it might prevent total disequilibrium. And so on a personal level I hope that this list of words that approximates to my story so far may operate as a contraflow to my family history, and so extend its half-life when the last of the Londons is gone.

When I left Oxford there was no pressing need for me to consider any career: I possessed the riches of a rock star, and had a sizeable estate to run, a business that already employed dozens of people. Had I been interested in politics (even to the extent that I am, say, now in the canton) I could have surfaced in the House of Lords and become a committee man (as it was, I never even took my seat). I could have retreated to Monaco, slumped around on yachts and maybe even had a try for one of those Callipygian Princesses. (I could have eaten either of the Grimaldi Girls with a spoon.) But what I opted for was a postgraduate course at Peterhouse, Cambridge, where, under the supervision of Helen Coates (then the doyenne of Augustan specialists), I hoped to become the first English Duke ever to achieve a doctorate by examination rather than honorary conferral – almost a vindication, in fact, of the Fairy Queen's vision of the future in *Iolanthe*, 'And a duke's exalted station/Be obtainable by competitive examination!'

It was a most agreeable life, combining all the advantages of a campus (which Oxford lacked) and its steady sense of slow burning, without the hectic brinkmanship that attaches to much undergraduate activity. I was not bound by terms and tutorials, and divided my time as best I pleased between London, Spellbrook and the house I had bought for myself in Westbury Street. I began to collect eighteenth-century books, I joined the College Literary Society, I participated in seminars, composed the odd learned little piece for *Notes and Queries*, gave the occasional tutorial to third-years struggling with my period, and worked at my research with a methodical application which would have delighted Angus Fraser, and, only a couple of years previously, would have astonished me as well. It was my first extended experience of putting something together for myself, amassing my own cairn, and even if the subject was of no great seismic significance (the poetry of Pope) I was doing it from choice, and the University Library felt like neither a cage nor a mineshaft – I was, rather, a worker in a hive, busy around the cells of knowledge, intent for once upon sweetness and light.

My progress was derailed one night towards the end of my second year of study, when I went to one of those bring-a-bottle parties, given by a fellow English graduate in Girton, and I was introduced to Susan Morris. My first words, on looking at her face, were, 'Oh, my God!' It was as if I had been shot in the spine.

I will describe Susan as she first appeared to me, though in view of what has intervened it is not exactly possible for me to be objective. She was tall and thin and pale, with short black hair. She wore no make-up that evening, and was dressed in black jeans and a white, polo-necked sweater, with the sleeves tucked up. She looked very serious as she replied to my inane opening enquiries about her work – she was reading History – and the first time I ever saw her smile was when I asked if she lived in College, and she said no, she lived with her boyfriend who was an agricultural scientist. It wasn't long before he came wandering up in search of her, so I had the pleasure of her introducing me to Bob Porter, a hydroponics expert from the Fison's Institute – a man no doubt literally expert in his field, but one of those party-killers who wears a seersucker jacket and knitted tie, cradles a tumbler of orange juice, and nods distractedly during any conversation with which he is evidently bored. Even before he put his hand in the small of her back and suggested they must be getting along home, I surmised to my complete satisfaction that Bob Porter was an International Class Grade A Hammerhead, with twin bars and optional oak-leaf cluster. I could not for the life of me imagine how he could have netted a siren like Susan, but then the *cattivo pensiero* crossed my mind that he must have been exceedingly hot in the cot, and I cursed myself for even speculating.

Ridiculous as it was, on the basis of a rather uninspired ten minutes of chit-chat over a glass of Vinho Verdhe, I found to my consternation that I could not get the electric sensation of Susan Morris's gaze to leave my memory. It was not that in any way she had deliberately provoked such a stimulus – I'm not even sure she registered my name – but I knew, with an unprecedented sense of conviction that left me queasy at the almost certain prospect of failure, that I had to track her down and see her again, on our own, anywhere would do, so she would notice me for the feverishly besotted swain I had become. I asked my Girton friend Jo – as casually as I could over tea – who that tall girl at her party had been, the one with some boyfriend who grew Brussels Sprouts for a living ('Honestly, Richard, he's one of their senior chemists'), and she told me that Susan had been born in Australia, her parents had divorced, and her mother was married to some farmer in Gloucestershire. 'But I reckon you can forget it, in case you've any ideas. Bob and Susie are a serious item. I'd concentrate on your card-index, or dust over your bibliography, instead.'

Bob and Susie are a serious item. It was almost more than I could bear, and was perhaps the single most provocative sentence I had heard in my life. I have never made it a policy to go around wrecking the interpersonal constructs of other couples, but in this case there was something else at stake, namely my own constructive aspirations: I had decided that Susan and I needed to have a talk. Like many a maniac before me, I knew she would see the light if only I engineered the circumstances.

In the event, it did not require elaborate machinations on my part: I saw her in the Harlequin Coffee Shop, *sans* Turnip Townsend, and although I felt my pancreas was going to implode and my knee-caps come spinning off as I approached her, I managed to remind her who I was (was then, at any rate), and she did not object when I slid on to the adjacent stool with my cardboard plate of baked potato with chili con carne filling and began to try my level best to enchant her. I have to say that it was slow work to begin with. Susan (*Susie!*) did not make me feel like I had any Charm School diplomas, and kept asking me to repeat what I had just said; I found her disconcerting, and I think she was not much taken by my habit of staring intently into her eyes. But I did manage to extract their phone number, and after a fortnight of excruciating but strategic self-restraint, I called to invite them both to supper in Westbury Street.

My dinner-party was perhaps only a qualified success. The food was alright, and, yes, I can remember the menu (one nearly always can, at such instances): I served chilled Redshot with croûtons and chopped chives, followed by pork fillets in a white wine and cream sauce (a recipe dinned into me by Iris), and the one pudding at which I excelled, viz. *crème brûlée* with peaches. The trouble was that my five guests were not appraised of the fact that the soup was vodka-based until we were all well into the scooping and slurping, and I was subsequently perhaps a little too persistent with topping everyone up with Chablis, the result being that we became precociously drinkative, and, heady from dragging in the powerful blue web of smoke from my third French lungfucker over the coffee, I asked Bob Porter if his life held any prospects more exciting than the mere culti-vation of carrots. He wrestled with the pathetic vestiges of his bruised and chipped manners, and retorted that there was an impending nutritional crisis of global proportions, about which even I as a student of the questionably useful Humanities might conceivably have heard, going on to explain that whereas the University continued to harbour postgraduates who were devoted to intellectual culture and the life of the mind, what he and his colleagues at the Institute found a more pressing concern was the prospect of people starving to death. It was a riposte that I was sorry to see met with general approbation, and I felt moved to ask him whether or not he thought the preservation of language as a medium for efficient communication was not worth a little subsidy, alongside his indubitably ground-break-ing work with corms and tubers, pods, roots, and multi-crop seasonal hybrids, given that the chemicals flushed down a lab-oratory sluice by the jet of a single faucet at the end of a day might cost the equivalent of an entire term's grant for someone wishing to determine how our civilization has arrived at its current level of deep-frozen, manipulative phraseology. But I fear that at this stage in the social proceedings Jo Rosse had to make a rush for the loo, and the assembled company began to fragment and take its leave, with thanks for a lovely evening, with congratulations on a sensational meal. With a kiss on my cheek from Susan. It was a beginning.

I took a calculated risk when I asked them down to Spellbrook for my birthday weekend, but I figured that Susan's curiosity might get the better of her, and that although Bob would probably object on some obscure point of political principle, he was hardly going to let her go on her own. I stressed it would be a casual couple of days (meaning that I had told Philip we would help ourselves to food from the sideboard, and I knew my mother was in Yorkshire) and mentioned that a London girlfriend was also coming (a young lady called Julia Sutherland, whom I had dated uneventfully twice, and whom I fear I was using shamelessly as a pawn on this occasion). It was Bob who rang and accepted, and it was Bob who had to squeeze into the back seat of the Aston as we left Cambridge, while above the exhaust notes of my roadster I talked to Susan for two hours and observed for the first time the naked splendour of her legs – a little like Leon admiring in Emma Bovary *'l'exaltation de son âme et les dentelles de sa jupe'*.

But it was Begg and his horses that won the day, I think. I knew that Susan was fond of riding, so on the Saturday morning I had him box up two of his finest and bring them to the stables from the London Equestrian Centre, and while Bob went off with one of the farmers to inspect the winter wheat, and I pleaded pressing business elsewhere on the estate, Julia and Susan (whom I was pleased to note were not exactly seeing eye to eye, already) went for what is known as a hack together. Under other circumstances I might have felt desire fingering at my denims as I watched Julia, small and blonde and immaculate in her jodhpurs and boots, swinging herself into the saddle, but Susan came clopping slowly past me, adjusting her girth, and this gave me the chance to hold the bridle until she was finished, and then, as casually as I could, I grasped her left boot by the heel, moved it briefly back and forth in the stirrup as if expertly appraising its fit, and caressed the rump of her horse. Susan was looking down at me quizzically, I saw her inhale and part her lips, and before she could make any remark I gave her my most *faux-naïf* of smiles and said, 'We can't take any risks, you know.' She widened her eyes, replying, 'Oh yes we can. You'd be surprised,' before they were off.

In many ways it was a predictably tense weekend, although the weather was so good that we were able to spend much of it outside. To defuse any suspicion of my motives, I had to feign burgeoning passion for the company of Julia, who I'm afraid seemed rather to welcome this, although I was discharging my duties as a host with infinitely greater punctiliousness in the direction of another. But it is one of those curious things about secret, burning emotion, that you forget it only consumes your vision of the world, and may not even be noticed by anyone else. So perhaps it was just as well that Julia was not a highly perceptive girl at the best of times, though even she could hardly fail to notice the condescension with which Susan treated her on occasion, professing to admire her pearls, her ruff-necked blouses, and her extensive knowledge of glazed chintz fabrics. Being a man possessed, I swept aside incipient feelings of guilt at putting the hapless Julia in such a position (I acknowledge now that it was a craven ploy, a rude attempt to kindle jealousy), and it was an act of dastardly ruthlessness when, early on the Saturday morning, after several hours of scotching the world to rights with Bob (he was not entirely beyond redemption, I discovered), I slid into Julia's room, found her still awake and apparently waiting, and engaged in a desultory *boffe de politesse* during the duration of which I imagined only the very different body of Susan Morris beneath mine.

Next morning I brought Julia her breakfast in bed, partly to assuage my pangs about being an unreconstructed shit and partly because it gave me an opportunity to tap discreetly on the door of the Print Room where my other house-guests were accommodated, to see if they, too, would like room service. It was Susan who answered, and said, yes, some tea and toast would be nice, and told me that Bob had already dressed and gone out for a walk (it was almost ten, but perhaps because he was built like an ox he did not need to sleep off his whisky quite in the way I did). I grew impatient with Philip as he minced around the pantry, fetching a miniature vase for the tray, dabbling marmalade into a glass dish. 'Your Grace is flustering me, you know,' he reprimanded, 'the ladies like these little touches in the morning,' and I said, 'Yes, Philip, I quite agree, they do.' Then up the stairs, with no time to be lost, rat-a-tat-tat, in with a waiterly flourish, and there is Susan, sitting up in the double-bed beneath its full-testa awning, with the sheet tucked into her armpit, her hard little shoulders above it bare.

'Where does Madam want it?'

She smoothed the quilt over her thighs, and said, 'Right here, please,' and as I delivered the tray I gave her a light, dry kiss on the forehead. 'Thank you,' she replied, as if I had just removed a dirty plate.

'Will there be anything else?' brushing imaginary crumbs off the foot of the folded counterpane.

'Not for now. Really, you'd better go.'

I may have been a fool, blinded perhaps like King Midas when the lenses of his spectacles turned to gold, but even in my crapulous morning state I realized she was right. As I turned the drop-handle on the inside of the door, but just before I tugged it open, I heard Susan say softly (could there have been a faint trace of disappointment in her voice, even?), 'You smell of sex.'

I turned. 'Well, so do you, as it happens.'

'You've been sleeping with your little decorator, haven't you?'

A risky moment. I pursed my lips, deliberating. 'Would it bother you if I had?'

This time there was no mistaking her disappointment. 'If only you realized how puerile this is,' said Susan coldly, 'I'm not interested in playing games.'

'What would interest you, then, I wonder?'

'You might, Richard, if you'd drop the act, and just grow up.' Her words stringing the air with steel as I left her room.

And it was Bob who wrote to thank me, sending a letter of embarrassing erudition and charm, so that my feelings of guilt were compounded, especially since I had decided that whatever the opposite of charisma was, he had it in spades. He wrote in fulsome appreciation of what he had seen on the estate (none of my doing, but he was generous enough to omit this point), the extent of my hospitality, and his delight at the creature comforts of Spellbrook. There was no air of resentment or stiffness, and I felt a heel for my combination of prejudice and subterfuge. There was no mention of Susan except implicitly in his signing-off, 'With good wishes from us both'. At this juncture, I decided to wait: I told myself I was 'confused', which, if you don't already know, is masculine emotional jargon for 'I know exactly what decision I should make, but can't accept it.' There was now rather a lot at stake, and no room for half-measures; I began to entertain doubts, and some of them got on so well together that they paired off and began to reproduce. I assured myself that I scarcely knew Susan Morris, was merely lusting for the thrill of a distant horizon, was deluding myself (not that it had ever stopped me before) that she was a tease and a cheat, a succubus and a gold digger, a lover of horses, a minx, a non-smoker, and besides, I did not like short hair. Round and round went my abrasive arguments, tumbling me like some rough stone in a gemmologist's polishing machine, making it all smooth and clear. On balance, it had all gone quite far enough. I snapped open my card-index box, and resolved to re-read before luncheon a most important essay by Peter R. Fussbaum entitled 'Implicit and Explicit Meanings in the Cosmetic Satires of Jonathan Swift' (*Tennessee Studies in Literature*, 12, 1971, pp. 21–33), a much more sensible course of action than sending any of the notes I had composed, an infinitely more rewarding decision, in the long run, than making some ghastly mistake of a personal nature. And thus, in the spirit of that exemplary scholar Dr Robin Tappen, I ignored as irrelevant what was only speculative, and fell to concentrating on the realm of the known.

Susan rang the doorbell in Westbury Street one morning

less than a month later, and I appeared with my face still partially coated in foam; she said she needed £2.50 for the cab, as she had left home in a hurry, and she wanted to use my phone. She cried a lot that evening, and we held each other, and she stayed that night; after a few days living together, during which time I knew I had found my partner in life, I organized a van and we went to collect her belongings. It was the first time I had been forced to face music of this cacophonous pitch, and Bob was understandably abusive and maudlin, and I quietly cursed the number of books she had amassed as I hoiked the cardboard boxes down the stairs and sweated like a wrestler. There was relief and exhaustion as we drove to my house, but with the elation came an undertow of shock, such as one might experience after narrowly missing a bad accident. After all, we both tacitly accepted that the journey was only the beginning.

We lived together in my Cambridge house until Susan finished her Finals the following summer. She came to stay regularly at Spellbrook where she overcame my mother's initial suspicions (I had seldom had a regular female guest) and took considerable pains to talk to her gently and at length (Susan was otherwise not one to mince her words, but I both loved and admired her for her tolerance of the Duchess's idiosyncrasies, at which she was more adept than I had ever been), and it became clear even to Gilbey and my mama that this was something serious.

We were dining together alone one evening, after Susan had returned to Gloucestershire, when my mother laid down her cutlery with elaborate care, dabbed her mouth, and said, 'I'm getting old, Rich, so you must forgive me if I forget things – but how old are you at the moment?'

'Twenty-four, Mother. I shall be twenty-five in September. Why do you ask, particularly?' I could see that some subterranean pressure was about to surface, and took an antidotal slug of burgundy.

She lit a cigarette and screwed up her face, fluttering the trailing smoke away with her free hand. 'May I ask if it has crossed your mind to become engaged to Susan? Because if it has, and you are in some doubt over it, I'd like to tell you now that I think she is one of the sweetest girls I have met, and I know you'd make a splendid couple. There's something, you know, about her' – she swept an arm up histrionically, spraying ash – 'and I think it's lovely. Young love, Rich, that's just what this house needs. Spellbrook has been starved of it for as long as I can remember. What a truly happy thing that would be, would it not?'

'Yes, it would, Mother. But Susan *is* young. She hasn't even taken her exams yet. And I have my thesis to complete next year. It's all a bit up in the air. But I am glad you like each other; that's really good.' More dark wine – I have had enough of this.

My mother pushed back her chair, placed her hands on the rim of the table, and delivered her curtain-line: 'Don't be like your father, Rich. Don't go through life being careful. Be young and swooping and fiery, like I was. You are the Duke of London – carry her off over your shoulder into your cave!' I helped her to her room, and kissed her on the cheek, and told her everything would be all right in good time. Which, indeed, I did believe.

I went to meet Susan's family, too, and this I did not find especially easy. Her mother Florence was a blowzy painter in her late forties, a woman who talked incessantly and enjoyed an accent somewhere in between Sydney and genteel English suburbia; and she was forever asking questions and eliciting one's views, and I found her exhausting. 'But that's the thing about Wimbledon, dontcha just think, Richard, all that build-up in the media, so you can't watch the tennis for what it is?', or, 'Now you tell me, is there any other country you can think of where the artistic life of such a dense population is so marginalized outside the metropolis?' I don't know how her husband put up with this sort of stuff on a daily basis, but evidently he had devised some formula, because he appeared to adore the whole caboodle, though I doubt he was quick enough to pursue all of her argumentative ramifications. Mike Rendell had been a cavalry officer before inheriting his farm from an uncle, and he now seemed to divide his time between tractor maintenance, his interest in a local wine-shipping firm, and fiddling distractedly with his signet ring while his wife spouted gossamer. They had no children of their own, and he doted on Susan like a daughter. I liked him very much, but even so I did not look forward to weekends at Norbrook Farm with much lively anticipation.

Susan graduated with a 2.1 in history, and on my twenty-fifth birthday we announced our engagement, and got our names in the newspaper. To me, her devotion was still a strange and beautiful fruit, weighed in the hand, snuffed and mouthed and nibbled, but as yet still unpeeled. There were areas of emotional remoteness between us that I then considered to be a positive advantage, but of course now I am not so sure about any of that. I was not used to the intense scrutiny of my behaviour that cohabitation entailed, and Susan was full of schemes for improvements and expansion in this department – an aspect of our 'relationship' which I am probably being churlish about now, although the time for recrimination is long since gone. And I cannot overlook the fact that Susan my fiancée was heart-stoppingly beautiful, with her sharply cut-away mouth, those eyes of cartoon-like refulgence, delicate lobes to her ears, and a wonderful therapeutic looseness when our bodies were together. I realize that I sound both resentful and elegiac, but such are the tricks of the light where I now sit, unravelling my thoughts into this machine, hoping something will spin its way out, a little fabric that has been put together rather than pulled apart. Susan Morris, just before she became my Duchess, was a blow-torch of my desire, the pride of all women I had met, and the heartbeat of my new universe. When we were geographically apart, I felt we were still connected by busy atmospheric impulses. We were implicated in the glistening, perilous funnel-web of the labyrinth that has twisted and turned more people round and round than any other illusion since the segregation of Eve's offspring in Eden. We went down without any clue, however.

Susan and I were married on Valentine's Day, 1983, on the beach at Sandy Lane in Barbados. Neither of us wanted a big church wedding, but of course Florence was not to be denied her grand social event, so there was a party in the Ballroom at Claridge's when we returned from honeymoon, and poor old Mike was landed with a bill for many thousands of pounds, so that none should miss the fact that his step daughter was now a Duchess.

When we moved into Spellbrook as a married couple there were several changes to be made. My mother was resettled in my grandfather's old wing, where she was looked after by the now semi-retired Mrs Pike; this entailed a great deal of protracted redecoration, which seemed to delight and preoccupy her, and in fairness I must say that she refrained from interfering with the new arrangements her daughter-in-law was making elsewhere in the ménage. Cosmo had graduated from the St Martin's School of Art and was trying to qualify as an architect; he had the Old Mill House on the estate, and visited us at weekends from time to time, occasionally with some young man in tow, but after gaining his diploma he emigrated to Texas, where he eventually established a fashionable practice. It was strange to feel at last the Master of the House, but I need not have worried about settling down with my carpet-slippers in the library while being waited on hand and foot; Susan was a tenacious and dynamic woman, with plenty of ideas about how I should be using my time, and she was adept at judging the *moment critique* for being confrontational. Spoilt, selfish and underhand as I was, she soon had the measure of me: I was to give up smoking before she would countenance trying to start a family, I was to continue with my doctorate and not to let it lapse, and she was going to take over the running of the household accounts. After only a few months, I was being highly organized.

The arrival of an equestrian duchess delighted Begg, who

once again was able to spend time at the Spellbrook stables proper, where Susan kept her own palomino which she brought up from Gloucestershire, along with two other beasts she persuaded me to buy (she had little trouble in getting her way with me, in those days). 'It's just like the old days, like,' enthused Begg, though I couldn't quite see it myself. Susan's interest was in dressage, to me the most numbingly dull form of equitation, and about on a par with having to watch synchronized swimming with only a single swimmer, though naturally I was slow to make such sentiments apparent. She disapproved of what she called 'bloodsports', however, and would have nothing to do with the local hunt, which suited me fine except that it engineered a tricky situation over the pheasant shoot. There was no question of discontinuing it, of course, because our commercial days were a valuable part of the estate's income, nor did Susan seek to convert me to her views (she was no form of fanatic), but she made it clear she would not wish to play hostess, as my mother had done for many years, to successive parties of weekend guns staying throughout the winter. I could invite friends to shoot, and they could have lunch and tea on the day, but she did not want them taking the place over. 'It's *our* home now, Rich, not some sort of sporting club. You can see that.' She could appear so sweetly reasonable, especially when she was sitting in my lap and I had my face in her hair.

Just before we celebrated our first anniversary I submitted my thesis under the title *The Mask and the Muse: strategies of self-reference in the poetry of Alexander Pope, 1711–38*, a masterpiece of academic flimflam and intellectual casuistry, if I say so myself. But the examiners swallowed it, and so I became the only doctor of any sort in the history of our family. I took the opportunity to commemorate this triumph by treating myself to yet another vehicle I coveted, but could not quite justify in terms of quotidian expenditure: a Lamborghini 4x4, finished in Flame Red. The LM004 was originally built for desert patrol work, and instead of a conventional boot it had a rear cockpit that could accommodate four armed personnel, although the interior of the passenger cabin (where the Sheikh or Sultan sat in air-conditioned comfort) was decked out with leather and walnut trim, just like any of the modified racers usually manu-factured by this marque. Powered by a 7.2-litre marine engine, this Lambo was the fastest jeep in the world, a boxy great head-turner of a brute with a 70-gallon fuel tank that formed irate queues at filling-stations (one of the things I loved about it, in fact). I still drive it here in the canton, and Herr Sitt upbraids me for having such an ecologically irresponsible machine, which gives me reason to gun a couple of extra revs from the loud pedal each time I turn up onto the main road opposite his house.

Despite her strictures concerning field sports, Susan proved to be an enthusiastic hostess, another of her attributes that won approval from the resident and ever-watchful Dowager. At Spellbrook we led a life that might be described as 'well-heeled Bohemian' – we had writers and journalists (the distinction is one preferred by the former), university friends who had gone on to be actors or work for the BBC, the odd art-dealer and PR executive, along with the occasional plutocrat to foment the brew. What we were not interested in cultivating was the company of anyone in the legal profession, aspiring politicoes, or representatives of the military–industrial complex. Nor did we have anything to do with the Merry House of Windsor. There was no crooking of the knee, except when sizing up a stroke in the snooker-room. Our guests were expected to be polite to the staff, but not necessarily to us. If they brought children, we all ate together in the dining-room. People took their cue from Susan, who tended to wander around barefoot (she had the most elegant feet, so arched and streamlined in the correct proportions, so neatly pedicured, with varnished shell-like nails, that sometimes I made love to them, *pars minima ipsa puella sua*, but obviously not when we had guests around), though we regularly gave slightly more formal dinner-parties for the express purpose of including my mother who, although a little dotty in some of her notions about modern society, was actually better company than she had ever been when I was a child (or should I say, when my father was alive?). We did not think of ourselves as the *jeunesse dorée*, but they were good times while they lasted. I have no regrets about those few years.

At four o'clock in the morning, 16 May 1984, I awoke to a chill draught and the sound of someone breathing beside my bed. Susan was staying in Durham Walk, because she had an appointment with her doctor the following day, but even if she had been with me, I would have recognized at once the grasshopper rasp of Charlie Sanga's voice.

'Charlie got to go now, Richard. Now is the time. No, sir, no need for extra light, not now,' he said, restraining my arm as I reached for the switch. 'I sorry I have to leave like this, but long time ago your father he been very sick, and I help to make him well, and promise to stay as Keeper for the family. But now there is something else, and time is right for me to disappear.'

As my eyes acclimatized to the dim light, I could see that Charlie was dressed only in his trousers, with his short white hunting-cloak slung diagonally across his torso. 'Christ, Charlie, what's going on? Are you in some kind of trouble?' But then he was gone. I clambered out of bed and went to the open window, a 30-foot drop to the flower-beds below, but there was no spectral figure racing away across the lawn, no sign that he had ever been in the room. Yet I was convinced it had not been some inebriate dream; I rang his cottage, and there was no reply. Later that morning, I drove round to see for myself, and his home was empty of all his possessions, as if he had never spent some thirty years on the estate.

I received a call from the Sussex police, in connection with the death of one John Preston, of Hillside Villas, Hove. On going through the deceased's effects, they had discovered papers relating to the time he was employed as a tutor at Spellbrook. Timothy Meech had been released from prison only earlier that week, and his body had been found by his landlady. The pathologist's report indicated that he had been dead for less than twenty-four hours, and they were treating it as murder – when would it be convenient for me to see someone who could ask me and my staff a few routine questions?

A detective-sergeant came to visit, and spent some time uneasily commenting on the contents of my library as we waited for tea to arrive. His manner was apologetic, and polite to an exaggerated degree, which made me suspicious in turn. He did not want to alarm me unduly, he said, but he was afraid they might be looking for a psychopath, or possibly the member of some bizarre cult. Any clues I could give him, any details at all about the habits of the man who latterly passed by the name of John Preston, would be most welcome. He knew, of course, about the case concerning Cosmo, to which he referred with professional tact.

Meech had apparently been clubbed and decapitated: his genitals had also been amputated, and forced up his anus. It was not clear in which order these actions had been performed. There was no evidence of any struggle, and the police suspected that his assailant must have been known to him, and possibly admitted voluntarily to his room, although none of the other lodgers had heard or seen a stranger enter the building. Given his known sexual proclivities, it was thought that he might have picked up some trade that proved too rough for him, yet there was no sign of recent sexual activity. He admitted that they were in the dark.

I told him what I could remember about the detestable Meech, making no attempt to conceal my opinions of him. He asked me if I could think of anyone who might harbour a motive for killing him.

'Good God, officer, I hope you are not suggesting that members of my family might be under suspicion of exacting revenge in such an appalling fashion?'

'Oh, rest assured, Your Grace, I meant to imply no such thing. Of course not. Though stranger things have happened, believe me. No, the purpose of my visit is to try to build up a picture of this man's movements over a long period of time, to deepen his profile, as it were.'

'Well, I should imagine you've got your work cut out. A pervert like Meech must have had dozens of people out for his blood, but you can take my word for it that his death has no connection with anyone at Spellbrook.'

He nodded, and put down his cup. 'We've only got one thing to go on, at present. A curious clue. Very odd thing altogether.' He pulled a small plastic bag from his pocket, and shook the contents down into his cupped palm. 'One of our men found this on the carpet. We think it must have belonged to the deceased, or his attacker. I wonder if you recognize it? Apparently it's human bone.'

And there in his hand, carved into the shape of a bounding cheetah, lay the youthful tip of Charlie Sanga's index finger.

I took an immediate gamble. Taking the bone from his palm, I frowned at it, turned it around in my fingers, as if making doubly certain of my memory, and said, 'Here I think I may be able to help you, because I distinctly remember him showing me this – or something very similar to it – when I was a boy. He used to carry it in the pocket of his cardigan, as some kind of lucky charm, or talisman. I recall thinking what a grisly item it was at the time, and being fascinated by it. You know the way kids are. Yes, I would say this was definitely the same object. It seems that Meech's supply of good luck ran out on him, in the end, however. Please put this horrible thing away again. I'm afraid the very thought of it makes me feel sick.'

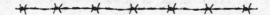

Before we were married, I had not realized that Susan had been anorexic as a teenager; she was well over it by the time we started living together, but there were complications when we tried to start a family. Eventually, in the spring of 1986, as I was climbing into bed for another bout of anxious intercourse, she told me to relax and be recreational for once, because that afternoon her pregnancy test had proved positive.

I find it now almost impossible to revive the feelings of pride and strange anticipation I experienced during those months; my views of the world seemed to swell and expand along with the ripening of Susan's uterus, and it was a time of tenderness and wonder between the two of us that was both fraught and blissful. She had to lie up during the second trimester, so we saw few other people and felt as if there was a cocoon around us – the three of us – there in the heart of Spellbrook. My mother was intrigued by the whole business, as if she had never had a baby herself, and fulfilled her role as expectant in-law by trotting out plenty of old wives' tales from the days when pregnancy often ended in death. She even dangled Susan's wedding-ring from one of her hairs, and pronounced that we were having a daughter, but by this stage in the Dowager's life it was impossible to discern whether she was demented or merely acting. My old nursery was refurbished, a monthly nurse was booked for October, huge amounts of equipment were purchased, the inevitable compendia of Christian names were acquired: it felt like the build-up to a State visit.

Like most men, I am pathetically squeamish about the very idea of childbirth (it's all very well going in there for the conception, but the honey-cup of your wife's snapdragon takes on all types of fearsome new dimensions once you study the obstetrical diagrams that show how the fruits of your passion will be emerging): so far as I could see, it was a feat on a par with expelling a large Jaffa orange through your nostril. I tried not to ponder this aspect of the business, but secretly marvelled (for the first time, but better late than never) at the entire secret history of women through the dark and dangerous centuries when there was no antisepsis, no anaesthetic, no regard for the mother if a longed-for heir presented complications and a choice had to be made between the survival of baby or wife, and little compunction in removing the infant piecemeal should it become breached. I read up the lurid history of childbirth, quaked at its past weaponry, with which the ingenuity of the Inquisition could scarcely compete, and saw it as not only proof that there is some progress in human history, but also a strong suggestion that there must be a God with a sense of humour not to my liking, who could come up with such perilous anatomical designs.

The time drew near, and we witnessed on the miraculous Ultrasound screen a picture like a satellite weather-map that brought the contours of our moving baby into focus. Like a couple of terrorists engaged in a suicide pact, our bodies clad in explosives, we gingerly made our way into restaurants and cinemas as if at any minute the world was going to go up, and this would be our last expedition together as ourselves. In the final week, we moved to Durham Walk, with both my mother and Florence in residence also, which did add to the tension. I hired a radiopager, and took Mike Rendell out to an extended lunch at Buck's, for which the women upbraided us. The bags were packed, my Thermos gaping like a triton next to the kettle (I was told by the midwife conducting the ante-natal classes that I would certainly require the sustaining effects of coffee or tea), emergency numbers taped to each phone extension. We were as ready as could be.

In the event, it was not an easy birth. Susan's canal was narrow, and the baby did not present correctly, so there had to be an emergency Caesar. For one who dislikes blood and the sight of needles, this was a vicarious ordeal for me, but I had promised Susan I would be with her at the birth, so I stayed. There was no time to sip tea. I remembered the prior advice not to look up into the operating lights (the metal shades can reflect the gory scene below), and stared, instead, more deeply into my wife's face than I had ever done before, the rictus of an agonized grin in both our expressions, though mine concealed by a mask. The medics slit and delved and applied spectacular-sounding hydraulic suction devices. My white slippers were splattered scarlet. Susan's grip on my hand became slack. And then the squalling cry from beyond the green cambric screen, the gynaecologist's announcement, 'A lovely baby boy!', and, maybe one minute later, smeared with vernix and still streaked with blood, his genitals distended and empurpled, a clamped umbilical worm lividly extending from his middle, his pinched face itself like a healed navel, our son and heir, now having his passages cleared before being laid on his mother's chest by the proudest Duke in all Christendom.

Later, while the two chief combatants were being cleaned and dressed and pacified, I wandered the corridors of the Lindo Wing, nodding and grinning to staff and strangers alike, as if I had just single-handedly liberated the entire city from which I drew my name. I felt like a hero, in fact, like most new fathers. I felt ultimately responsible for the victorious result. And we had a boy, to boot! The soft lunulae of his buttocks, the nectar-ine soles of his feet, the startled concentration with which he filled his first, amazing nappies with inky, neonatal scoria. Per-fect! Perfect down to his exhaust system. Already an Aston, a Lambo amongst babies. I delivered almost the entire contents of Pulbrook and Gould to Susan's room that evening: red roses, tuberoses, potted hyacinths, a stand of white orchids. She smiled out of the hinterlands of morphia, and our little Waterstock was asleep in his grim red clench of a face. I kissed the down on his pate, and wondered if he was dreaming: do babies dream, and if so, of what? I regarded him in his transparent cradle and wondered what colourful shapes might be racing round and round the peachy pulse of his several fontanelles. There are miracles that we don't understand, and I think we are not meant to understand them.

I cannot dwell much here on the next five years. Our lives seemed set fair, but these were changeling years that wore the aspect of joy at first, then grew into something unrecognizably alien. All I can say is that our son Peter grew, and was loved, and these are some of the pictures I have of his childhood before the vessels of my memory were cauterized.

Peter hurtling around the nursery in his wheeled baby-walker like a stripped-down Dalek, his tongue sticking out between closed lips, lunging for anything that was out of reach, giving vent to rainforest shrieks, stamping the carpet with his sausage feet and saying 'Baba' indiscriminately to all members of his audience. He was not a placid baby, already as strong-willed as his mother, and would not brook being ignored for more than a few minutes of his wakeful day; although we had a rather strict nanny called Elaine, who took no nonsense under such circumstances, he was spoiled with indulgence by his father, for which I do not apologize for one second. His antic moods entranced me, and he was already an adept flirt with both sexes; he had the promising beginnings of a guttural dirty laugh; most people agreed that he looked like me, which I found ridiculously pleasing, even though it was not necessarily intended as a compliment. Yes, yes, Peter was a Daddy's boy, for better or for worse; I used to tell him of all the things we were going to do together as he grew up, whispered him prom-ises as he glugged at the mudhole of Milupa surrounding his mouth, sang soaringly to him as I walked him round and round for winding, and made clownish noises of encouragement as he sent a sour cataract of regurgitate down the back of my latest sweater. I had never known a baby even slightly before and he could do no wrong. If my attitude was uncritical and irrespon-sible, I acknowledge it along with the joy, that sense of rediscov-ery, that a small child's exploration of his world can bring to even an awkward English heart.

These were busy times at Spellbrook. Susan had begun to contribute articles and reviews to magazines ('You don't think I'm going to turn into a trophy mother, I hope, and start discussing prep schools and charity balls?'), writing under her maiden name, and achieving what I regarded as a considerable degree of success (*Harper's*, the *Spectator*, the odd piece in the *TLS*, even), though she was impatient with her efforts and editors alike, and frustrated by the extent to which marriage and motherhood had slackened her historical acumen. To be honest, I think it took her at least a year to recover from the experience of Peter's birth, not only psychologically (one is braced for that, in a way) but from the sheer physical trauma of the operation and its not entirely tranquil aftermath, for which we were less well prepared. Where I found Peter a dark cherubim (I confess I did not have to deal with him on anything other than an optional basis, and Susan had three months of breast-feeding as an entrée) she seemed to resent his demands, and became intermittently exasperated with him, telling me she never wanted to have another baby (not that we were trying: that was another rude change to our marital life), reminding me that she was an intellectual woman who had no intention of spending the rest of her life shackled to children. These were only understandable outbursts, of course, but I secretly found them a little shocking, and realized that I still had a long way to go before I could presume to empathize with anyone else, even with the woman I adored.

Susan also began to ask me what plans I had for my own work, now that we had a child. 'What is he going to say when he grows up,' she once enquired of me, 'that his father is a Duke? Is that it, then? What exactly does a Duke *do* in today's world? Are you a farmer, or a dilettante with a Ph.D, or what?'

'I'm a businessman, darling. You know that. We run a business here, with the Golf Club, the Equestrian Centre, the bottling-plant. Spellbrook Spring water has captured more than 10 per cent of the supermarket sales in the last eighteen months. There's the market-garden, the shoot, the wine merchants in the village. Honestly, I don't bother you with all the minutiae of these things, but they have to be headed up by someone, and that person is me.'

'I know, but I wish you'd do something really useful, as well.'

'Such as what – charity work? For God's sake, I'm patron of six, and on the steering committee of four more. And what do you define as "useful", while we're about it?' I felt antagonized, wrenched on to some Procrustean bed of her own dissatisfaction. And I felt she might have a point, which made it worse.

'You could publish something, and let us all in on your great discoveries.'

'I don't see why you have to wax sarcastic. I do not deprecate your own writing – in fact, I think I have been very supportive. The world of glossy magazines holds little allure for me, and I think there is enough crap published as it is.'

'Well, thank you. But you could publish something better, if only you put what used to be your mind to it.'

At times like that, I really yearned for a lungfucker. 'Listen,' I said, 'this is getting silly. Let's not row. I'll think about it. But right now I'm busy, and we'll just leave it at that.'

'Up in the air, as usual.'

'Up in the air, for the time being. Yes.'

Peter raced across the croquet lawn when the sprinkler was on (you could do that, in those days), leaping and dancing through the thin flails of water, a naiad, a miniature narcissist playing to the gallery, scampering through the promise of temporary rainbows and the seething arc of a supplement to the Spellbrook climate: the cold sear of water, then tripping away across the scimitars of grass, the final summons to a warm bath, and exhaustion beneath the swathe of his duvet. *Thomas the Tank Engine* from me, perhaps, then a song or two from *Mary Poppins*, and sleep: the clear-lidded sleep that few adults can experience, the clean, sudden cleft of sleep that belongs only to the first seven years of life. Exhaustion brought home from prancing through a world laced with stinging silver, suddenly flung open and free, jets sending diamond and teardrop and tinsel and brief, crystal seed against the high blue of the summer skies. A sleep that belongs to the first seven years, if that.

I wanted us to have another baby, but it was not easy. We tried for three years, with all sorts of special consultation and diets and programmes and even performative exercises, but something was wrong. I did my best to relax and follow instructions, but by the time Peter was four it was pretty clear that we had been lucky to have one child in the first place. Resentment was building up on both sides of the wire.

Peter's fourth birthday: I invited Finny back for the occasion, and asked him to restage one of his performances from my own childhood. He treated the assembled company to a memorable impersonation of Long John Silver, and Peter and his friends ran around brandishing plastic cutlasses, before settling to their puppet show. I gave him a remote-controlled jeep, as red a version of my own as I could find at Hamley's, and they all squabbled over it afterwards, in the courtyard. 'I'll say one thing for him, Your Grace,' Flynn volunteered, 'he won't have any trouble getting his own way.'

Without very much warning, Susan announced in the summer of 1990 that she had a scheme for launching a jewellery business in partnership with a designer she knew, called Bernard Cook. I was more than happy to finance the venture, and before long they had opened a shop in Beauchamp Place. It was called London Jewels. Running this business required new periods when Susan spent nights in Durham Walk, and I had reason to believe she was not spending those nights alone. I became suspicious of the plausible Bernard, and resistant to his expansionist schemes. I began to suspect Susan of cheating on me, and as soon as this had crossed my mind I began to read all types of guilt into her behaviour: the note of disappointment in her voice when once I rang her and she said, 'Oh, it's you'; her vagueness of reply to my questions about Bernard's private life, and her apparent reluctance to discuss him with me at all; her air of listlessness when away from London (the city, not the man). I had no proof, and was wary of voicing my suspicions, even in the form of some contrived jocularity. We were tense enough with one another, as it was. I wanted to clear the air, but the risks seemed too great: if I was deluded (as with most men, my capacity for self-delusion approached the infinite), I was not sure I could weather the ensuing storm, and if I was right – no, better let this one blow over, especially if it was all in my imagination.

Peter's first day at Weston House school, in Knightsbridge: Susan and I photograph him in his black and white blazer and stripey tie, before delivering him to Miss Miranda, his form teacher. Suddenly, uncharacteristically shy, he clings to my jacket and says, 'Don't leave me, Daddy. I don't want to be here. I want to stay home.'

'It's only till lunchtime, darling: and Miss Miranda is going to keep a special eye on you, for your first morning.'

'Will you be home when I come?'

'Daddy will always be there, whenever you want me,' I said. It was a promise I will never forgive myself for breaking.

At the beginning of his summer term, I took Susan away for a week's holiday at the Gazelle d'Or, in Morocco: we were both wound up, and I thought something approaching a second honeymoon might relieve the pressure. We were now apart several nights a week, and when in the country I was morose and pettish and my nocturnal drinking was hardening into a fierce pattern. I had been half-heartedly fiddling with a piece of fiction, but my writing seemed to be going round in circles (I never did finish it). I was relieved when Susan greeted the idea of a holiday on our own with surprised pleasure, and I took it as a sign that my fears had been ill-founded. In fact, as we began to talk properly to each other once again, and the icy cyst that had somehow formed between us started to thaw, I found an occasion to confess my suspicions, fortified by a little Scotch courage. Susan's laugh awakened me from my paranoid dream.

'But how *could* you, Richard? I mean, he's practically bald – and you know I don't go for bald men. You are so stupid; is that what this has all been about?'

We had four days of hedonistic lounging by the pool, delicious afternoon sleeps together, long evenings of wine and dancing and teasing each other back into humour, into a more temperate zone. We wandered through the *souk* like lovers, haggling for useless carved artefacts and constructs of hide and gourd. We made resolutions and plans, and disported ourselves in bed. We had baled our vessel, made staunch the hull, and were back on course under the wheeling stars.

I was deep into a siesta when the manager knocked at the door of our suite on the Saturday afternoon. There was an urgent phone call from England. The line was bad, deluged with interference, as I heard Philip tell me there had been an accident. Peter had fallen into the lake. Our son had drowned.

The official cause of death was given as accidental, but, like many people, I do not now think accidents happen by chance. He had been playing on the Chinese bridge, and Elaine had been reading up on the hill, when his kite blew into the water. He fell in, trying to rescue it, his tracksuit became waterlogged, he sank rapidly amongst the weeds. We were six hours away, but however hard my mind flies, whatever prodigious inhalations of breath I take to strain after him, I can never make up that distance. He was the little apple of my eye, and when he disappeared it was as if something in my senses went numb for ever: as if I, too, had fallen head-first below water, and could never again see or hear properly what was around me.

It is dark and cold down here, and yet I do not wish to surface. I have become accustomed to my liquid world, and will not be coming up for air. I must hold this breath for the rest of my life.

What really happened, I wonder? Did he hear a shout, see a strange, older boy – exactly how much older he could never have imagined – running towards him round the magnolias? Was it this which caused him, in alarm, to lose his balance, to slip and fall . . . ?

I had promised him I would always be there. But for as long as I hold my breath, I have not entirely lost him: he has gone to join the hidden ones, in the submarine weather of my heart.

ELEVEN

Although it is an historical event probably still too recent to be susceptible to objective analysis, the seed-crystal of the military Push seems to me to belong to the defence cuts approved seven years ago and gradually implemented by a purblind Tory administration that failed to appreciate the social implications of militarily trained personnel during an unprecedented era of minimal combat opportunities. The martial scree that was to generate a landslide first began slithering off the peaks on 1 August 1992, when the initial two regular Army regiments – the 5th Royal Inniskilling Dragoon Guards, and the 4th/7th Dragoon Guards – were officially amalgamated to form the Royal Dragoons.

As others followed, thousands of highly trained and motivated men and women were being made redundant, and realized they were being replaced by equally expensive technology; disaffection was soon rife among the other ranks who were offered inadequate housing and often no more than twenty-eight days of retraining for civilian life. Dangerous numbers began leaching from the Services into a direct continuation of their careers with various mercenary units then punching their way through the shattered cities of what was Eastern Europe. Despite reassurances from the Army Council, it was clear to those who remained that the intention was to abolish the entire regimental system; this bred resistance at both county and family level, not just among the officer classes it threatened to dispossess; although I had precious little first-hand knowledge of this world (and – this was the point – nor did the Civil Service, or many of the politicians), I had been at school with several career soldiers, and what they told me in Buck's and the Turf (where I often repaired to drink at lunchtime) sounded none too good.

With so many battalions repatriated, there had never before been so many people in uniform and on home territory. The situation with hindsight looks so obviously explosive that one wonders at anybody being surprised at the result, but at that stage the general consensus, even in Clubland, was that: it Could Never Happen Here, Of Course.

After a period of clinging and numbness, Susan and I began once again to float adrift. In silent ways we fed each other bitterness and blame. Perhaps it would have been different if we had managed to conceive another child, but by then we both knew this was too late. I was not affected by any concerns about dynastic succession (now I am resigned to the matter), and I would have stayed with her had there been any hope of harmony between us, of permanent consolation; but the daily resentments grew, building up lethally, like arsenic in the bones, until we both felt sick. Less than a year after Peter's death, we separated; I bought Susan the lease on a house in Notting Hill, and made arrangements for her to be financially independent, though before long she had secured a job for herself as the Assistant Features Editor on a magazine called *Contemporary Europe*. So began another life for her, and no doubt she found it intellectually more fulfilling than the one she had shared with me, though we seldom spoke of such matters: our relationship became businesslike, and only on a couple of occasions when I rang her, intoxicated and maudlin from the country, did we ever broach the subject of our loss. It is the peculiarly English way of not forgetting.

Meanwhile, England itself was becoming progressively more sullen and defeatist, developing an ugly face fashioned by boredom and alcohol and the bemusement of the television screen – again, people had been predicting this for years, but they were experts speaking through the media, and therefore regarded with suspicion on the one hand (perhaps the English are a touch more attentive these days), and disbelief on the other. But even the most committed adherent to beliefs about the native superiority and resilience of the British Way of Life could not pretend the Government still had the social situation in hand: if there was one phenomenon of which every citizen was aware, it was the rapid escalation of violent crime and the concomitant failure of confidence in the police – perhaps the last factor which had for so long distinguished us from the United States.

It was the *Daily Express*, I think, which originally coined the term 'Crim' as a generic tag for the pandemic underclass of vandalistic gangs that began to proliferate, not just in the inner cities but throughout all but the most rurally isolated parts of Britain; the name was intended to distinguish these mobs from the historically defined 'professional' class of criminal, and it caught the ear of the public because it chimed with 'grim', was a trim version of an outdated and legalistic word, and sounded like a nickname, and this had the effect of slightly defusing the menace, along the lines of familiar gangland argot (The Firm, The Tigers, Mods, Beatniks, what have you). It meant their activities could be discussed in shorthand, and, so long as this could be conducted, it was presumed that the threat was containable. It proved to be, eventually, but not by dint of editorial semantics. In the meantime there were real dangers to be faced.

The middle years of the decade could be characterized by a mania for personal security. It became clear that the police could not cope when their spokesmen abandoned even giving the impression that they would automatically try to solve all reported crimes: car thefts, muggings, rapes and trespass would only be the subject of traditional investigation if they had additional elements such as involvement with a celebrity, huge amounts of valuables, sexual grotesquerie, or 'human interest' that might make it to a front page. I'm not sure I can blame the police for their realistic new attitudes, because funding was genuinely short and new recruits hard to come by on that sort of salary (the private security firms paid much better, and there was always the chance of a good bit of grievous down an alley). Even when the inevitable happened, the officers routinely went on patrol armed with a Solaro .38 just for checking out a domestic, or wading in to arbitrate a clunk of bumpers, they couldn't really attract the right calibre of constable. The situation remained as it had for years: those who wanted action and were any good joined the Army, and those who couldn't scrape into the police, but craved a uniform, became traffic wardens. I don't believe the Push would have happened if the Tories had taken the trouble to revivify the police force.

They were increasingly losing credibility in the prosecution system as well, and one of the undeniable benefits to the nation introduced by the military was the replacement of the ancient adversarial process of the courts in favour of tribunals. The instances of wrongful conviction, and subsequent investigations (running into millions of public funds), with exposure of corruption and the falsification of evidence (all part of the desire to show results) by the office of the Director of Public Prosecutions (for years reluctant to take much initiative), meant that in the matter of a short space of time the vigilante mentality that had bobbed up previously with groups like the Underground Angels now surfaced, as it were, with a vengeance. Not only did every pub and club and sports hall begin to depend on its team of bouncers, the more genteel residential enclaves clubbed together and hired some uniformed help. The Neighbourhood Watch schemes of the eighties began to stump up cash, and show their teeth.

There was a boom in sales of passive security systems, too, ones which are unrelated to the police. Where once the dinner-party chat was (as Susan rightly divined it) all about nannies and schools, now you would have been more likely to hear the latest buzz about access control, perimeter barriers, physical systems. Very few affluent folk depended on the liveware response of the police to their new circuitry: you either made your property as impregnable as possible, or you got hold of auxiliaries. The Duke of Atholl was no longer the only British subject to have private militia at his own disposal. And here I can speak from experience – an experience that contributed more than any other to my decision to leave the country.

In these last years of the United Kingdom, there was an increasingly embattled state of affairs in the protection of my own domain. Webbed across as it was by bridle-paths and public rights of way (some spuriously created deep in the past by a *canard* that the route taken by a coffin established freedom of access to the *canaille* in perpetuity), the acres of Spellbrook were regularly invaded by greenroaders, ramblers, snoopers and marauders from Dorking and Guildford and London itself. These interpolators set fire to barns, destroyed fences and thus released livestock, catapulted my ducks, shot with airguns the frogs and cruising carp, and attempted to invade the precincts to stage *ad hoc* festivals. It took on the proportions, and the spooky atmosphere, of guerilla warfare. Distasteful and expensive as it was, I had to step up security at Spellbrook to a level alarmingly more severe than anything that complied with police guidelines.

One night I was stopped driving down a private road that ran through Home Farm by a tree felled across my path as a roadblock. A group of men, numbering maybe six, none of whom I knew, closed in on my car and began to drive crowbars and baseball bats through the side-window and the main windscreen. Had it not been for the fact that my Lambo was a left-hand drive vehicle, I feel sure I would have been killed; as it was, I managed to circumvent the immediate obstacle (taking a wire fence with me for half a mile), and contact my own operatives on one of my mobile telephones. But after this incident I realized that it was time to take the gloves off when dealing with Crim. I equipped myself with a Blaser Starlight capable of delivering a 50,000 volt light-shock, whenever I had to venture abroad after dark, and, illegal as it still was, I took the precaution of importing three guard-dogs from the Continent. There was no point in pretending: we had to play hardball.

These were Japanese tosas crossbred with Neapolitan mastiffs, and they cost me £5,000 apiece. I called them Hunter, Repeater and Rolex – or Rex for short for the latter, since he was a king among watchdogs. A certain bitter humour was setting in, as no doubt you will have observed, but otherwise there was nothing faintly amusing about my new accessories, each one of which stood as high as a pony, weighed in at seventeen stone, and regarded the pitbulls they sometimes encountered as the canine equivalent of finger-food. Word got around, as you can imagine, and for a while Spellbrook was given a wide berth by Crim. But then we had a disaster, a fiasco that would never have occurred in the days when Charlie Sanga held sway. I got my name in the papers, and it was not good. It was not good at all.

At that time, practically everyone who owned more than 10 acres was employing some form of armed security; my own force comprised four ex-Gurkhas and two personal bodyguards from the Marines. It was not difficult to employ such men, and there was a feeling of straining at the leash when you talked to them, as their attitude towards public indifference (Ireland, the Falklands, the Gulf Wars) was, shall we say, rather pronounced. The agency through which I engaged them demanded a prodigious fee, but I was assured I would be employing the best. The Asians were particularly inclined to take matters into their own hands, and in the wake of an outbreak from Crim (whom they despised as amateurs) of incendiary devices planted near the main house, they decided to booby-trap the Long Walk with punji-sticks. They posted conspicuous notices advertising the danger, but this was no defence during the subsequent proceedings. An intruder aged fifteen was impaled and killed, and it did not help that she was a local girl. In the days before the Push there were no such people as Outlaws in Britain, and my men were brought to trial: trespass was not in itself a criminal offence, and all you were permitted to do was employ 'reasonable force' to arrest someone who was committing an offence on your property – you were forbidden to sabotage it with traps, guns or even wiring to electricity. Of course, thousands of households were taking such precautions, and more, but causing the death of an adolescent girl with a Vietnamese device constructed from sharpened bamboo poles inflamed certain sections of the media (now silenced forever), despite the fact that the body in question was found to be carrying several petrol bombs, a serrated carving-knife and several phials of the strength-giving designer drug known as Ultramarine.

It was a bad business, and I sensed a losing battle. The whole notion of privacy was going to the wall, and if this is a lament that would have been branded as politically incorrect a decade ago by the *soi-disant* 'thinking classes', well, bully for them. To my way of thinking, martial law is about as politically correct as rape and pillage: they had it coming to them, the cress-eating liberals.

For three years I was forced to inhabit a high-tech stockade – 'The Avenues to his Castle were guarded with Turn-pikes, and Palissadoes, all after the Modern way of Fortification', as Dean Swift wrote of the spider's citadel in his fable. I was living in a reticulated web of tripwires and barbed steel, and was beginning to ponder the alternatives.

Spidersilk comprises a various range of specialized compositions, some as thin as one-millionth of an inch, and it can be five times the strength of an equivalent steel filament. It is both a weapon and an instrument. A thick cob has healing properties as a styptic, a staunch against bleeding, while individual strands are still used in the manufacture of optical equipment, for silk is unrivalled by any synthetic substance as a material for the cross-hairs in micrometer eye-pieces. It is incorporated into the weave of bullet-proof jackets, such is its lightness and resilience. It is one of the miracle products of the animal world.

The spider is a spectacular engineer, constructing diving-bells, casting-nets, rafts, bolases and trap-doors. She fashions orbs, sheets, scaffolds and stars; she can live under the sea, and above the snow-line; she is adept at mimicry and camouflage, disguising herself as twigs, leaves, ants and lichen. When insects evolved wings to escape her, she devised fresh mutations to deceive them. The Javanese crab-spider imitates the bird-droppings on which butterflies like to settle; another has an abdomen resembling the flower of the heather plant, and lurks, like an ogre beneath the bridge, to drain the noble blood of the working bee.

Araneid venom is universally feared in folklore (cures for the bite include a slit barbel, Love-in-the-Mist, and the blood of the sea-tortoise), but even the largest of our native species would scarcely be able to puncture human skin, even if deliberately cornered and provoked. While more enlightened persons realized that the spider was innocuous – Elizabeth I regarded a large house-spider as a great delicacy, and the astronomer Lalande used to nibble some before engaging in coitus – elsewhere in Europe the legend persisted that all spiders were a sac of venom. Frederick the Great saw a spider dead in his cup of hot, fashionable chocolate, and sent it back to the kitchen; shortly thereafter he heard a gunshot, and was told that his chef had been blackmailed into poisoning him, and presumed his ploy had been discovered. There is a large spider painted on the ceiling of the ante-room at Sans-souci, to this day.

Different, however, is *Latrodectus mactans*, the night-stinger, redback, malmignatte, or black widow. Unlike the slow but horrid giants commonly called tarantulas, she is a real hit-and-run arachnid, a ready biter with a venom fifteen times as toxic as that of the rattlesnake. She is the teleologic archetype of the spider world: her neurotoxin arcs like an electric current through your blood, causing sweats, restlessness, lack of motor co-ordination, urinary dereliction, delirium, and death. The little male, by contrast, possesses venom that is harmless to humans. He is equipped only to subdue roaches and bugs.

In March 1994, I decided to put Spellbrook on the market. It had been our family home for more than a century, and my mother was horrified at the prospect. I explained to her that I was no longer happy living there, the place was now woven with uneasy memories, and that I sensed there was anyway something in the air, some spring-cleaning of a drastic sort impending, that I wished to avoid. She thought me alarmist – 'Honestly, Rich, all this republican talk is perfect nonsense. Your trouble is that you've been brooding down there on your own for too long. You should come and spend more time in London: it's not as bad as everyone makes out.' When she saw that I was adamant, she accepted my invitation to come to the house and take away any contents she desired. I made Susan a similar offer, but she declined.

Applying for resident's papers from the Swiss authorities was the single most complicated aspect of the operation, not least because the recent wave of strikes and riots which shuddered across Britain had given many of my compatriots a similar idea. I could satisfy the financial requirements with little difficulty, even before I arranged for Hoare's to transfer the balance of my assets, but I could not enter the cantons as an unemployed citizen. It was sheer luck that I found a post at the Institute in time to coincide with my plans, especially since I had relatively little teaching experience; but here in Schwyz a First from Oxford and a doctorate from Cambridge still cut a little ice, as it were, and I was contracted to begin my courses in September of that year.

Spellbrook was offered in several lots: the farmland went quickly enough, especially with the prospect of lucrative planning permission in the out-lying areas, and in June the house and grounds were sold to the Rainbow Leisure Group, who initially converted Spellbrook into a country club with a new golf course and Amenities Centre. The contents were dealt with in a variety of ways: the more unwieldy pieces of furniture were auctioned, I put some of the pictures and porcelain into store in case either Cosmo or myself should return and wish to display them in some future house, I had most of the *objets de vertu*, silver, family memorabilia and small furniture to which I had some sentimental attachment, containerized and shipped to the

Continent, and I donated four of the family canvases to the National Portrait Gallery. They're probably stacked in a vault somewhere now, or decorating an office in some ministry presided over by a brigadier who has never seen active service; but the painting of my grandmother Jane, on whom neither I nor her husband ever laid eyes during her lifetime, is here with me in Schwyz, where it fits over the mantelpiece in my sitting-room, so I can recall there was at least one member of our family who was known for her smile.

On 4 August, I drove my Lambo to the Folkestone Tunnel terminal, and at the ticketing concourse I took my last look at Great Britain. Under a dead-mackerel sky the teeming motorway and the blades of the rail-link ran back to the horizon, bringing little Englanders towards their tense foreign holidays; there were queues to the Euroshops (last chance to get marmalade, and some decent sliced bread), and men in lightweight anoraks (never know what sort of weather you're going to come across abroad, these days) were busy tugging at straps on roof-racks, inspecting tyres, taking instructions from spouses leaning across from the passenger seats ('Move on, Harry, people are starting to honk' or, 'Take your time. Pay no attention to *them*'). I was not going to miss any of this in my new home, of that I felt sure as I swung in behind the steering-wheel and sent a last blue plume of exhaust into the air of my native country. I sensed that something was going to happen to these people quite soon, and although its probable source did not suggest it would culminate in any reprisals such as the events of Ekaterinburg, I knew that some kind of front was building up, and that it was time for what Kit Hamilton had called *el disappearo*.

Over the next few months I followed developments through my *Daily Telegraph* with growing concern. The Tory party's privatized state was becoming increasingly dishevelled, and dissatisfaction was running high; for all the talk of tackling inflation and market mechanisms, the unemployment figures were reaching five million, and the riots, though largely per-

petrated by bands of younger Crim, were clearly activated by
the frustrated male workers whose wives and daughters were
securing jobs (because they were still cheaper and more industri-
ous). In the ranks of the police squads combating 'demon-
strators' in Coventry, Bristol and Liverpool there were
occasionally recognized faces of men supposed to be serving
with the Armed Forces in Northern Ireland.

'It's not as bad as everyone makes out,' my mother reiterated, in one of her early letters to my Swiss eyrie, 'but you do
see some strange characters on the streets, these days, even in
the better parts of town. And the needles are everywhere. It is
genuinely worrying, and they will have to do something about
it before too long. After all, it's not as if the Government is
blind to this state of affairs. But I suppose things always have
to get a little worse, before they improve.' I was very concerned
about my mother, and used to ring her regularly, trying to
persuade her to come out and join me, but she would have none
of it (I think she regarded my departure as slightly treasonable).
'You need not worry about your mother,' Gilbey added to one
of her notes, in his identifiable Dervish script, 'because I am
happy, and utterly confident of the future. Can you say the
same of yourself, I wonder?'

The events of 1995 would probably not have occurred if
the Royal Family had not appeared so fly-blown during recent
years. I must say, I never thought they would get rid of the
Saxe-Coburg-Gothas while Her Majesty the Queen was still
reigning, but the climate of public opinion was whirling round
very rapidly, like so much else, and the fact that the Queen
Mum died had a profound effect on the country. Brilliant as I
regard the last monarch to have been in her busy silence over
political matters, there can be no doubt that her mother was
the final exemplar of Royal Patriotism – she had been a symbol
of the nation during the war, and nothing even that Princess
could achieve under very different circumstances could equal
this. The Queen Mother was deified in the Press as The Last
Really Useful Queen, and there was apparently nothing the

antiquated and inept Palace officials could do to counter this image: the case for retaining the monarchy was finding fewer and shriller voices. When the Wales couple formally separated, I suppose it was almost a foregone conclusion. The entire Windsor dynasty suffered from appalling advice over public relations: as a family they made the mistake of making too many concessions to the public, too late. If they had remained aloof, despite the constant summons from the gutter to step on down and go walk-about with their emotions, they would have remained as impervious to the changing times as any other attraction, like those ravens with their clipped wings in the Tower of London.

But they ran up against a moraine compounded of bad luck and historical pressure, as one sometimes does. In amongst all the political gavotting and vacillation came the long-overdue *exposé* by the media about an ancient indiscretion on the part of the Prime Minister, a revelation about a liaison that he had enjoyed long before attaining senior office. It was a storm in a tea-cup, but in the usual way it was alleged that this proved he was not reliable; possible breaches of security were ruled out, but his credibility as a leader was thoroughly questioned, he resigned, and in the ensuing squabble about who should head up the Government a State of Emergency was declared by the brave General.

With so many of his troops already in control of running key services across the nation, it was not difficult for Fenwick and the Chiefs of Staff to implement their coup. Special Forces entered Buckingham Palace and Downing Street simultaneously, and the Queen was persuaded to dissolve Parliament for the last time.

She and most of her family were out of the country within hours, leaving behind only the Princess, who remains there as a private citizen, living quietly with her successful Brigadier near Salisbury, useful propaganda for the new administration whenever the busy apologists need to stress the voluntary nature of the Royal exodus to those folk still inexplicably nostalgic for the *status quo ante*. The General meanwhile appeared on television and explained the usual points about the National Interest, and announced a number of strictly temporary measures designed to restore order to the country – the borders were to be sealed, there was to be a nationwide curfew for six weeks, petrol was rationed, and all liquor stores were now under State control. Martial law was imposed under the newly constituted Civil Defence Council, and so began his period of caretaker dictatorship that is still flourishing today under his Presidency.

There was much rhetorical but little physical opposition – no reports of rape and pillage, those builder's perks of traditional revolutions. Most citizens appeared relieved that at last somebody was in control; everyone blamed everyone else, and this gave the nation something new to talk about, in addition to the weather. There were rumours of resistance (especially in Scotland; Ulster was rapidly turned over to a Peace Force from the UN), but with the Forces in charge of the media during those early weeks the image that emerged was one of pacific resignation. The noise of church bells may no longer drift across sleepy Sunday mornings in the shires, but the citizens of the new Republic seem to have adjusted to their new regime; there might not be quite the freedom of expression previously enjoyed and abused in certain quarters, but people reassure one another that this will return once the country settles down. For the time being, though, the unofficial motto of the administration is, 'You can think what you like, so long as you do what you're told.' I'm sure Nanny Mottram would have approved.

Meanwhile, I had settled to my own new life, and my refreshing professional identity – I rarely use my hereditary name here, and as I said, the Swiss are more impressed by the title 'Doctor'. So I have become, for the foreseeable future, and to most intents and purposes, Dr Richard Slide, Instructor in English Language and Literature, at the Schwyz International Institute.

We get a lot of visitors here, in season: along with the usual academics toting their ludicrous research grants there are plenty of foreign folk for whom the combination of the remarkable air and the museum-like qualities of our culture (notice the ease with which I have begun to refer to Swiss history with the collective possessive) seems to offer a powerful source of attraction. And, indeed, there is much to absorb. A little down the road, towards Zug, is the lake known as Lauerzesee, where a certain W. Tell purportedly jumped from a boat and thus escaped prison. All the apple-shooting stuff happened further south, in the Uri canton, if at all, and so far as we are concerned in this neck of the woods, that is an entirely foreign province. In Altdorf they do stage frequent performances of Schiller's play *Wilhelm Tell* – his last, and hugely boring, work – and it is invariably greeted by such visitors with rapture. That lone defiance against tyranny! The sheer *sprezzatura* of the symbolic marksmanship! Well, quite.

One thing about the sainted Schiller has always intrigued me: it is said that he used to keep in one of the drawers of his desk a layer of rotting apples, which apparently he liked to sniff, for the purposes of poetic inspiration. I guess he would have been moved to all kinds of verse by a quick whiff of our family tree, as it now stands. But – we were singing the praises of the Institute.

The place was founded seven years ago, to commemorate the Seven-Hundredth Anniversary of the Everlasting League formed by the original cantons. The funding came initially from Berne and overseas sources in equal proportions, with the initial impetus being to create a degree-giving research and teaching centre that embraced every aspect of Swiss culture (no, no: we don't have a Department of Cheese), but after several years it became clear that foreign sponsorship was tending towards the pharmaceutical and biotechnological fields for which the country has become important in recent decades, and the Directors set about redressing the balance by opening small faculties that offered courses in foreign Arts and Humanities subjects. The emphasis may still be on the genome project, transgenic biology and nuclear medicine, but all students registered for an undergraduate programme have to undertake coursework across the spectrum, so at some stage in their three years I get all the eco-physicists, nutritionists and astro-chemists, as well as those few students majoring in my 'discipline', and I derive a peculiar satisfaction from my task of introducing these shapers and twitchers of our future world to the complexities of Post-modernism, neo-classicist critical theory, the history of the English prosody (this is where Chris Jenkins and his notes come in), and the Restoration Comedies. I rather enjoy baffling the boffins, before trying to make all clear; and the process operates both ways, because they try to explain to me the significance of their other, scientific work. Only last week, I was drinking in the canteen with two Koreans who informed me that their project supervisor was believed to be not much more than two years away from definitively calculating the centre of the universe. This will no doubt prove very helpful to those of us who wish to take our bearings, as the millennium arrives. I may not know much about science, but I know what I like.

I met Magda when she took my course during my second year: she is a mathematician from St Gallen, very clever, and not yet half my age. I was not guilty of gross moral turpitude until after she had left the Literature Department, but sex has not really been much of a feature between us. We have been living together for three months, but she is technically my lodger (there's a peppercorn rent, but the catch is that she has to look after me when I need help, which is becoming increasingly often): she will complete her programme next summer, and I shall be alone again. Magda has a world ahead of her, and I would not dream of trying to persuade her to stay with me. My world has shrunk to these surroundings, where in the end there will only ever be room for one. I am divorced, now, and tech-nically free to seek another permanent partner, but there are other reasons. I have come across something that has so disturbed me that I don't think I could entrust myself to another woman.

In an attempt to reduce storage charges and sort out some

of their contents, I spent three days going through the strong-boxes I had deposited in the vaults of my bank in Geneva; they contained certain legal documents of family import, my silver collection, jewellery, and useless but historic stuff such as our ducal regalia. I selected a pearl necklace with a diamanté clasp (that had belonged to my grandmother) and took it back as a present for Magda, having opened all the boxes and drawn up a fresh inventory for my records. There were several I had not seen inside before, and one of these contained some personal papers in my father's hand: I took this back to Schwyz, too, although now I wish I had never done so.

I cannot tell you if I was ever intended to read these words. Certainly there was no accompanying letter, and no explanation. The deductions have therefore been my own. The black japanned box contained little fragments of what must have been an occasional journal, but when it was written up I do not know – I assume it was over a period of years, but nothing is dated, and the notes are on loose sheets of varying sizes. I do not intend to reproduce it verbatim, and indeed I cannot; except for details I transcribed, it no longer survives, and, when it is complete, my own account will be locked away in that same box in the strong-room.

There was a doctor at Innsbergen (the camp where my father was imprisoned) by the name of Riemann. He was supervising the psychological programme to break down his prisoner's resistance. They tried the usual tactics – sleep-deprivation, propaganda about the confessions of colleagues, strategic electricity, leading him before a firing-squad. The document was terse and routine in this respect, with no details about torture, to begin with. Since it could not have been written in the camp, I must assume his staccato comments were set down later as some kind of rudimentary *aide-memoire*; there were notes about the weather (*The sky dull, and everything close. Terrible flies*) and glimpses of fellow prisoners (*I saw Jack taken out, and his head put beneath the tap. His left leg was trailing. Do not think he saw me*), and a reiterated comment, *No data*, which

I think refers to his continued refusal to disclose information, but it might mean there was no news of the war.

There came a break in this defiance. *Probably March. Riemann discovers my fear. Very bad. Terror, but no data at first. What he did – the memory of such a man merely pollutes. Now dead, and I saw it.*

My father suffered morbidly from arachnophobia, and once the expert inquisitioner had diagnosed this, they confined him to a chamber where spiders in different species were a constant presence. It must have been like being locked in a cell of his own brain, with its resident nightmare. They starved him, and then mixed spiders into his food; they put live specimens in tumblers, and taped them over his eyes; they strapped him down and let the creatures roam freely over his naked body. There were details here, and I could only read them in partial disbelief, but perhaps he found the very act of writing them down was some help in exorcising his memory. *On the white-washed walls everywhere, the splintery shapes. Like bullet-holes from stray riflefire.*

So far as I can see, he gave in and told them something. He did not record what it was, and it may have been invention, but it made them stop. *And then the relief. Slept two nights, but still not able to eat.* There followed a description of the liberation of the camp, in quite different style.

If that had been all, it would have altered my perception of my father beyond all measure – I could understand his reluctance to discuss the war, and perhaps even his general remoteness. But there were later pieces of paper in the box which made me wonder if he had been rendered insane by this experience, and indeed the nature of his apparent psychosis was such that I suspect he may not have been my biological parent after all (I would stress that this is all speculation on my part, made questionable by the irrational state I am now in myself).

Some time after the war he began to suffer from what he called *sudden attacks of the Noise, insomnia, hands shaking, shifting of vision, nausea*; there were several entries recording this, but no mention of medical advice. I would say it might be what is nowadays called post-traumatic stress disorder. Whatever the condition, something was evidently corroding his mind during this period; there was an entry merely headed *Paris*, which made me realize that. *Afterwards, could not sleep. Yellow light from her lamp, as Nicole slept. I touch her lips, a film of dried saliva. Arrange cushions, but the room filling with the Noise. Something is there, hiding between her legs dribbling silk.*

How else shall I say this? My father became obsessed with the delusion that the female genitalia were a form of parasitic spider. This notion arrested his brain, and there were pages and pages of notes about the behaviour of these arthropods; he seemed to be convinced there was a conspiracy of silence about this fact, with dozens of details about witchcraft and alchemy and arcane celestial lore, suggesting that the spider was some kind of mythological key to the entire female principle, an all-pervasive symbol of the feminine and the forbidden. One piece of card simply had these words on it: *The diaphanous membrane encasing the spinal cord and the whole human brain, underlying the Dura Mater, is the arachnoid membrane. It is recognized as the web around our centre of consciousness.* I will summarize certain salient points of my father's conviction, in my own words, but one thing is for sure (don't we often say that, when concealing uncertainty?): the facts do not speak for themselves.

Ariadne was the daughter of Pasiphaë, Cretan goddess of the Moon, who manipulated the tides with her complex threads; her daughter was the spinner of the original clue, that assisted Theseus out of the maze, but when he spurned her love she hanged herself. Before she died, she hurled her crown into the sky, where it became a constellation: light still comes down from the cluster that surrounded the labyrinthian brain of the woman who hangs by a cord.

Arachne (or Aranea, as she later became) was an ill-starred weaver from Lydia who thought herself a match for Athena, the goddess of handiwork; she defeated the jealous immortal in a tapestry contest, and then hanged herself. Athena sprinkled her corpse with the juice of aconite, and at once the hair, nose and ears fell off, the torso shrivelled up, and she was transformed into a black spinster, a spider.

Arianrod, lady of the silver wheel (or web), was the Celtic goddess of the Moon, daughter of Don, the *Corona borealis* or Northern Crown. Her symbol is the spider, which is both creator and destroyer, growing its web and then harvesting death like the wax and wane of the tides, the flux of the seasons. The spider is therefore an image of the Fates, those female spinners and shearers (snip, snap) familiar to so many cultures.

During the Flight from Egypt, the Holy Family took refuge in a cave, and a spider wove a thick web across its mouth, and a dove made a nest in it; when Herod's soldiers passed it by, the dove became the symbol of the Holy Spirit – and the spider? Have you examined the shape of a Celtic cross, a wheel of fortune, an auspicious (right-handed) swastika? She is the umbilicus from the vaginal bush, the silver cord, the vessel of creation.

This was all unsettling to read, but the next page did not seem to make any sense at all, at first.

Later that night Charlie takes me to a village, where they put me in his father's hut. My head is ablaze. Kitimu a very tall man, says I am thabu and cursed by my actions. I think he is going to kill me. They say I must be purified. A stone is placed on my chest, they burn leaves that fill the eyes with water, flick water on me from some animal-leg. The stone is boiled, and set down in doorway. I drink the water, and it makes me sleep. I don't know for how long, but it is still night, and must return to town. Charlie is to come with me. Feel cold.

Into the clearing, and the old men of the tribe staring at me round a fire. Sit opposite Charlie, and they club an ox between its eyes. Two lumps of liver are fried on sticks. Kitimu painted with white clay, ghostly in the firelight, with a blade in his hand. Scrapes around

*my arm, navel and chest until blood comes, wipes liver in it, passes it
over to Charlie in a gourd. He eats it, and they do same to him.*

At the bottom of the box was a little clutch of newspaper
cuttings from 1952, relating to the trial of Onymayu Tamboto,
a Mau-Mau terrorist who was executed for the murder and
mutilation of two white women and (although he denied all
charges) became notorious as The Scissor Man. After killing his
victims, he performed a clitoridectomy upon their corpses, that
was presumed to be a symbolic revenge against a culture that
had banned the traditional ceremony of female circumcision as
practised among several Kenyan tribes on all girls between the
ages of ten and fourteen – the single slash of a stone blade,
followed by a poultice of chicken feathers. After Tamboto was
killed, there were more murders, but never again with this
grisly signature.

There was no confession, no explanation, no further notes
about my father's life, merely a circumstantial and interrupted
archive, but I could only account for its very existence by
forming a conclusion that was almost impossible to contemplate: that it was my father George Waterstock who was The
Scissor Man.

At first, I felt sick, like a medical student diagnosing in his
own physique the symptoms of each ailment about which he
learns; the very fact that I had arrived at this interpretation made
me ill at ease, suggesting a mind made febrile by drink and
remorse. But I could think of no other reason why those clip-
pings had been preserved; Charlie had told me once that my
father had been ill when they met, but what were the actions
that had so defiled my father that he had to be purified, and
have Charlie, the son of the medicine-man, become his blood-
brother and mentor for life? Could it be that he detected the
deep malaise afflicting my father, and undertook to heal him,
rather than turn him in? Or was the crisis from which the Yaaku
rescued my father something else altogether, nothing to do with
the dead German women? I do not know. This is unfinished
business, but I am contaminated by doubts. I would like to
know the truth, however late in the day.

Had he lived, would he have explained any of this to me – the psychosis, the symbolic obsessions, the dark events in Kenya, the reason why Charlie Sanga became a part of our lives? Is that why my mother embraced Gilbey, sensing something strange lurking in the London blood-line? Night thoughts, unclear reasoning. Logical processes of induction and deduction submerged in several tumblers of Scotch. Too much fear in the throat. But fear is a barbed and isolating thing: as I speculate, I feel myself falling into the middle distance of my own picture, like one of those feverish, childhood dreams. What if this madness (of which I have convinced myself) is an hereditary condition? Tomorrow I will be someone slightly different – will I awake one morning and find I have a desire to . . . ?

It does strange things to your mind, having always thought of your father as a war hero, and now suspecting him of having been a psychosexual murderer. The notion so haunts me that I have even considered going to Kenya and trying to trace Charlie, who must surely have gone to rejoin what is left of his tribe (HIV is running at almost 80 per cent in some areas of East Africa, now). Perhaps one day I will, when I have recovered my composure, although that is becoming increasingly difficult. I have entertained ideas that he could not have been my father, not with those sorts of delusions about women in his head – pehaps my true father was some thespian lush with whom my mother consorted in town during her idle afternoons, and who may even now be living somewhere in the New Britain. (This would mean, of course, that I never should have become a Duke, in the first place.) Or maybe in some miraculous, spiritous way, it was old Gilbey, making me a gin-baby rather than a whisky-duke, the opposite of an abortion in a boiling bath. Maybe I only ever existed in the dreamy fantasies of an unfulfilled and beautiful actress, whose husband could not bring himself to contemplate her body. (Ah, yes, we are just brains in bottles, connected to machines, observed by a laboratory full of alien scientists in some experiment. I know. Enough.)

But there is one thing more. Family history may indeed have a way of repeating itself. The year before his debts forced him to sell his father's estate, Clive (the third Duke) left behind him an unsolved case involving the death of a servant, a girl – as Robert Hodgson phrases it in his book – 'whose body was found, according to the only surviving record I have been able to consult, in a remote part of the Waterstock grazings on 7 July 1827. The corpse had been mutilated, whether by feral scavengers or human hand it was never concluded, but the Northampton coroner recorded "her injuries were of so grave and intimate a nature, that I could not suffer my assistant (being but a youth) to view them, and instructed him to depart the chamber." Clive had Becky Wilson's parents evicted from their cottage two months after her funeral, when her father was allegedly apprehended poaching game from the estate.'

In 1887, my esteemed ancestor Harry met his American heiress in London, and three years later they retired to the newly-acquired Spellbrook. Just prior to this period (the only time in the Canny Duke's adulthood when he lived in London), eight women were killed in the East End by a murderer whose identity has never been discovered, but who remains widely regarded as having been a senior member of the aristocracy, and possibly someone who moved in royal circles. His sobriquet was, of course, Jack the Ripper, another Scissor Man. But, enough.

Earlier this year, I made the mistake of revisiting Britain, primarily with the intention of making sure my mother was really as safe and comfortable as she kept assuring me. She had repeatedly turned down my invitations to visit Schwyz, and her conversations on the phone were as erratic as ever (she seldom turned on the screen, saying it made her uneasy). I found her in good heart, though it was difficult to tell whether she was looking after Mrs Pike, or vice versa; the capital had certainly improved since last I was there, although I found the English as bad-mannered and collectively stupid as I had remembered, slouching around in their leisure-wear as if permanently disaffected at some gigantic car-boot sale.

My trip to Spellbrook was not a success: the countryside was caked with cracked mud in the drought (this is the second year there has been no winter in Northern Europe) and the river-beds I saw from the monotrak out to Guildford looked like bleached tortoise-shell. The new trains do run on time, it is true, but you have to be authorized to catch one; as a foreign national whose residential status abroad predates the new administration, I am privileged to have an open, ten-day travel pass, though three days is all it takes to convince me that I do not intend to return.

My former home has been turned into a Heritage Centre: I knew that much, before I went. My grandfather's orchard has been felled to make way for a Visitors Reception Point (no apostrophe, of course, they have dispensed with such niceties), and the lake where my son drowned is now an arid picnic pit. There are jars of Heritage Chutney, and Spellbrook dishcloths on sale at the Gift Shop, an auto-repeat videobox retailing a spurious history of the house and its owners every fifteen minutes, a miniature railway where parents can photograph their children, and a Historium which consists of a trip around the ground floor of the house in what resembles an electric coal-cart, viewing roped-off vestibules stuffed with waxwork dummies in 'period' clothing, and a kitchen where amid a riotous array of cooking utensils and stuffed gamebirds, a red-faced mannequin in a lace bob-cap boggles glassily at her skillet full of unpeeled onions, and a spit bearing chipped plaster facsimiles of chicken carcasses rotates eternally, infernally, before a fire of winking, coloured shards. At every doorway stands a uniformed 'guard' with nicotine hair, grey complexion, tattooed thumbs, distinguished grandly from the fee-paying *Lumpenproletariat* only by his scrawny epaulettes, and the ridiculous pride of his sentinel stance.

It was unwise of me to have taken that trip, but it confirmed something else I had suspected, which was useful: the past is not a foreign country, it is the visitor who is foreign. The past was still there, where it mattered, and it was I who had become a voluntary stranger. I found the graveyard without much difficulty, and there was the Spellbrook Seedling, now thick of trunk above Arthur's grave; I plucked some leaves, and placed them by the austere headstone of my father, in the knowledge that he had been more tormented than I had ever guessed.

I sat for some while with my back against the side of the stone cross we had set over Peter, and realized I would probably never be there again. Lying above my son's bones was curiously restful: I would not return to this foreign country, but the past would remain quick in my memory, however much the place itself had changed, and I could always see a boy leaping through a curtain of water swishing high above the old Spellbrook lawn whenever I chose to close my eyes, and hold my breath. I would not be a stranger to his memory any longer.

'Their souls dwell in the house of tomorrow', wrote Kahlil Gibran, about children, 'which you cannot visit, not even in your dreams.' The house of tomorrow may be empty, but I now know I can slip into the garden of the past, where children still run through an orchard, even if it is light-years away, and the seasons will observe their cycle, and there will be fruit on the trees when the time is right. I can hear the voices whispering in to me from the shadows, the hidden ones from my life reassuring me of their real presence – Arthur, Peter, Nanny Mottram. I see my father, even, caught in that searchlight, with one arm across his face. There are two boys with kites. A giant is demolishing a wall with his axe. I must go home.

The day grows old, and goes blind. Very little light is coming through the window, now, and I feel cold. I am on my own here, with my cobweb of words, and it is getting late. If I move my chair to the side of the desk – just here – I can see the peaks of the Mitre and the curving red line that is the last of the sun. The sky seems to promise fine weather tomorrow, which I would welcome, but it might be just another industrial sunset.

We will see.